PEARSON CUSTOM
ELECTRONICS TECHNOLOGY

ENGR 2210
Utah State
Volume II

Pearson Learning Solutions

New York   Boston   San Francisco
London   Toronto   Sydney   Tokyo   Singapore   Madrid
Mexico City   Munich   Paris   Cape Town   Hong Kong   Montreal

Senior Vice President, Editorial and Marketing: Patrick F. Boles
Executive Marketing Manager: Nathan L. Wilbur
Senior Acquisition Editor: Debbie Coniglio
Development Editor: Christina Martin
Editorial Assistant: Jeanne Martin
Operations Manager: Eric M. Kenney
Production Manager: Jennifer Berry
Art Director: Renée Sartell
Cover Designer: Kristen Kiley

Cover Art: "Air Traffic Controller at Work, Radar in Foreground," courtesy of Roger Tully/Getty Images; "Young Man Enjoying Music with Headphones," courtesy of Geni Corwin/iStockphoto; "Rov Ventana Submersible is Lowered by Crane from MBARI Ship, Point Lobos, Monterey Bay, California," courtesy of Norbert Wu/Getty Images; "Air Traffic Control Room, Two Men Studying with Radar Screen, Rear View," courtesy of Paul Chesley/Getty Images; "Autonomous Submersible," courtesy of Norbert Wu/Getty Images.

Please visit our website at *www.pearsoncustom.com/custom-library/pearson-custom-electronics-technology*.

Attention bookstores: For permission to return any unsold stock, contact us at *pe-uscustomreturns@pearson.com*.

Pearson Learning Solutions, 501 Boylston Street, Suite 900, Boston, MA 02116
A Pearson Education Company
www.pearsoned.com

ISBN 10: 0-558-88891-7
ISBN 13: 978-0-558-88891-6

Attention Students!
Important Information Regarding Supplemental Materials for Your Customized Book

Your custom book may come with additional student resources designed to aid you in further understanding material covered in your text. These supplements are available to you via the following website, searchable by author last name and title:

http://www.pearsoned.com/electronics

When you encounter a text reference to the website above, simply follow these instructions to access the supplemental materials.

Accessing the Student Data Files in the Pearson Custom Publishing Program in Electronics Technology:

1. **From an open Web browser go to:** http://www.pearsoned.com/electronics. **Note:** You should consider bookmarking this URL, as it may contain links to additional supplements that you will be using in your class.

2. **Select the book from which your custom chapter is derived.** In order to determine this, go to the first page of the chapter in which you are currently working. At the bottom of the first page you will see a credit line that includes a book title and author name. On the website, click on the first letter of the author's last name. **Note:** If the author has written more than one text, all titles will be listed. Simply select the appropriate book title for your chapter.

3. **Select the corresponding chapter to access supplemental materials.** Since you have a custom book, refer only to chapter titles – not the original chapter numbers which appear in parentheses. This is because your instructor may have re-ordered the sequence of chapters for your customized book. Simply browse through the chapter titles to locate the one that matches the title of the chapter you are reading. **Note:** If unsure of your chapter title, again refer to the first page of the chapter in which you are currently working.

4. **Locate the file that you need.** You may open to view it immediately, or you may save the file to a specific location on your hard drive. We recommend saving the files to your desktop to find them easily. **Note:** Student data file names may have numbers that differ from your custom book's chapter numbers. Again, this will occur if your instructor re-ordered the chapters when creating your custom book.

Contents

INTRODUCTORY CONCEPTS

CHAPTER OUTLINE

1 Digital and Analog Quantities
2 Binary Digits, Logic Levels, and Digital Waveforms
3 Basic Logic Operations
4 Introduction to the System Concept
5 Fixed-Function Integrated Circuits
6 Test and Measurement Instruments
7 Introduction to Programmable Logic

CHAPTER OBJECTIVES

- Explain the basic differences between digital and analog quantities
- Show how voltage levels are used to represent digital quantities
- Describe various parameters of a pulse waveform such as rise time, fall time, pulse width, frequency, period, and duty cycle
- Explain the basic logic operations of NOT, AND, and OR
- Describe several types of logic functions and explain their application in an example system
- Identify fixed-function digital integrated circuits according to their complexity and the type of circuit packaging
- Identify pin numbers on integrated circuit packages
- Recognize various instruments and understand how they are used in measurement and troubleshooting digital circuits and systems
- Describe programmable logic, discuss the various types, and describe how PLDs are programmed

KEY TERMS

Key terms are in order of appearance in the chapter.

- Analog
- Digital
- Binary
- Bit
- Pulse
- Duty cycle
- Clock
- Timing diagram
- Data
- Serial
- Parallel
- Logic
- Input
- Output

- Gate
- NOT
- Inverter
- AND
- OR
- Integrated circuit (IC)
- Fixed-function logic
- Troubleshooting
- Programmable logic
- SPLD
- CPLD
- FPGA
- Compiler

INTRODUCTION

The term *digital* is derived from the way operations are performed, by counting digits. For many years, applications of digital electronics were confined to computer systems. Today, digital technology is applied in a wide range of areas in addition to computers. Such applications as television, communications systems, radar, navigation and guidance systems, military systems, medical instrumentation, industrial process control, and consumer electronics use digital techniques. Over the years digital technology has progressed from vacuum-tube circuits to discrete transistors to complex integrated circuits, some of which contain millions of transistors.

This chapter introduces you to digital electronics and provides a broad overview of many important concepts, components, and tools.

From *Digital Fundamentals*, Tenth Edition, Thomas L. Floyd. Copyright © 2009 by Pearson Education, Inc. Published by Prentice Hall. All rights reserved.

1 DIGITAL AND ANALOG QUANTITIES

Electronic circuits can be divided into two broad categories, digital and analog. Digital electronics involves quantities with discrete values, and analog electronics involves quantities with continuous values. Although you will be studying digital fundamentals in this book, you should also know something about analog because many applications require both; and interfacing between analog and digital is important.

After completing this section, you should be able to

◆ Define *analog*

◆ Define *digital*

◆ Explain the difference between digital and analog quantities

◆ State the advantages of digital over analog

◆ Give examples of how digital and analog quantities are used in electronics

An **analog*** quantity is one having continuous values. A **digital** quantity is one having a discrete set of values. Most things that can be measured quantitatively occur in nature in analog form. For example, the air temperature changes over a continuous range of values. During a given day, the temperature does not go from, say, 70° to 71° instantaneously; it takes on all the infinite values in between. If you graphed the temperature on a typical summer day, you would have a smooth, continuous curve similar to the curve in Figure 1. Other examples of analog quantities are time, pressure, distance, and sound.

▶ FIGURE 1

Graph of an analog quantity (temperature versus time).

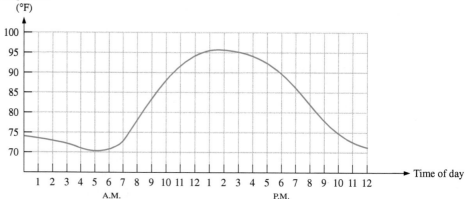

Rather than graphing the temperature on a continuous basis, suppose you just take a temperature reading every hour. Now you have sampled values representing the temperature at discrete points in time (every hour) over a 24-hour period, as indicated in Figure 2. You have effectively converted an analog quantity to a form that can now be digitized by representing each sampled value by a digital code. It is important to realize that Figure 2 itself is not the digital representation of the analog quantity.

---

*The blue bold terms are key terms and are included in a Key Term glossary at the end of the chapter.

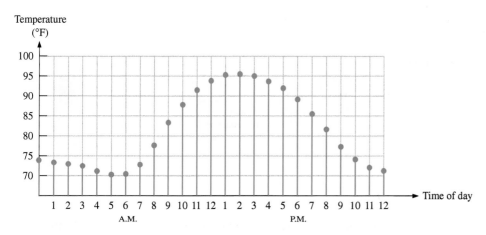

◄ FIGURE 2

Sampled-value representation (quantization) of the analog quantity in Figure 1. Each value represented by a dot can be digitized by representing it as a digital code that consists of a series of 1s and 0s.

The Digital Advantage Digital representation has certain advantages over analog representation in electronics applications. For one thing, digital data can be processed and transmitted more efficiently and reliably than analog data. Also, digital data has a great advantage when storage is necessary. For example, music when converted to digital form can be stored more compactly and reproduced with greater accuracy and clarity than is possible when it is in analog form. Noise (unwanted voltage fluctuations) does not affect digital data nearly as much as it does analog signals.

An Analog Electronic System

A public address system, used to amplify sound so that it can be heard by a large audience, is one simple example of an application of analog electronics. The basic diagram in Figure 3 illustrates that sound waves, which are analog in nature, are picked up by a microphone and converted to a small analog voltage called the audio signal. This voltage varies continuously as the volume and frequency of the sound changes and is applied to the input of a linear amplifier. The output of the amplifier, which is an increased reproduction of input voltage, goes to the speaker(s). The speaker changes the amplified audio signal back to sound waves that have a much greater volume than the original sound waves picked up by the microphone.

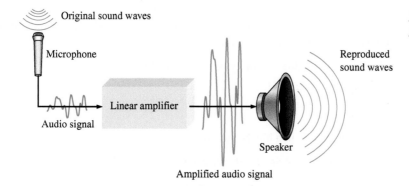

◄ FIGURE 3

A basic audio public address system.

A System Using Digital and Analog Methods

The compact disk (CD) player is an example of a system in which both digital and analog circuits are used. The simplified block diagram in Figure 4 illustrates the basic principle. Music in digital form is stored on the compact disk. A laser diode optical

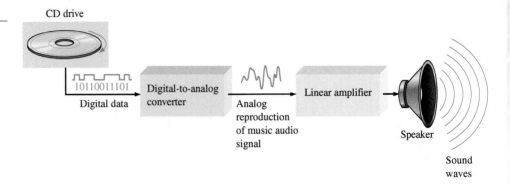

► FIGURE 4

Basic block diagram of a CD player. Only one channel is shown.

system picks up the digital data from the rotating disk and transfers it to the **digital-to-analog converter (DAC).** The DAC changes the digital data into an analog signal that is an electrical reproduction of the original music. This signal is amplified and sent to the speaker for you to enjoy. When the music was originally recorded on the CD, a process, essentially the reverse of the one described here, using an **analog-to-digital converter (ADC)** was used.

SECTION 1 CHECKUP
Answers are at the end of the chapter.

1. Define *analog*.
2. Define *digital*.
3. Explain the difference between a digital quantity and an analog quantity.
4. Give an example of a system that is analog and one that is a combination of both digital and analog. Name a system that is entirely digital.

---

2 BINARY DIGITS, LOGIC LEVELS, AND DIGITAL WAVEFORMS

Digital electronics involves circuits and systems in which there are only two possible states. These states are represented by two different voltage levels: A HIGH and a LOW. The two states can also be represented by current levels, bits and bumps on a CD or DVD, etc. In digital systems such as computers, combinations of the two states, called *codes,* are used to represent numbers, symbols, alphabetic characters, and other types of information. The two-state number system is called *binary,* and its two digits are 0 and 1. A binary digit is called a *bit.*

After completing this section, you should be able to

♦ Define *binary*

♦ Define *bit*

♦ Name the bits in a binary system

♦ Explain how voltage levels are used to represent bits

♦ Explain how voltage levels are interpreted by a digital circuit

♦ Describe the general characteristics of a pulse

♦ Determine the amplitude, rise time, fall time, and width of a pulse

♦ Identify and describe the characteristics of a digital waveform

- Determine the amplitude, period, frequency, and duty cycle of a digital waveform
- Explain what a timing diagram is and state its purpose
- Explain serial and parallel data transfer and state the advantage and disadvantage of each

Binary Digits

Each of the two digits in the binary system, 1 and 0, is called a bit, which is a contraction of the words *binary digit*. In digital circuits, two different voltage levels are used to represent the two bits. Generally, 1 is represented by the higher voltage, which we will refer to as a HIGH, and a 0 is represented by the lower voltage level, which we will refer to as a LOW. This is called **positive logic** and will be used throughout the book.

$$\text{HIGH} = 1 \quad \text{and} \quad \text{LOW} = 0$$

Another system in which a 1 is represented by a LOW and a 0 is represented by a HIGH is called *negative logic*.

Groups of bits (combinations of 1s and 0s), called *codes,* are used to represent numbers, letters, symbols, instructions, and anything else required in a given application.

COMPUTER NOTE

The concept of a digital computer can be traced back to Charles Babbage, who developed a crude mechanical computation device in the 1830s. John Atanasoff was the first to apply electronic processing to digital computing in 1939. In 1946, an electronic digital computer called ENIAC was implemented with vacuum-tube circuits. Even though it took up an entire room, ENIAC didn't have the computing power of your handheld calculator.

Logic Levels

The voltages used to represent a 1 and a 0 are called *logic levels.* Ideally, one voltage level represents a HIGH and another voltage level represents a LOW. In a practical digital circuit, however, a HIGH can be any voltage between a specified minimum value and a specified maximum value. Likewise, a LOW can be any voltage between a specified minimum and a specified maximum. There can be no overlap between the accepted range of HIGH levels and the accepted range of LOW levels.

Figure 5 illustrates the general range of LOWs and HIGHs for a digital circuit. The variable $V_{H(max)}$ represents the maximum HIGH voltage value, and $V_{H(min)}$ represents the minimum HIGH voltage value. The maximum LOW voltage value is represented by $V_{L(max)}$, and the minimum LOW voltage value is represented by $V_{L(min)}$. The voltage values between $V_{L(max)}$ and $V_{H(min)}$ are unacceptable for proper operation. A voltage in the unacceptable range can appear as either a HIGH or a LOW to a given circuit. For example, the HIGH input values for a certain type of digital circuit technology called CMOS may range from 2 V to 3.3 V and the LOW input values may range from 0 V to 0.8 V. If a voltage of 2.5 V is applied, the circuit will accept it as a HIGH or binary 1. If a voltage of 0.5 V is applied, the circuit will accept it as a LOW or binary 0. For this type of circuit, voltages between 0.8 V and 2 V are unacceptable.

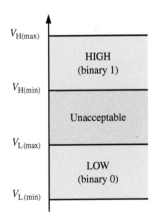

Digital Waveforms

Digital waveforms consist of voltage levels that are changing back and forth between the HIGH and LOW levels or states. Figure 6(a) shows that a single positive-going pulse is generated when the voltage (or current) goes from its normally LOW level to its HIGH level and then back to its LOW level. The negative-going pulse in Figure 6(b) is generated when the voltage goes from its normally HIGH level to its LOW level and back to its HIGH level. A digital waveform is made up of a series of pulses.

▲ FIGURE 5

Logic level ranges of voltage for a digital circuit.

► FIGURE 6

Ideal pulses.

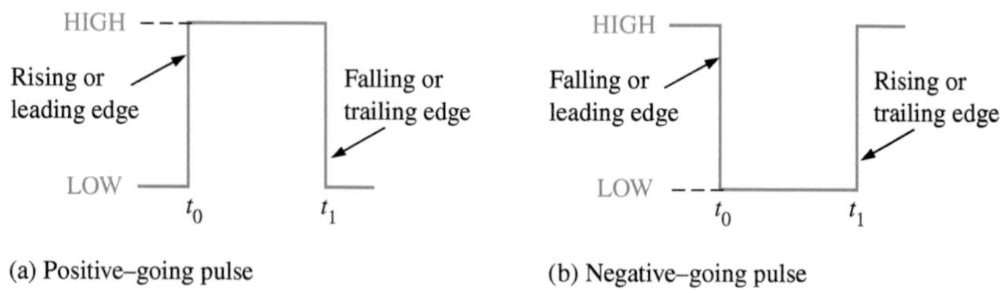

HIGH — —

Rising or
leading edge

Falling or
trailing edge

LOW

t_0 t_1

(a) Positive–going pulse

HIGH —

Falling or
leading edge

Rising or
trailing edge

LOW — —

t_0 t_1

(b) Negative–going pulse

The Pulse As indicated in Figure 6, a pulse has two edges: a **leading edge** that occurs first at time t_0 and a **trailing edge** that occurs last at time t_1. For a positive-going pulse, the leading edge is a rising edge, and the trailing edge is a falling edge. The pulses in Figure 6 are ideal because the rising and falling edges are assumed to change in zero time (instantaneously). In practice, these transitions never occur instantaneously, although for most digital work you can assume ideal pulses.

Figure 7 shows a nonideal pulse. In reality, all pulses exhibit some or all of these characteristics. The overshoot and ringing are sometimes produced by stray inductive and capacitive effects. The droop can be caused by stray capacitive and circuit resistance, forming an *RC* circuit with a low time constant.

► FIGURE 7

Nonideal pulse characteristics.

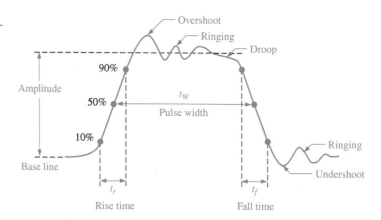

The time required for a pulse to go from its LOW level to its HIGH level is called the **rise time** (t_r), and the time required for the transition from the HIGH level to the LOW level is called the **fall time** (t_f). In practice, it is common to measure rise time from 10% of the pulse **amplitude** (height from baseline) to 90% of the pulse amplitude and to measure the fall time from 90% to 10% of the pulse amplitude, as indicated in Figure 7. The bottom 10% and the top 10% of the pulse are not included in the rise and fall times because of the nonlinearities in the waveform in these areas. The **pulse width** (t_W) is a measure of the duration of the pulse and is often defined as the time interval between the 50% points on the rising and falling edges, as indicated in Figure 7.

Waveform Characteristics Most waveforms encountered in digital systems are composed of series of pulses, sometimes called *pulse trains,* and can be classified as either periodic or nonperiodic. A **periodic** pulse waveform is one that repeats itself at a fixed interval, called a **period** (T). The **frequency** (f) is the rate at which it repeats itself and is measured in hertz (Hz). A nonperiodic pulse waveform, of course, does not repeat itself at fixed intervals and may be composed of pulses of randomly differing pulse widths and/or randomly differing time intervals between the pulses. An example of each type is shown in Figure 8.

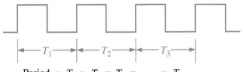

(b) Nonperiodic

Period $= T_1 = T_2 = T_3 = \ldots = T_n$
Frequency $= \frac{1}{T}$

(a) Periodic (square wave)

▲ FIGURE 8

Examples of digital waveforms.

The frequency (f) of a pulse (digital) waveform is the reciprocal of the period. The relationship between frequency and period is expressed as follows:

$$f = \frac{1}{T}$$ Equation 1

$$T = \frac{1}{f}$$ Equation 2

An important characteristic of a periodic digital waveform is its **duty cycle,** which is the ratio of the pulse width (t_W) to the period (T). It can be expressed as a percentage.

$$\textbf{Duty cycle} = \left(\frac{t_W}{T}\right)\textbf{100\%}$$ Equation 3

EXAMPLE 1

A portion of a periodic digital waveform is shown in Figure 9. The measurements are in milliseconds. Determine the following:

(a) period   **(b)** frequency   **(c)** duty cycle

▶ FIGURE 9

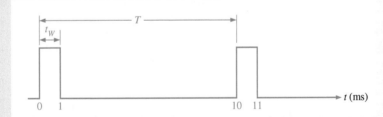

Solution   **(a)** The period is measured from the edge of one pulse to the corresponding edge of the next pulse. In this case T is measured from leading edge to leading edge, as indicated. T equals **10 ms.**

(b) $f = \dfrac{1}{T} = \dfrac{1}{10 \text{ ms}} = \textbf{100 Hz}$

(c) Duty cycle $= \left(\dfrac{t_W}{T}\right)100\% = \left(\dfrac{1 \text{ ms}}{10 \text{ ms}}\right)100\% = \textbf{10\%}$

*Related Problem**   A periodic digital waveform has a pulse width of 25 μs and a period of 150 μs. Determine the frequency and the duty cycle.

* Answers are at the end of the chapter.

A Digital Waveform Carries Binary Information

COMPUTER NOTE

The speed at which a computer can operate depends on the type of microprocessor used in the system. The speed specification, for example 3.5 GHz, of a computer is the maximum clock frequency at which the microprocessor can run.

Binary information that is handled by digital systems appears as waveforms that represent sequences of bits. When the waveform is HIGH, a binary 1 is present; when the waveform is LOW, a binary 0 is present. Each bit in a sequence occupies a defined time interval called a **bit time.**

The Clock In digital systems, all waveforms are synchronized with a basic timing waveform called the clock. The clock is a periodic waveform in which each interval between pulses (the period) equals the time for one bit.

An example of a clock waveform is shown in Figure 10. Notice that, in this case, each change in level of waveform *A* occurs at the leading edge of the clock waveform. In other cases, level changes occur at the trailing edge of the clock. During each bit time of the clock, waveform *A* is either HIGH or LOW. These HIGHs and LOWs represent a sequence of bits as indicated. A group of several bits can be used as a piece of binary information, such as a number or a letter. The clock waveform itself does not carry information.

▶ FIGURE 10

Example of a clock waveform synchronized with a waveform representation of a sequence of bits.

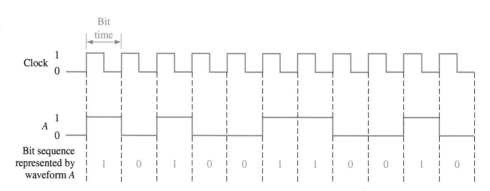

Timing Diagrams A timing diagram is a graph of digital waveforms showing the actual time relationship of two or more waveforms and how each waveform changes in relation to the others. By looking at a timing diagram, you can determine the states (HIGH or LOW) of all the waveforms at any specified point in time and the exact time that a waveform changes state relative to the other waveforms. Figure 11 is an example of a timing diagram made up of four waveforms. From this timing diagram you can see, for example, that the three waveforms *A*, *B*, and *C* are HIGH only during bit time 7 (shaded area) and they all change back LOW at the end of bit time 7.

▶ FIGURE 11

Example of a timing diagram.

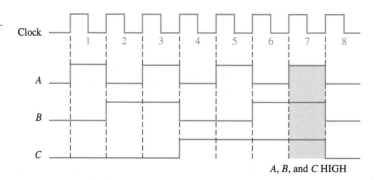

Data Transfer

Data refers to groups of bits that convey some type of information. Binary data, which are represented by digital waveforms, must be transferred from one circuit to another within a digital system or from one system to another in order to accomplish a given purpose. For example, numbers stored in binary form in the memory of a computer must be transferred

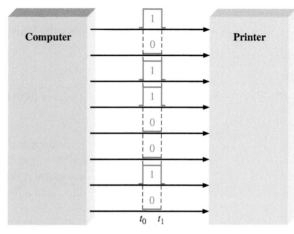

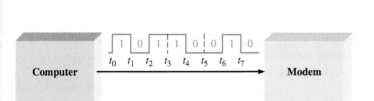

(a) Serial transfer of 8 bits of binary data from computer to modem. Interval t_0 to t_1 is first.

(b) Parallel transfer of 8 bits of binary data from computer to printer. The beginning time is t_0.

▲ FIGURE 12

Illustration of serial and parallel transfer of binary data. Only the data lines are shown.

to the computer's central processing unit in order to be added. The sum of the addition must then be transferred to a monitor for display and/or transferred back to the memory. In computer systems, as illustrated in Figure 12, binary data are transferred in two ways: serial and parallel.

When bits are transferred in **serial** form from one point to another, they are sent one bit at a time along a single line, as illustrated in Figure 12(a) for the case of a computer-to-modem transfer. During the time interval from t_0 to t_1, the first bit is transferred. During the time interval from t_1 to t_2, the second bit is transferred, and so on. To transfer eight bits in series, it takes eight time intervals.

When bits are transferred in **parallel** form, all the bits in a group are sent out on separate lines at the same time. There is one line for each bit, as shown in Figure 12(b) for the example of eight bits being transferred from a computer to a printer. To transfer eight bits in parallel, it takes one time interval compared to eight time intervals for the serial transfer.

To summarize, an advantage of serial transfer of binary data is that a minimum of only one line is required. In parallel transfer, a number of lines equal to the number of bits to be transferred at one time is required. A disadvantage of serial transfer is that it takes longer to transfer a given number of bits than with parallel transfer at the same clock frequency. For example, if one bit can be transferred in 1 μs, then it takes 8 μs to serially transfer eight bits but only 1 μs to parallel transfer eight bits. A disadvantage of parallel transfer is that it takes more lines than serial transfer.

COMPUTER NOTE

Universal Serial Bus (USB) is a serial bus standard for device interfacing. It was originally developed for the personal computer but has become widely used on many types of handheld and mobile devices. USB is expected to replace other serial and parallel ports. USB operated at 12 Mbps (million bits per second) when first introduced in 1995, but it now operates at 480 Mbps.

EXAMPLE 2

(a) Determine the total time required to serially transfer the eight bits contained in waveform A of Figure 13, and indicate the sequence of bits. The left-most bit is the first to be transferred. The 1 MHz clock is used as reference.

(b) What is the total time to transfer the same eight bits in parallel?

▶ FIGURE 13

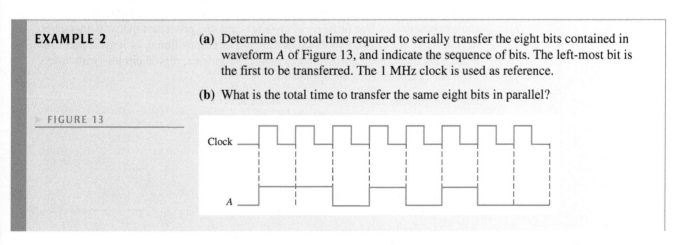

Solution   **(a)** Since the frequency of the clock is 1 MHz, the period is

$$T = \frac{1}{f} = \frac{1}{1 \text{ MHz}} = 1 \ \mu s$$

It takes 1 μs to transfer each bit in the waveform. The total transfer time for 8 bits is

$$8 \times 1 \ \mu s = \mathbf{8 \ \mu s}$$

To determine the sequence of bits, examine the waveform in Figure 13 during each bit time. If waveform *A* is HIGH during the bit time, a 1 is transferred. If waveform *A* is LOW during the bit time, a 0 is transferred. The bit sequence is illustrated in Figure 14. The left-most bit is the first to be transferred.

FIGURE 14

(b) A parallel transfer would take **1 μs** for all eight bits.

Related Problem   If binary data are transferred on a USB at the rate of 480 million bits per second (480 Mbps), how long will it take to serially transfer 16 bits?

SECTION 2 CHECKUP

1. Define *binary*.
2. What does *bit* mean?
3. What are the bits in a binary system?
4. How are the rise time and fall time of a pulse measured?
5. Knowing the period of a waveform, how do you find the frequency?
6. Explain what a clock waveform is.
7. What is the purpose of a timing diagram?
8. What is the main advantage of parallel transfer over serial transfer of binary data?

---

3   BASIC LOGIC OPERATIONS

In its basic form, logic is the realm of human reasoning that tells you a certain proposition (declarative statement) is true if certain conditions are true. Propositions can be classified as true or false. Many situations and processes that you encounter in your daily life can be expressed in the form of propositional, or logic, functions. Since such functions are true/false or yes/no statements, digital circuits with their two-state characteristics are applicable.

After completing this section, you should be able to

♦ List three basic logic operations

♦ Define the NOT operation

♦ Define the AND operation

♦ Define the OR operation

Several propositions, when combined, form propositional, or logic, functions. For example, the propositional statement "The light is on" will be true if "The bulb is not burned out" is true and if "The switch is on" is true. Therefore, this logical statement can be made: *The light is on only if the bulb is not burned out and the switch is on.* In this example the first statement is true only if the last two statements are true. The first statement ("The light is on") is then the basic proposition, and the other two statements are the conditions on which the proposition depends.

In the 1850s, the Irish logician and mathematician George Boole developed a mathematical system for formulating logic statements with symbols so that problems can be written and solved in a manner similar to ordinary algebra. Boolean algebra, as it is known today, is applied in the design and analysis of digital systems.

The term **logic** is applied to digital circuits used to implement logic functions. Several kinds of digital logic **circuits** are the basic elements that form the building blocks for such complex digital systems as the computer. We will now look at these elements and discuss their functions in a very general way. Later chapters will cover these circuits in detail.

Three basic logic operations (NOT, AND, and OR) are indicated by standard distinctive shape symbols in Figure 15. The lines connected to each symbol are the **inputs** and **outputs.** The inputs are on the left of each symbol and the output is on the right. A circuit that performs a specified logic operation (AND, OR) is called a logic **gate.** AND and OR gates can have any number of inputs, as indicated by the dashes in the figure.

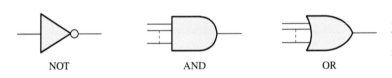

NOT   AND   OR

◀ FIGURE 15

The basic logic operations and symbols.

In logic operations, the true/false conditions mentioned earlier are represented by a HIGH (true) and a LOW (false). Each of the three basic logic operations produces a unique response to a given set of conditions.

NOT

The **NOT** operation changes one logic level to the opposite logic level, as indicated in Figure 16. When the input is HIGH (1), the output is LOW (0). When the input is LOW, the output is HIGH. In either case, the output is *not* the same as the input. The NOT operation is implemented by a logic circuit known as an **inverter.**

◀ FIGURE 16

The NOT operation.

AND

The **AND** operation produces a HIGH output only when all the inputs are HIGH, as indicated in Figure 17 for the case of two inputs. When one input is HIGH *and* the other input is HIGH, the output is HIGH. When any or all inputs are LOW, the output is LOW. The AND operation is implemented by a logic circuit known as an *AND gate.*

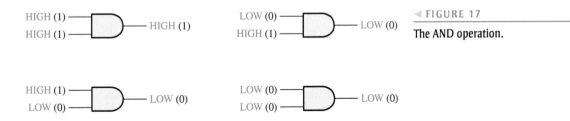

◀ FIGURE 17

The AND operation.

OR

The OR operation produces a HIGH output when one or more inputs are HIGH, as indicated in Figure 18 for the case of two inputs. When one input is HIGH *or* the other input is HIGH *or* both inputs are HIGH, the output is HIGH. When both inputs are LOW, the output is LOW. The OR operation is implemented by a logic circuit known as an *OR gate.*

▶ FIGURE 18

The OR operation.

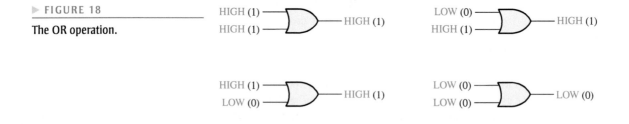

**SECTION 3
CHECKUP**

1. When does the NOT operation produce a HIGH output?
2. When does the AND operation produce a HIGH output?
3. When does the OR operation produce a HIGH output?
4. What is an inverter?
5. What is a logic gate?

4 INTRODUCTION TO THE SYSTEM CONCEPT

The three basic logic elements AND, OR, and NOT can be combined to form various types of logic functions: comparison, arithmetic, code conversion, encoding, decoding, data selection, counting, and storage. A digital system is an arrangement of the individual logic functions connected to perform a specified operation or produce a defined output. This section provides an overview of important logic functions and illustrates how they can be used in a specific system.

After completing this section, you should be able to

♦ List several types of logic functions

♦ Describe comparison and list the four arithmetic functions

♦ Describe code conversion, encoding, and decoding

♦ Describe multiplexing and demultiplexing

♦ Describe the counting function

♦ Describe the storage function

♦ Explain the operation of the tablet-bottling system

The Comparison Function

Magnitude comparison is performed by a logic circuit called a **comparator.** A comparator compares two quantities and indicates whether or not they are equal. For example, suppose you have two numbers and wish to know if they are equal or not equal and, if not equal, which is greater. The comparison function is represented in Figure 19. One number

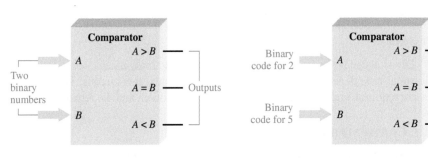

(a) Basic magnitude comparator

(b) Example: *A* is less than *B* (2 < 5) as indicated by the HIGH output (*A* < *B*)

in binary form (represented by logic levels) is applied to input *A*, and the other number in binary form (represented by logic levels) is applied to input *B*. The outputs indicate the relationship of the two numbers by producing a HIGH level on the proper output line. Suppose that a binary representation of the number 2 is applied to input *A* and a binary representation of the number 5 is applied to input *B*. A HIGH level will appear on the $A < B$ (*A* is less than *B*) output, indicating the relationship between the two numbers (2 is less than 5). The wide arrows represent a group of parallel lines on which the bits are transferred.

The Arithmetic Functions

Addition Addition is performed by a logic circuit called an **adder.** An adder adds two binary numbers (on inputs *A* and *B* with a carry input C_{in}) and generates a sum (Σ) and a carry output (C_{out}), as shown in Figure 20(a). Figure 20(b) illustrates the addition of 3 and 9. You know that the sum is 12; the adder indicates this result by producing 2 on the sum output and 1 on the carry output. Assume that the carry input in this example is 0.

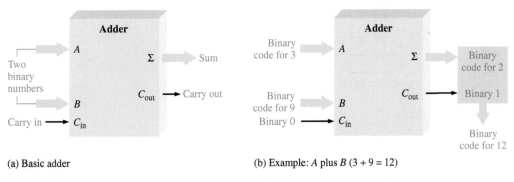

(a) Basic adder

(b) Example: *A* plus *B* (3 + 9 = 12)

The addition function.

Subtraction Subtraction is also performed by a logic circuit. A **subtracter** requires three inputs: the two numbers that are to be subtracted and a borrow input. The two outputs are the difference and the borrow output. When, for instance, 5 is subtracted from 8 with no borrow input, the difference is 3 with no borrow output. Subtraction can actually be performed by an adder because subtraction is simply a special case of addition.

Multiplication Multiplication is performed by a logic circuit called a *multiplier.* Numbers are always multiplied two at a time, so two inputs are required. The output of the multiplier is the product. Because multiplication is simply a series of additions with shifts in

COMPUTER NOTE

In a microprocessor, the arithmetic logic unit (ALU) performs the operations of add, subtract, multiply, and divide as well as the logic operations on digital data as directed by a series of instructions. A typical ALU is constructed of many thousands of logic gates.

the positions of the partial products, it can be performed by using an adder in conjunction with other circuits.

Division Division can be performed with a series of subtractions, comparisons, and shifts, and thus it can also be done using an adder in conjunction with other circuits. Two inputs to the divider are required, and the outputs generated are the quotient and the remainder.

The Code Conversion Function

A **code** is a set of bits arranged in a unique pattern and used to represent specified information. A code converter changes one form of coded information into another coded form. Examples are conversion between binary and other codes such as the binary coded decimal (BCD) and the Gray code.

The Encoding Function

The encoding function is performed by a logic circuit called an **encoder.** The encoder converts information, such as a decimal number or an alphabetic character, into some coded form. For example, one certain type of encoder converts each of the decimal digits, 0 through 9, to a binary code. A HIGH level on the input corresponding to a specific decimal digit produces logic levels that represent the proper binary code on the output lines.

Figure 21 is a simple illustration of an encoder used to convert (encode) a calculator keystroke into a binary code that can be processed by the calculator circuits.

▶ FIGURE 21

An encoder used to encode a calculator keystroke into a binary code for storage or for calculation.

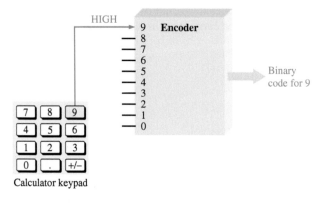

The Decoding Function

The decoding function is performed by a logic circuit called a **decoder.** The decoder converts coded information, such as a binary number, into a noncoded form, such as a decimal form. For example, one particular type of decoder converts a 4-bit binary code into the appropriate decimal digit.

Figure 22 is a simple illustration of one type of decoder that is used to activate a 7-segment display. Each of the seven segments of the display is connected to an output line

▶ FIGURE 22

A decoder used to convert a special binary code into a 7-segment decimal readout.

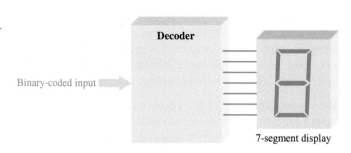

from the decoder. When a particular binary code appears on the decoder inputs, the appropriate output lines are activated and light the proper segments to display the decimal digit corresponding to the binary code.

The Data Selection Function

Two types of circuits that select data are the multiplexer and the demultiplexer. The **multiplexer,** or mux for short, is a logic circuit that switches digital data from several input lines onto a single output line in a specified time sequence. Functionally, a multiplexer can be represented by an electronic switch operation that sequentially connects each of the input lines to the output line. The **demultiplexer** (demux) is a logic circuit that switches digital data from one input line to several output lines in a specified time sequence. Essentially, the demux is a mux in reverse.

Multiplexing and demultiplexing are used when data from several sources are to be transmitted over one line to a distant location and redistributed to several destinations. Figure 23 illustrates this type of application where digital data from three sources are sent out along a single line to three terminals at another location.

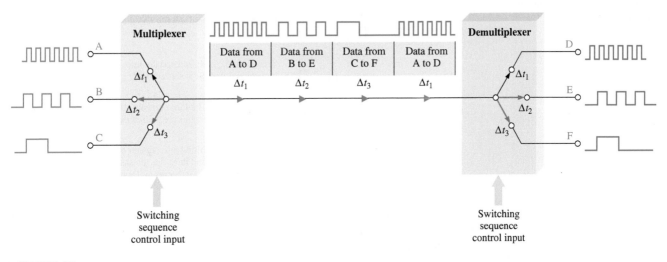

Illustration of a basic multiplexing/demultiplexing application.

In Figure 23, data from input A are connected to the output line during time interval Δt_1 and transmitted to the demultiplexer that connects them to output D. Then, during interval Δt_2, the multiplexer switches to input B and the demultiplexer switches to output E. During interval Δt_3, the multiplexer switches to input C and the demultiplexer switches to output F.

To summarize, during the first time interval, input A data go to output D. During the second time interval, input B data go to output E. During the third time interval, input C data go to output F. After this, the sequence repeats. Because the time is divided up among several sources and destinations where each has its turn to send and receive data, this process is called *time division multiplexing* (TDM).

The Storage Function

Storage is a function that is required in most digital systems, and its purpose is to retain binary data for a period of time. Some storage devices are used for short-term storage and some are used for long-term storage. A storage device can "memorize" a bit or a group of bits and retain the information as long as necessary. Common types of storage devices are flip-flops, registers, semiconductor memories, magnetic disks, magnetic tape, and optical disks (CDs).

COMPUTER NOTE

The internal computer memories, RAM and ROM, as well as the smaller caches are semiconductor memories. The registers in a microprocessor are constructed of semiconductor flip-flops. Opto-magnetic disk memories are used in the internal hard drive and for the CD-ROM.

Flip-flops   A **flip-flop** is a bistable (two stable states) logic circuit that can store only one bit at a time, either a 1 or a 0. The output of a flip-flop indicates which bit it is storing. A HIGH output indicates that a 1 is stored and a LOW output indicates that a 0 is stored. Flip-flops are implemented with logic gates.

Registers   A **register** is formed by combining several flip-flops so that groups of bits can be stored. For example, an 8-bit register is constructed from eight flip-flops. In addition to storing bits, registers can be used to shift the bits from one position to another within the register or out of the register to another circuit; therefore, these devices are known as *shift registers*.

The two basic types of shift registers are serial and parallel. The bits are stored in a serial shift register one at a time, as illustrated in Figure 24. A good analogy to the serial shift register is loading passengers onto a bus single file through the door. They also exit the bus single file.

▶ FIGURE 24

Example of the operation of a 4-bit serial shift register. Each block represents one storage "cell" or flip-flop.

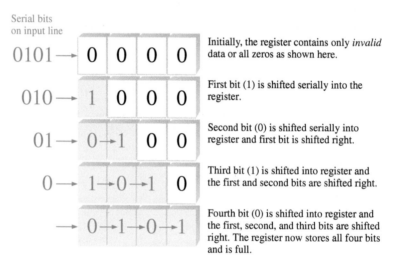

Initially, the register contains only *invalid* data or all zeros as shown here.

First bit (1) is shifted serially into the register.

Second bit (0) is shifted serially into register and first bit is shifted right.

Third bit (1) is shifted into register and the first and second bits are shifted right.

Fourth bit (0) is shifted into register and the first, second, and third bits are shifted right. The register now stores all four bits and is full.

The bits are stored in a parallel register simultaneously from parallel lines, as shown in Figure 25. For this case, a good analogy is loading passengers on a roller coaster where they enter all of the cars in parallel.

▶ FIGURE 25

Example of the operation of a 4-bit parallel shift register.

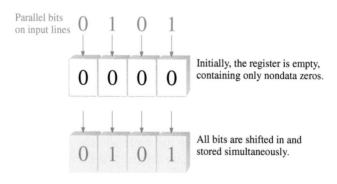

Initially, the register is empty, containing only nondata zeros.

All bits are shifted in and stored simultaneously.

Semiconductor Memories   Semiconductor memories are devices typically used for storing large numbers of bits. In one type of memory, called the *read-only memory* or ROM, the binary data are permanently or semipermanently stored and cannot be readily changed. In the *random-access memory* or RAM, the binary data are temporarily stored and can be easily changed.

Magnetic Memories   Magnetic disk memories are used for mass storage of binary data. Examples are the so-called floppy disks used in computers and the computer's internal hard disk. Magneto-optical disks use laser beams to store and retrieve data. Magnetic tape is still used in memory applications and for backing up data from other storage devices.

The Counting Function

The counting function is important in digital systems. There are many types of digital **counters,** but their basic purpose is to count events represented by changing levels or pulses. To count, the counter must "remember" the present number so that it can go to the next proper number in sequence. Therefore, storage capability is an important characteristic of all counters, and flip-flops are generally used to implement them. Figure 26 illustrates the basic idea of counter operation.

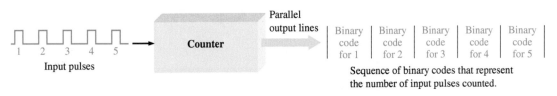

▲ FIGURE 26

Illustration of basic counter operation.

A Process Control System

A system for bottling vitamin tablets is shown in the block diagram of Figure 27. To begin, the tablets are fed into a large funnel-type hopper. The narrow neck of the hopper creates a serial flow of tablets into a bottle on the conveyor belt below. Only one tablet at a time passes the sensor, so the tablets can be counted.

The system controls the number of tablets into each bottle and displays a continually updated readout of the total number of tablets bottled. This system utilizes all of the basic logic functions that have been introduced in this section and illustrates how these functions can be connected to work together to produce a specified result. This system is purely for instructional purposes and is not intended to necessarily represent the most efficient or best way to implement the operation.

General Operation   The maximum number of tablets per bottle is entered from the keypad, changed to a code by the *Encoder,* and stored in *Register A.* Decoder A changes the code stored in the register to a form appropriate for turning on the display. *Code converter A* changes the code to a binary number and applies it to the *A* input of the *Comparator* (Comp).

An optical sensor in the neck of the hopper detects each tablet that passes and produces a pulse. This pulse goes to the *Counter* and advances it by one count; thus, any time during the filling of a bottle, the binary state of the counter represents the number of tablets in the bottle. The binary count is transferred from the counter to the *B* input of the comparator (Comp). The *A* input of the comparator is the binary number for the maximum tablets per bottle. Now, let's say that the present number of tablets per bottle is 50. When the binary number in the counter reaches 50, the $A = B$ output of the comparator goes HIGH, indicating that the bottle is full.

The HIGH output of the comparator causes the valve in the neck of the hopper to close and stop the flow of tablets. At the same time, the HIGH output of the comparator activates the conveyor, which moves the next empty bottle into place under the hopper. When the bottle is in place, the conveyor control issues a pulse that resets the counter to zero. As a result, the output of the comparator goes back LOW and causes the hopper valve to restart the flow of tablets.

For each bottle filled, the maximum binary number in the counter is transferred to the *A* input of the *Adder.* The *B* input of the adder comes from *Register B* that stores the total number of tablets bottled up through the last bottle filled. The adder produces a new cumulative sum that is then stored in register B, replacing the previous sum. This keeps a running total of the tablets bottled during a given run.

The cumulative sum stored in register B goes to *Code Converter B,* which changes it into a code that *Decoder B* then uses to activate the decimal display. The binary sum in register B also goes to the *Multiplexer* (MUX) for conversion from parallel to serial form and

17

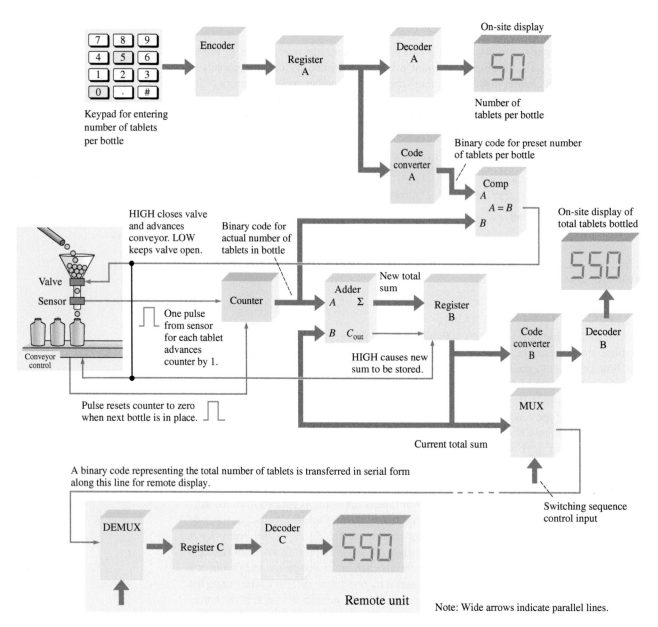

▲ FIGURE 27

Block diagram of a tablet-bottling system.

transmission over the single line to the remote *Demultiplexer* (DEMUX), which changes the number back to parallel form for storage in *Register C*. The number is then decoded by *Decoder C* for display at the remote location.

SECTION 4 CHECKUP	
	1. What does a comparator do?
	2. What are the four basic arithmetic operations?
	3. Describe encoding and give an example.
	4. Describe decoding and give an example.
	5. Explain the basic purpose of multiplexing and demultiplexing.
	6. Name four types of storage devices.
	7. What does a counter do?

5 FIXED-FUNCTION INTEGRATED CIRCUITS

All the logic elements and functions that have been discussed are generally available in integrated circuit (IC) form. Digital systems have incorporated ICs for many years because of their small size, high reliability, low cost, and low power consumption. It is important to be able to recognize the IC packages and to know how the pin connections are numbered, as well as to be familiar with the way in which circuit complexities and circuit technologies determine the various IC classifications.

After completing this section, you should be able to

- Recognize the difference between through-hole devices and surface-mount fixed-function devices
- Identify dual in-line packages (DIP)
- Identify small-outline integrated circuit packages (SOIC)
- Identify plastic leaded chip carrier packages (PLCC)
- Identify leadless ceramic chip carrier packages (LCC)
- Determine pin numbers on various types of IC packages
- Explain the complexity classifications for fixed-function ICs

A monolithic **integrated circuit (IC)** is an electronic circuit that is constructed entirely on a single small chip of silicon. All the components that make up the circuit—transistors, diodes, resistors, and capacitors—are an integral part of that single chip. Fixed-function logic and programmable logic are two broad categories of digital ICs. In **fixed-function logic**, the logic functions are set by the manufacturer and cannot be altered.

Figure 28 shows a cutaway view of one type of fixed-function IC package with the circuit chip shown within the package. Points on the chip are connected to the package pins to allow input and output connections to the outside world.

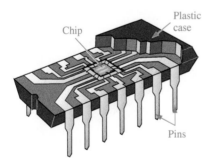

Chip
Plastic case
Pins

◀ FIGURE 28

Cutaway view of one type of fixed-function IC package (dual in-line package) showing the chip mounted inside, with connections to input and output pins.

IC Packages

Integrated circuit (IC) packages are classified according to the way they are mounted on printed circuit (PC) boards as either through-hole mounted or surface mounted. The through-hole type packages have pins (leads) that are inserted through holes in the PC board and can be soldered to conductors on the opposite side. The most common type of through-hole package is the dual in-line package (**DIP**) shown in Figure 29(a).

Another type of IC package uses surface-mount technology (**SMT**). Surface mounting is a space-saving alternative to through-hole mounting. The holes through the PC board are unnecessary for SMT. The pins of surface-mounted packages are soldered directly to conductors on one side of the board, leaving the other side free for additional circuits. Also, for a circuit with the same number of pins, a surface-mounted package is much smaller than a

Examples of through-hole and surface-mounted devices. The DIP is larger than the SOIC with the same number of leads. This particular DIP is approximately 0.785 in. long, and the SOIC is approximately 0.385 in. long.

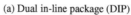

(a) Dual in-line package (DIP)   (b) Small-outline IC (SOIC)

dual in-line package because the pins are placed closer together. An example of a surface-mounted package is the small-outline integrated circuit (**SOIC**) shown in Figure 29(b).

Various types of SMT packages are available in a range of sizes, depending on the number of leads (more leads are required for more complex circuits and lead configurations). Examples of several types are shown in Figure 30. As you can see, the leads of the **SSOP** (shrink small-outline package) are formed into a "gull-wing" shape. The leads of the **PLCC** (plastic-leaded chip carrier) are turned under the package in a J-type shape. Instead of leads, the **LCC** (leadless ceramic chip) has metal contacts molded into its ceramic body. The LQFP also has gull-wing leads. Both the CSP (chip scale package) and the FBGA (fine-pitch ball grid array) have contacts embedded in the bottom of the package.

(a) SSOP (153 × 193 mils)   (b) PLCC (350 × 350 mils)   (c) LCC (350 × 350 mils)

(d) LQFP (7 × 7 mm)   (e) Laminate CSP (3.5 × 3.5 mm)   (f) FBGA (4 × 4 mm)

▲ FIGURE 30

Examples of SMT package configurations. Parts (e) and (f) show bottom views.

Pin Numbering

All IC packages have a standard format for numbering the pins (leads). The dual in-line packages (DIPs) and the shrink small-outline packages (SSOP) have the numbering arrangement illustrated in Figure 31(a) for a 16-pin package. Looking at the top of the package, pin 1 is indicated by an identifier that can be either a small dot, a notch, or a beveled edge. The dot is always next to pin 1. Also, with the notch oriented upward, pin 1 is always the top left pin, as indicated. Starting with pin 1, the pin numbers increase as you go down, then across and up. The highest pin number is always to the right of the notch or opposite the dot.

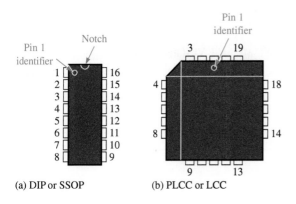

Pin numbering for standard types of IC packages. Top views are shown.

(a) DIP or SSOP   (b) PLCC or LCC

The PLCC and LCC packages have leads arranged on all four sides. Pin 1 is indicated by a dot or other index mark and is located at the center of one set of leads. The pin numbers increase going counterclockwise as viewed from the top of the package. The highest pin number is always to the right of pin 1. Figure 31(b) illustrates this format for a 20-pin PLCC package.

Complexity Classifications for Fixed-Function ICs

Fixed-function digital ICs are classified according to their complexity. They are listed here from the least complex to the most complex. The complexity figures stated here for SSI, MSI, LSI, VLSI, and ULSI are generally accepted, but definitions may vary from one source to another.

+ **Small-scale integration (SSI)** describes fixed-function ICs that have up to ten equivalent gate circuits on a single chip, and they include basic gates and flip-flops.

+ **Medium-scale integration (MSI)** describes integrated circuits that have from 10 to 100 equivalent gates on a chip. They include logic functions such as encoders, decoders, counters, registers, multiplexers, arithmetic circuits, small memories, and others.

+ **Large-scale integration (LSI)** is a classification of ICs with complexities of from more than 100 to 10,000 equivalent gates per chip, including memories.

+ **Very large-scale integration (VLSI)** describes integrated circuits with complexities of from more than 10,000 to 100,000 equivalent gates per chip.

+ **Ultra large-scale integration (ULSI)** describes very large memories, larger **microprocessors,** and larger single-chip computers. Complexities of more than 100,000 equivalent gates per chip are classified as ULSI.

Integrated Circuit Technologies

The types of transistors with which all integrated circuits are implemented are either MOSFETs (metal-oxide semiconductor field-effect transistors) or bipolar junction transistors. A circuit technology that uses MOSFETs is CMOS (complementary MOS). One type of fixed-function digital circuit technology uses bipolar junction transistors and is sometimes called TTL (transistor-transistor logic). BiCMOS uses a combination of both CMOS and bipolar.

All gates and other functions can be implemented with either type of circuit technology. SSI and MSI circuits are generally available in both CMOS and bipolar. LSI, VLSI, and ULSI are generally implemented with CMOS or NMOS because it requires less area on a chip and consumes less power.

SECTION 5
CHECKUP

1. What is an integrated circuit?
2. Define the terms DIP, SMT, SOIC, SSI, MSI, LSI, VLSI and ULSI.
3. Generally, in what classification does a fixed-function IC with the following number of equivalent gates fall?

    (a) 10   (b) 75   (c) 500

    (d) 15,000   (e) 200,000

6 TEST AND MEASUREMENT INSTRUMENTS

Troubleshooting is the process of systematically isolating, identifying, and correcting a fault in a circuit or system. A variety of instruments are available for use in troubleshooting and testing. Some common types of instruments are introduced and discussed in this section.

After completing this section, you should be able to

♦ Distinguish between an analog and a digital oscilloscope

♦ Recognize common oscilloscope controls

♦ Determine amplitude, period, frequency, and duty cycle of a pulse waveform with an oscilloscope

♦ Discuss the logic analyzer and some common formats

♦ Describe the purpose of the data pattern generator, the digital multimeter (DMM), the dc power supply, the logic probe, and the logic pulser

The Oscilloscope

The oscilloscope (scope for short) is one of the most widely used instruments for general testing and troubleshooting. The scope is basically a graph-displaying device that traces the graph of a measured electrical signal on its screen. In most applications, the graph shows how signals change over time. The vertical axis of the display screen represents voltage, and the horizontal axis represents time. Amplitude, period, and frequency of a signal can be measured using the oscilloscope. Also, the pulse width, duty cycle, rise time, and fall time of a pulse waveform can be determined. Most scopes can display at least two signals on the screen at one time, enabling their time relationship to be observed. Typical digital oscilloscopes are shown in Figure 32.

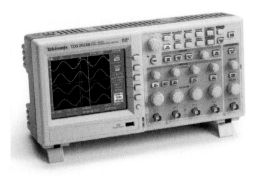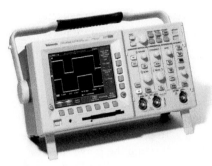

▲ FIGURE 32

Typical digital oscilloscopes. Used with permission from Tektronix, Inc.

Two basic types of oscilloscopes, analog and digital, can be used to view digital waveforms. As shown in Figure 33(a), the analog scope works by applying the measured waveform directly to control the up and down motion of the electron beam in the cathode-ray tube (CRT) as it sweeps across the display screen. As a result, the beam traces out the waveform pattern on the screen. As shown in Figure 33(b), the digital scope converts the measured waveform to digital information by a sampling process in an analog-to-digital converter (ADC). The digital information is then used to reconstruct the waveform on the screen.

The digital scope is more widely used than the analog scope. However, either type can be used in many applications; each has characteristics that make it more suitable for certain

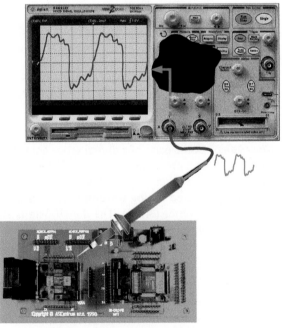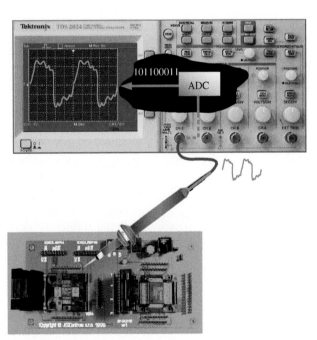

(a) Analog oscilloscope. Displayed waveform is created directly from the analog input signal.

(b) Digital oscilloscope. Displayed waveform is created by converting the analog input signal to digital form for processing and then reconstructing it.

▲ FIGURE 33

Basic comparison of analog and digital oscilloscope operation.

situations. An analog scope displays waveforms as they occur in "real time." Digital scopes are useful for measuring transient pulses that may occur randomly or only once. Also, because information about the measured waveform can be stored in a digital scope, it may be viewed at some later time, printed out, or thoroughly analyzed by a computer or other means.

Basic Operation of Analog Oscilloscopes To measure a voltage, a **probe** must be connected from the scope to the point in a circuit at which the voltage is present. Generally, a ×10 probe is used that reduces (attenuates) the signal amplitude by ten. The signal goes through the probe into the vertical circuits where it is either further attenuated or amplified, depending on the actual amplitude and on where you set the vertical control of the scope. The vertical circuits then drive the vertical deflection plates of the CRT. Also, the signal goes to the trigger circuits that trigger the horizontal circuits to initiate repetitive horizontal sweeps of the electron beam across the screen using a sawtooth waveform. There are many sweeps per second so that the beam appears to form a solid line across the screen in the shape of the waveform. This basic operation is illustrated in Figure 34.

▶ FIGURE 34

Block diagram of an analog oscilloscope.

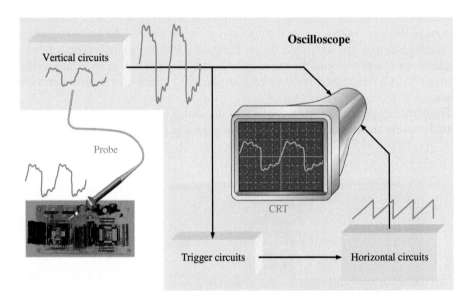

Basic Operation of Digital Oscilloscopes Some parts of a digital scope are similar to the analog scope. However, the digital scope is more complex than an analog scope and typically has an LCD screen rather than a CRT. Rather than displaying a waveform as it occurs, the digital scope first acquires the measured analog waveform and converts it to a digital format using an analog-to-digital converter (ADC). The digital data is stored and processed. The data then goes to the reconstruction and display circuits for display in its original analog form. Figure 35 shows a basic block diagram for a digital oscilloscope.

Oscilloscope Controls A front panel view of a typical digital oscilloscope is shown in Figure 36. Instruments vary depending on model and manufacturer, but most have certain common features. For example, the four vertical sections contain a Position control, a channel menu button, and a volts/div control. The horizontal section contains a sec/div control.

Some of the main oscilloscope controls are now discussed. Refer to the user manual for complete details of your particular scope.

Vertical Controls In the vertical section of the scope in Figure 36, there are identical controls for each of the four channels (CH1, CH2, CH3, and CH4). The Position control

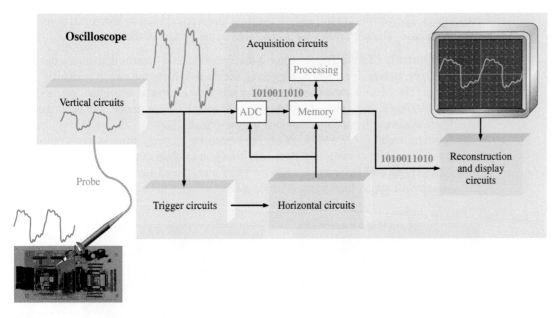

▲ FIGURE 35

Block diagram of a digital oscilloscope.

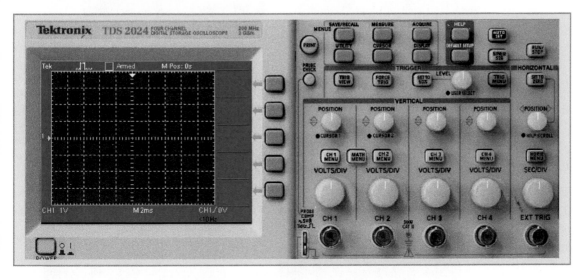

▲ FIGURE 36

Representation of a typical digital oscilloscope front panel. Numbers below screen indicate the values for each division on the vertical (voltage) and horizontal (time) scales and can be varied using the vertical and horizontal controls on the scope.

lets you move a displayed waveform up or down vertically on the screen. The buttons on the right side of the screen provide for the selection of several items that appear on the screen, such as the coupling modes (ac, dc, or ground), coarse or fine adjustment for the volts/div, signal inversion, and other parameters. The volts/div control adjusts the number of volts represented by each vertical division on the screen. The volts/div setting for each channel is displayed on the bottom of the screen.

Horizontal Controls In the horizontal section, the controls apply to all channels. The Position control lets you move a displayed waveform left or right horizontally on the screen. The Menu button provides for the selection of several items that appear on the screen such as the main time base, expanded view of a portion of a waveform, and other parameters. The sec/div control adjusts the time represented by each horizontal division or main time base. The sec/div setting is displayed at the bottom of the screen.

Trigger Controls   In the Trigger control section, the Level control determines the point on the triggering waveform where triggering occurs to initiate the sweep to display input waveforms. The Menu button provides for the selection of several items that appear on the screen, including edge or slope triggering, trigger source, trigger mode, and other parameters. There is also an input for an external trigger signal.

Triggering stabilizes a waveform on the screen or properly triggers on a pulse that occurs only one time or randomly. Also, it allows you to observe time delays between two waveforms. Figure 37 compares a triggered to an untriggered signal. The untriggered signal tends to drift across the screen, producing what appears to be multiple waveforms.

▶ FIGURE 37

Comparison of an untriggered and a triggered waveform on an oscilloscope.

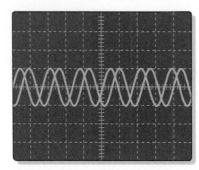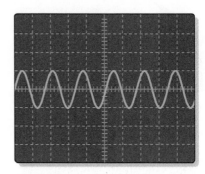

(a) Untriggered waveform display   (b) Triggered waveform display

Coupling a Signal into the Scope   Coupling is the method used to connect a signal voltage to be measured into the oscilloscope. DC and AC coupling are usually selected from the Vertical menu on a scope. DC coupling allows a waveform including its dc component to be displayed. AC coupling blocks the dc component of a signal so that you see the waveform centered at 0 V. The Ground mode allows you to connect the channel input to ground to see where the 0 V reference is on the screen. Figure 38 illustrates the result of DC and AC coupling using a pulse waveform that has a dc component.

▶ FIGURE 38

Displays of the same waveform having a dc component.

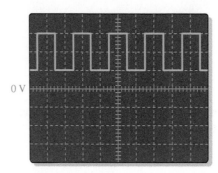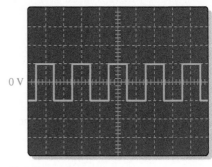

(a) DC coupled waveform   (b) AC coupled waveform

The voltage probe, shown in Figure 39, is essential for connecting a signal to the scope. Since all instruments tend to affect the circuit being measured due to loading, most scope probes provide a high series resistance to minimize loading effects. Probes that have a series resistance ten times larger than the input resistance of the scope are called ×10 probes. Probes with no series resistance are called ×1 probes. The oscilloscope adjusts its calibration for the attenuation of the type of probe being used. For most measurements, the ×10 probe should be used. However, if you are measuring very small signals, a ×1 may be the best choice.

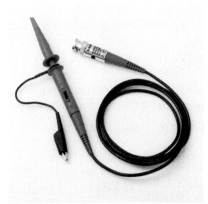

◀ FIGURE 39

An oscilloscope voltage probe. Used with permission from Tektronix, Inc.

The probe has an adjustment that allows you to compensate for the input capacitance of the scope. Most scopes have a probe compensation output that provides a calibrated square wave for probe compensation. Before making a measurement, you should make sure that the probe is properly compensated to eliminate any distortion introduced. Typically, there is a screw or other means of adjusting compensation on a probe. Figure 40 shows scope waveforms for three probe conditions: properly compensated, undercompensated, and overcompensated. If the waveform appears either over- or undercompensated, adjust the probe until the properly compensated square wave is achieved.

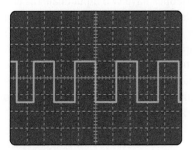
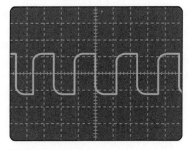
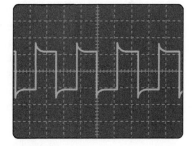

Properly compensated   Undercompensated   Overcompensated

▲ FIGURE 40

Probe compensation conditions.

EXAMPLE 3

Based on the readouts, determine the amplitude and the period of the pulse waveform on the screen of a digital oscilloscope as shown in Figure 41. Also, calculate the frequency.

▶ FIGURE 41

Ch1   1 V   10 μs

Solution   The volts/div setting is 1 V. The pulses are three divisions high. Since each division represents 1 V, the pulse amplitude is

$$\text{Amplitude} = (3\,\text{div})(1\,\text{V/div}) = \mathbf{3\,V}$$

The sec/div setting is 10 μs. A full cycle of the waveform (from beginning of one pulse to the beginning of the next) covers four divisions; therefore, the period is

$$\text{Period} = (4\,\text{div})(10\,\mu\text{s/div}) = \mathbf{40\,\mu s}$$

The frequency is calculated as

$$f = \frac{1}{T} = \frac{1}{40\,\mu s} = \mathbf{25\,kHz}$$

Related Problem   For a volts/div setting of 4 V and sec/div setting of 2 ms, determine the amplitude and period of the pulse shown on the screen in Figure 41.

The Logic Analyzer

Logic analyzers are used for measurements of multiple digital signals and measurement situations with difficult trigger requirements. Basically, the logic analyzer came about as a result of microprocessors in which troubleshooting or debugging required many more inputs than an oscilloscope offered. Many oscilloscopes have two input channels and some are available with four. Logic analyzers are available with from 34 to 136 input channels. Generally, an oscilloscope is used either when amplitude, frequency, and other timing parameters of a few signals at a time or when parameters such an rise and fall times, overshoot, and delay times need to be measured. The logic analyzer is used when the logic levels of a large number of signals need to be determined and for the correlation of simultaneous signals based on their timing relationships. A typical logic analyzer is shown in Figure 42, and a simplified block diagram is in Figure 43.

▷ FIGURE 42

Typical logic analyzer. Used with permission from Tektronix, Inc.

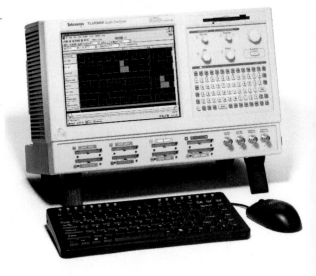

Data Acquisition   The large number of signals that can be acquired at one time is a major factor that distinguishes a logic analyzer from an oscilloscope. Generally, the two types of data acquisition in a logic analyzer are the timing acquisition and the state acquisition. Timing acquisition is used primarily when the timing relationships among the various signals need to be determined. State acquisition is used when you need to view the sequence of states as they appear in a system under test.

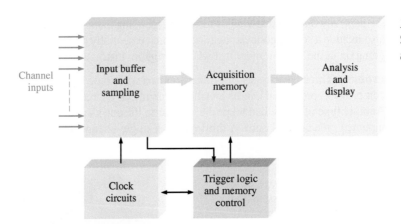

◀ FIGURE 43

Simplified block diagram of a logic analyzer.

It is often helpful to have correlated timing and state data, and most logic analyzers can simultaneously acquire that data. For example, a problem may initially be detected as an invalid state. However, the invalid condition may be caused by a timing violation in the system under test. Without both types of information available at the same time, isolating the problem could be very difficult.

Channel Count and Memory Depth Logic analyzers contain a real-time acquisition memory in which sampled data from all the channels are stored as they occur. Two features that are of primary importance are the channel count and the memory depth. The acquisition memory can be thought of as having a width equal to the number of channels and a depth that is the number of bits that can be captured by each channel during a certain time interval.

Channel count determines the number of signals that can be acquired simultaneously. In certain types of systems, a large number of signals are present, such as on the data bus in a microprocessor-based system. The depth of the acquisition memory determines the amount of data from a given channel that you can view at any given time.

Analysis and Display Once data has been sampled and stored in the acquisition memory, it can typically be used in several different display and analysis modes. The waveform display is much like the display on an oscilloscope where you can view the time relationship of multiple signals. The listing display indicates the state of the system under test by showing the values of the input waveforms (1s and 0s) at various points in time (sample points). Typically, this data can be displayed in hexadecimal or other formats. Figure 44 shows simplified versions of these two display modes. The listing display samples correspond to the sampled points shown in red on the waveform display.

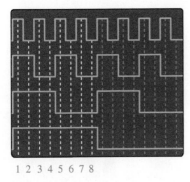

Sample	Binary	Hex	Time
1	1111	F	1 ns
2	1110	E	10 ns
3	1101	D	20 ns
4	1100	C	30 ns
5	1011	B	40 ns
6	1010	A	50 ns
7	1001	9	60 ns
8	1000	8	70 ns

1 2 3 4 5 6 7 8

(a) Waveform display   (b) Listing display

◀ FIGURE 44

Two logic analyzer display modes.

Two more modes that are useful in computer and microprocessor-based system testing are the instruction trace and the source code debug. The instruction trace determines and displays instructions that occur, for example, on the data bus in a microprocessor-based system. In this mode the op-codes and the mnemonics (English-like names) of instructions are generally displayed as well as their corresponding memory address. Many logic analyzers also include a source code debug mode, which essentially allows you to see what is actually going on in the system under test when a program instruction is executed.

Probes Three basic types of probes are used with logic analyzers. One is a multichannel compression probe that can be attached to points on a circuit board, as shown in Figure 45. Another type of multichannel probe, similar to the one shown, plugs into dedicated sockets mounted on a circuit board. A third type is a single-channel clip-on probe.

▶ FIGURE 45

A typical multichannel logic analyzer probe. Used with permission from Tektronix, Inc.

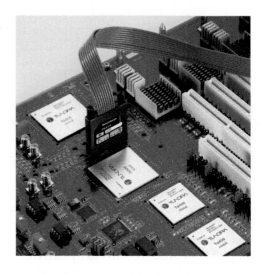

Signal Generators

Logic Signal Source These instruments are also known as pulse generators and data pattern generators. They are specifically designed to generate digital signals with precise edge placement and amplitudes and to produce the streams of 1s and 0s needed to test computer buses, microprocessors, and other digital systems.

Arbitrary Waveform Generators and Data Pattern Generators The arbitrary waveform generator can be used to generate standard signals like sine waves, triangular waves, and pulses as well as signals with various shapes and characteristics. Waveforms can be defined by mathematical or graphical input. A typical arbitrary waveform generator is shown in Figure 46(a).

The data pattern generator, shown in Figure 46(b), provides digital waveforms with programmable bit patterns. The function generator, shown in part (c), provides pulse, sine,

(a) Arbitrary waveform generator

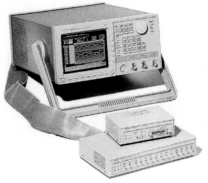

(b) Data pattern generator

(c) Function generator

▲ FIGURE 46

Typical signal generators. Used with permission from Tektronix, Inc.

and triangular waveforms, often with programmable capability. Signal generators have logic-compatible outputs to provide the proper level and drive for inputs to digital circuits.

The Digital Multimeter (DMM)

The digital multimeter (DMM) is a versatile instrument found on virtually all workbenches. All DMMs can make basic ac and dc voltage, current, and resistance measurements. Voltage and resistance measurements are the principal quantities measured with DMMs. For current measurements, the leads are switched to a separate set of jacks and placed in series with the current path. In this mode, the meter acts like a short circuit, so serious problems can occur if the meter is incorrectly placed in parallel.

In addition to the basic measurements, most DMMs can also test diodes and capacitors and frequently will have other capabilities such as frequency measurements. Most new DMMs have an autoranging feature, meaning that the user is not required to select a range for making a measurement. If the range is not set automatically, the user needs to set the range switch for voltage measurements *higher* than the expected reading to avoid damage to the meter.

In digital circuits, DMMs are the preferred instrument for setting dc power supply voltages or checking the supply voltage on various points in the circuit. Because digital signals are nonsinusoidal, the DMM is generally *not* used for measurements of digital signals (although the average or rms value can be determined in some cases). For signal measurements, the oscilloscope is the preferred instrument.

In addition, DMMs are used in digital circuits for testing continuity between points in a circuit and checking resistors with the ohmmeter function. For checking a circuit path or looking for a short, DMMs are the instrument of choice. Many DMMs sound a beep or tone when there is continuity between the leads, making it handy to trace paths without having to look at the display. If the DMM is not equipped with a continuity test, the ohmmeter function can be used instead. Measurements of continuity or resistance are never done in "live" circuits, as any circuit voltage will disrupt the readings and can be dangerous.

Typical test bench and handheld DMMs are shown in Figure 47.

◀ FIGURE 47

Typical DMMs. Courtesy of B+K Precision.®

The DC Power Supply

This instrument is an indispensable instrument on any test bench. The power supply converts ac power from the standard wall outlet into regulated dc voltage. All digital circuits require dc voltage. Most logic circuits require from 1.2 V to 5 V to operate. The power supply is used to power circuits during design, development, and troubleshooting when in-system power is not available. Typical test bench dc power supplies are shown in Figure 48.

The Logic Probe and Logic Pulser

The logic probe is a convenient, inexpensive handheld tool that provides a means of troubleshooting a digital circuit by sensing various conditions at a point in a circuit, as illustrated

▶ FIGURE 48

Typical dc power supplies. Courtesy of B+K Precision.®

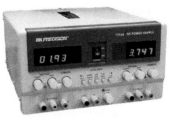

in Figure 49. The probe can detect high-level voltage, low-level voltage, single pulses, repetitive pulses, and opens on a PC board. The probe lamp indicates the condition that exists at a certain point, as indicated in the figure.

The logic pulser produces a repetitive pulse waveform that can be applied to any point in a circuit. You can apply pulses at one point in a circuit with the pulser and check another point for resulting pulses with a logic probe.

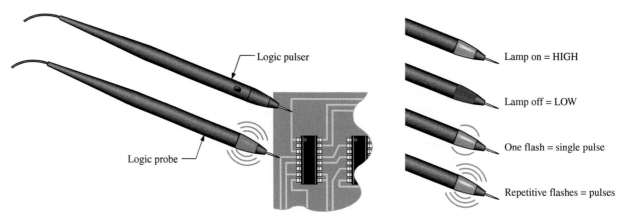

▲ FIGURE 49

Illustration of how a typical logic pulser and a logic probe can be used to apply a pulse to a given point and check for resulting pulse activity at another part of the circuit. Indications may vary depending on manufacturer.

SECTION 6 CHECKUP

1. What is the main difference between a digital and an analog oscilloscope?
2. Name two main differences between a logic analyzer and an oscilloscope?
3. What does the volts/div control on an oscilloscope do?
4. What does the sec/div control on an oscilloscope do?
5. What is the purpose of a function generator?

---

7 INTRODUCTION TO PROGRAMMABLE LOGIC

Programmable logic requires both hardware and software. **Programmable logic** devices can be programmed to perform specified logic functions by the manufacturer or by the user. One advantage of programmable logic over fixed-function logic is that the devices use much less board space for an equivalent amount of logic. Another advantage is that, with programmable logic, designs can be readily changed without rewiring or replacing components. Also, a logic design can generally be implemented faster and with less cost with programmable logic than with fixed-function ICs.

After completing this section, you should be able to

- State the major types of programmable logic and discuss the differences
- Discuss methods of programming
- List the major programming languages used for programmable logic
- Discuss the programmable logic design process

Types of Programmable Logic Devices

Many types of programmable logic are available, ranging from small devices that can replace a few fixed-function devices to complex high-density devices that can replace thousands of fixed-function devices. Two major categories of user-programmable logic are **PLD** (programmable logic device) and **FPGA** (field-programmable gate array), as indicated in Figure 50. PLDs are either SPLDs (simple PLDs) or CPLDs (complex PLDs).

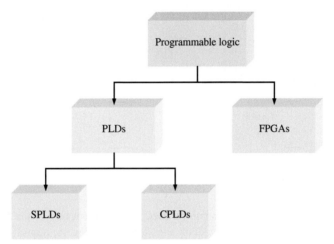

◀ FIGURE 50

Programmable logic.

Simple Programmable Logic Device (SPLD)   The SPLD was the original PLD and is still available for small-scale applications. Generally, an **SPLD** can replace up to ten fixed-function ICs and their interconnections, depending on the type of functions and the specific SPLD. Most SPLDs are in one of two categories: PAL and GAL. A **PAL** (programmable array logic) is a device that can be programmed one time. It consists of a programmable array of AND gates and a fixed array of OR gates, as shown in Figure 51(a). A **GAL**

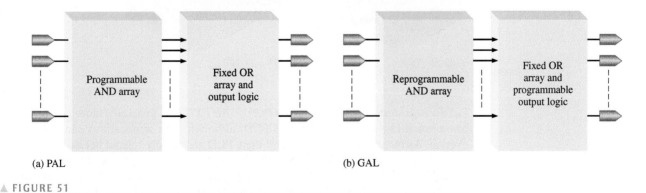

(a) PAL

(b) GAL

▲ FIGURE 51

Block diagrams of simple programmable logic devices (SPLDs).

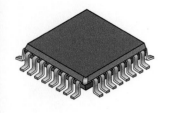

A typical SPLD package.

(generic array logic) is a device that is basically a PAL that can be reprogrammed many times. It consists of a reprogrammable array of AND gates and a fixed array of OR gates with programmable ouputs, as shown in Figure 51(b). A typical SPLD package is shown in Figure 52 and generally has from 24 to 28 pins.

Complex Programmable Logic Device (CPLD) As technology progressed and the amount of circuitry that could be put on a chip (chip density) increased, manufacturers were able to put more than one SPLD on a single chip and the CPLD was born. Essentially, the **CPLD** is a device containing multiple SPLDs and can replace many fixed-function ICs. Figure 53 shows a basic CPLD block diagram with four logic array blocks (LABs) and a programmable interconnection array (PIA). Depending on the specific CPLD, there can be from two to sixty-four LABs. Each logic array block is roughly equivalent to one SPLD.

▷ FIGURE 53

General block diagram of a CPLD.

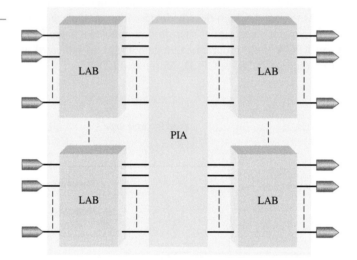

Generally, CPLDs can be used to implement any of the logic functions discussed earlier, for example, decoders, encoders, multiplexers, demultiplexers, and adders. They are available in a variety of configurations, typically ranging from 44 to 160 pin packages. Examples of CPLD packages are shown in Figure 54.

▷ FIGURE 54

Typical CPLD packages.

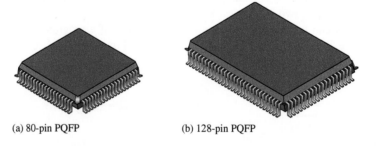

(a) 80-pin PQFP   (b) 128-pin PQFP

Field-Programmable Gate Array (FPGA) An **FPGA** is generally more complex and has a much higher density than a CPLD, although their applications can sometimes overlap. As mentioned, the SPLD and the CPLD are closely related because the CPLD basically contains a number of SPLDs. The FPGA, however, has a different internal structure (architecture), as illustrated in Figure 55. The three basic elements in an FPGA are the logic block, the programmable interconnections, and the input/output (I/O) blocks.

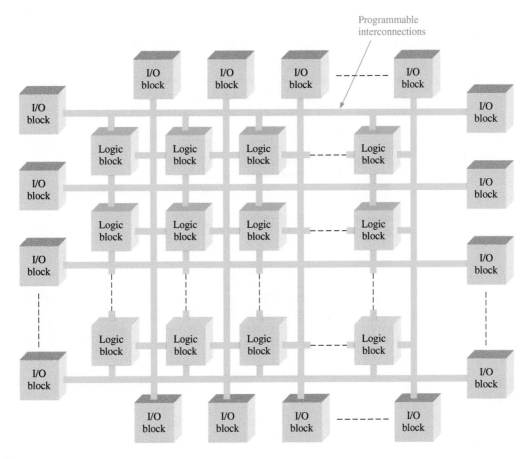

▲ FIGURE 55

Basic structure of an FPGA.

The logic blocks in an FPGA are not as complex as the logic array blocks (LABs) in a CPLD, but generally there are many more of them. When the logic blocks are relatively simple, the FPGA architecture is called *fine-grained*. When the logic blocks are larger and more complex, the architecture is called *coarse-grained*. The I/O blocks are on the outer edges of the structure and provide individually selectable input, output, or bidirectional access to the outside world. The distributed programmable interconnection matrix provides for interconnection of the logic blocks and connection to inputs and outputs. Large FPGAs can have tens of thousands of logic blocks in addition to memory and other resources. A typical FPGA ball-grid array package is shown in Figure 56. These types of packages can have over 1000 input and output pins.

◀ FIGURE 56

A typical ball-grid array (BGA) package.

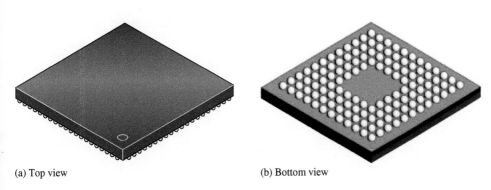

(a) Top view

(b) Bottom view

The Programming Process

An SPLD, CPLD, or FPGA can be thought of as a "blank slate" on which you implement a specified circuit or system design using a certain process. This process requires a software development package installed on a computer to implement a circuit design in the programmable chip. The computer must be interfaced with a development board or programming fixture containing the device, as illustrated in Figure 57.

► FIGURE 57

Basic setup for programming a PLD or FPGA.

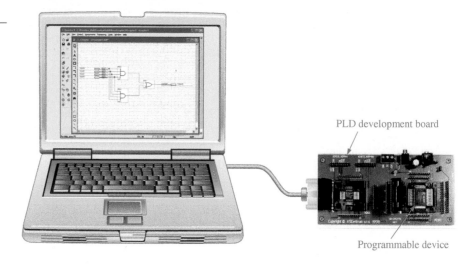

PLD development board

Programmable device

Several steps, called the *design flow,* are involved in the process of implementing a digital logic design in a programmable logic device. A block diagram of a typical programming process is shown in Figure 58. As indicated, the design flow has access to a design library.

► FIGURE 58

Basic programmable logic design flow block diagram.

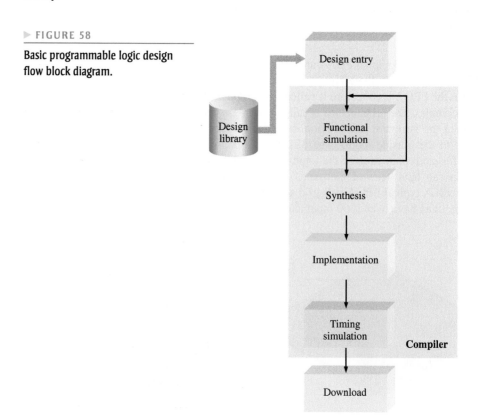

Design Entry   This is the first programming step. The circuit or system design must be entered into the design application software using text-based entry, graphic entry (schematic capture), or state diagram description. Design entry is device independent. Text-based entry is accomplished with a hardware description language (HDL) such as VHDL, Verilog, or AHDL. Graphic (schematic) entry allows prestored logic functions from a library to be selected, placed on the screen, and then interconnected to create a logic design. State-diagram entry requires specification of both the states through which a sequential logic circuit progresses and the conditions that produce each state change.

Once a design has been entered, it is compiled. A **compiler** is a program that controls the design flow process and translates source code into object code in a format that can be logically tested or downloaded to a target device. The source code is created during design entry, and the object code is the final code that actually causes the design to be implemented in the programmable device.

Functional Simulation   The entered and compiled design is simulated by software to confirm that the logic circuit functions as expected. The simulation will verify that correct outputs are produced for a specified set of inputs. A device-independent software tool for doing this is generally called a *waveform editor.* Any flaws demonstrated by the simulation would be corrected by going back to design entry and making appropriate changes.

Synthesis   **Synthesis** is where the design is translated into a netlist, which has a standard form and is device independent.

Implementation   **Implementation** is where the logic structures described by the netlist are mapped into the actual structure of the specific device being programmed. The implementation process is called *fitting* or *place and route* and results in an output called a bitstream, which is device dependent.

Timing Simulation   This step comes after the design is mapped into the specific device. The timing simulation is basically used to confirm that there are no design flaws or timing problems due to propagation delays.

Download   Once a bitstream has been generated for a specific programmable device, it has to be downloaded to the device to implement the software design in hardware. Some programmable devices have to be installed in a special piece of equipment called a *device programmer* or on a development board. Other types of devices can be programmed while in a system—called in-system programming (ISP)—using a standard JTAG (Joint Test Action Group) interface. Some devices are volatile, which means they lose their contents when reset or when power is turned off. In this case, the bitstream data must be stored in a memory and reloaded into the device after each reset or power-off. Also, the contents of an ISP device can be manipulated or upgraded while it is operating in a system. This is called "on-the-fly" reconfiguration.

SECTION 7 CHECKUP	1. List three major categories of programmable logic devices and specify their acronyms.
	2. How does a CPLD differ from an SPLD?
	3. Name the steps in the programming process.
	4. Briefly explain each step named in question 3.

SUMMARY

- ◆ An analog quantity has continuous values.
- ◆ A digital quantity has a discrete set of values.
- ◆ A binary digit is called a bit.
- ◆ A pulse is characterized by rise time, fall time, pulse width, and amplitude.

37

◆ The frequency of a periodic waveform is the reciprocal of the period. The formulas relating frequency and period are

$$f = \frac{1}{T} \quad \text{and} \quad T = \frac{1}{f}$$

◆ The duty cycle of a pulse waveform is the ratio of the pulse width to the period, expressed by the following formula as a percentage:

$$\text{Duty cycle} = \left(\frac{t_W}{T}\right)100\%$$

◆ A timing diagram is an arrangement of two or more waveforms showing their relationship with respect to time.

◆ Three basic logic operations are NOT, AND, and OR. The standard symbols for these are given in Figure 59.

▷ FIGURE 59

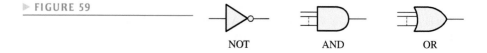

NOT   AND   OR

◆ The basic logic functions are comparison, arithmetic, code conversion, decoding, encoding, data selection, storage, and counting.

◆ The two broad physical categories of IC packages are through-hole mounted and surface mounted.

◆ Three families of fixed-function integrated circuits are CMOS, bipolar, and BiCMOS.

◆ Bipolar is also known as TTL (transistor-transistor logic).

◆ The categories of ICs in terms of circuit complexity are SSI (small-scale integration), MSI (medium-scale integration), LSI, VLSI, and ULSI (large-scale, very large-scale, and ultra large-scale integration).

◆ Two types of SPLDs (simple programmable logic devices) are PAL (programmable array logic) and GAL (generic array logic).

◆ The CPLD (complex programmable logic device) contains multiple SPLDs with programmable interconnections.

◆ The FPGA (field-programmable gate array) has a different internal structure than the CPLD and is generally used for more complex circuits and systems.

◆ Common instruments used in testing and troubleshooting digital circuits are the oscilloscope, logic analyzer, arbitrary waveform generator, data pattern generator, function generator, dc power supply, digital multimeter, logic probe, and logic pulser.

KEY TERMS

Analog Being continuous or having continuous values.

AND A basic logic operation in which a true (HIGH) output occurs only when all the input conditions are true (HIGH).

Binary Having two values or states; describes a number system that has a base of two and utilizes 1 and 0 as its digits.

Bit A binary digit, which can be either a 1 or a 0.

Clock The basic timing signal in a digital system; a periodic waveform used to synchronize operation.

Compiler A program that controls the design flow process and translates source code into object code in a format that can be logically tested or downloaded to a target device.

CPLD A complex programmable logic device that consists basically of multiple SPLD arrays with programmable interconnections.

Data Information in numeric, alphabetic, or other form.

Digital Related to digits or discrete quantities; having a set of discrete values.

Duty cycle The ratio of the pulse width to the period of a digital waveform, expressed as a percentage.

Fixed-function logic A category of digital integrated circuits having functions that cannot be altered.

FPGA Field-programmable gate array.

Gate A logic circuit that performs a basic logic operation such as AND or OR.

Input The signal or line going into a circuit.

Integrated circuit (IC) A type of circuit in which all of the components are integrated on a single chip of semiconductive material of extremely small size.

Inverter A NOT circuit; a circuit that changes a HIGH to a LOW or vice versa.

Logic In digital electronics, the decision-making capability of gate circuits, in which a HIGH represents a true statement and a LOW represents a false one.

NOT A basic logic operation that performs inversions.

OR A basic logic operation in which a true (HIGH) output occurs when one or more of the input conditions are true (HIGH).

Output The signal or line coming out of a circuit.

Parallel In digital systems, data occurring simultaneously on several lines; the transfer or processing of several bits simultaneously.

Programmable logic A category of digital integrated circuits capable of being programmed to perform specified functions.

Pulse A sudden change from one level to another, followed after a time, called the pulse width, by a sudden change back to the original level.

Serial Having one element following another, as in a serial transfer of bits; occurring in sequence rather than simultaneously.

SPLD Simple programmable logic device.

Timing diagram A graph of digital waveforms showing the time relationship of two or more waveforms.

Troubleshooting The technique or process of systematically identifying, isolating, and correcting a fault in a circuit or system.

TRUE/FALSE QUIZ

Answers are at the end of the chapter.

1. An analog quantity is one having continuous values.
2. A digital quantity has ten discrete values.
3. There are two digits in the binary system.
4. The term *bit* is short for binary digit.
5. In positive logic, a LOW level represents a binary 1.
6. If the period of a pulse waveform increases, the frequency also increases.
7. A timing diagram shows the timing relationship of two or more digital waveforms.
8. The basic logic operations are AND, OR, and MAYBE.
9. If the input to an inverter is a 1, the output is a 0.
10. Two broad types of digital integrated circuits are fixed-function and programmable.

SELF-TEST

Answers are at the end of the chapter.

1. A quantity having continuous values is
   - **(a)** a digital quantity
   - **(b)** an analog quantity
   - **(c)** a binary quantity
   - **(d)** a natural quantity

2. The term *bit* means

  (a) a small amount of data (b) a 1 or a 0

  (c) binary digit (d) both answers (b) and (c)

3. The time interval on the leading edge of a pulse between 10% and 90% of the amplitude is the

  (a) rise time (b) fall time

  (c) pulse width (d) period

4. A pulse in a certain waveform occurs every 10 ms. The frequency is

  (a) 1 kHz (b) 1 Hz (c) 100 Hz (d) 10 Hz

5. In a certain digital waveform, the period is twice the pulse width. The duty cycle is

  (a) 100% (b) 200% (c) 50%

6. An inverter

  (a) performs the NOT operation

  (b) changes a HIGH to a LOW

  (c) changes a LOW to a HIGH

  (d) does all of the above

7. The output of an AND gate is HIGH when

  (a) any input is HIGH (b) all inputs are HIGH

  (c) no inputs are HIGH (d) both answers (a) and (b)

8. The output of an OR gate is HIGH when

  (a) any input is HIGH (b) all inputs are HIGH

  (c) no inputs are HIGH (d) both answers (a) and (b)

9. The device used to convert a binary number to a 7-segment display format is the

  (a) multiplexer (b) encoder

  (c) decoder (d) register

10. An example of a data storage device is

  (a) the logic gate (b) the flip-flop (c) the comparator

  (d) the register (e) both answers (b) and (d)

11. A fixed-function IC package containing four AND gates is an example of

  (a) MSI (b) SMT (c) SOIC (d) SSI

12. An LSI device has a circuit complexity of from

  (a) 10 to 100 equivalent gates

  (b) more than 100 to 10,000 equivalent gates

  (c) 2000 to 5000 equivalent gates

  (d) more than 10,000 to 100,000 equivalent gates

13. VHDL is a

  (a) logic device

  (b) PLD programming language

  (c) computer language

  (d) very high density logic

14. A CPLD is a

  (a) controlled program logic device

  (b) complex programmable logic driver

  (c) complex programmable logic device

  (d) central processing logic device

15. An FPGA is a

  (a) field-programmable gate array (b) fast programmable gate array

  (c) field-programmable generic array (d) flash process gate application

PROBLEMS

Answers to odd-numbered problems are at the end of the chapter.

Section 1 **Digital and Analog Quantities**

1. Name two advantages of digital data as compared to analog data.

2. Name an analog quantity other than temperature and sound.

3. List three common products that can have either a digital or analog output.

Section 2 **Binary Digits, Logic Levels, and Digital Waveforms**

4. Explain the difference between positive and negative logic.

5. Define the sequence of bits (1s and 0s) represented by each of the following sequences of levels:

   (a) HIGH, HIGH, LOW, HIGH, LOW, LOW, LOW, HIGH

   (b) LOW, LOW, LOW, HIGH, LOW, HIGH, LOW, HIGH, LOW

6. List the sequence of levels (HIGH and LOW) that represent each of the following bit sequences:

   (a) 1 0 1 1 1 0 1   (b) 1 1 1 0 1 0 0 1

7. For the pulse shown in Figure 60, graphically determine the following:

   (a) rise time   (b) fall time   (c) pulse width   (d) amplitude

► FIGURE 60

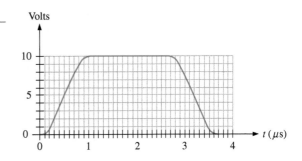

8. Determine the period of the digital waveform in Figure 61.

9. What is the frequency of the waveform in Figure 61?

10. Is the pulse waveform in Figure 61 periodic or nonperiodic?

11. Determine the duty cycle of the waveform in Figure 61.

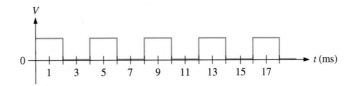

▲ FIGURE 61

12. Determine the bit sequence represented by the waveform in Figure 62. A bit time is 1 μs in this case.

13. What is the total serial transfer time for the eight bits in Figure 62? What is the total parallel transfer time?

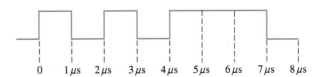

▲ FIGURE 62

14. What is the period if the clock frequency is 3.5 GHz?

Section 3   **Basic Logic Operations**

15. Form a single logical statement from the following information:

   (a) The light is ON if SW1 is closed.

   (b) The light is ON if SW2 is closed.

   (c) The light is OFF if both SW1 and SW2 are open.

16. A logic circuit requires HIGHs on all its inputs to make the output HIGH. What type of logic circuit is it?

17. A basic 2-input logic circuit has a HIGH on one input and a LOW on the other input, and the output is LOW. Identify the circuit.

18. A basic 2-input logic circuit has a HIGH on one input and a LOW on the other input, and the output is HIGH. What type of logic circuit is it?

Section 4   **Introduction to the System Concept**

19. Name the logic function of each block in Figure 63 based on your observation of the inputs and outputs.

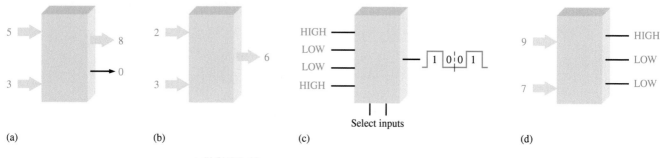

(a)   (b)   (c)   (d)

▲ FIGURE 63

20. A pulse waveform with a frequency of 10 kHz is applied to the input of a counter. During 100 ms, how many pulses are counted?

21. Consider a register that can store eight bits. Assume that it has been reset so that it contains zeros in all positions. If you transfer four alternating bits (0101) serially into the register, beginning with a 1 and shifting to the right, what will the total content of the register be as soon as the fourth bit is stored?

Section 5   **Fixed-Function Integrated Circuits**

22. A fixed-function digital IC chip has a complexity of 200 equivalent gates. How is it classified?

23. Explain the main difference between the DIP and SMT packages.

24. Label the pin numbers on the packages in Figure 64. Top views are shown.

▶ FIGURE 64

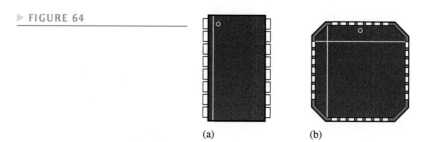

(a)   (b)

Section 6   **Test and Measurement Instruments**

25. A pulse is displayed on the screen of an oscilloscope, and you measure the base line as 1 V and the top of the pulse as 8 V. What is the amplitude?

26. A logic probe is applied to a contact point on an IC that is operating in a system. The lamp on the probe flashes repeatedly. What does this indicate?

Section 7 Introduction to Programmable Logic

27. Which of the following acronyms do not describe a type of programmable logic?

PAL, GAL, SPLD, VHDL, CPLD, AHDL, FPGA

28. What do each of the following stand for?

(a) SPLD   **(b)** CPLD   **(c)** HDL   **(d)** FPGA   **(e)** GAL

29. Define each of the following PLD programming terms:

(a) design entry   **(b)** simulation   **(c)** compilation   **(d)** download

30. Describe the process of place-and-route.

ANSWERS

SECTION CHECKUPS

Section 1 Digital and Analog Quantities

1. *Analog* means continuous.

2. *Digital* means discrete.

3. A digital quantity has a discrete set of values and an analog quantity has continuous values.

4. A public address system is analog. A CD player is analog and digital. A computer is all digital.

Section 2 Binary Digits, Logic Levels, and Digital Waveforms

1. Binary means having two states or values.

2. A bit is a binary digit.

3. The bits are 1 and 0.

4. Rise time: from 10% to 90% of amplitude. Fall time: from 90% to 10% of amplitude.

5. Frequency is the reciprocal of the period.

6. A clock waveform is a basic timing waveform from which other waveforms are derived.

7. A timing diagram shows the time relationship of two or more waveforms.

8. Parallel transfer is faster than serial transfer.

Section 3 Basic Logic Operations

1. When the input is LOW

2. When all inputs are HIGH

3. When any or all inputs are HIGH

4. An inverter is a NOT circuit.

5. A logic gate is a circuit that performs a logic operation (AND, OR).

Section 4 Introduction to the System Concept

1. A comparator compares the magnitudes of two input numbers.

2. Add, subtract, multiply, and divide

3. Encoding is changing a familiar form such as decimal to a coded form such as binary.

4. Decoding is changing a code to a familiar form such as binary to decimal.

5. Multiplexing puts data from many sources onto one line. Demultiplexing takes data from one line and distributes it to many destinations.

6. Flip-flops, registers, semiconductor memories, magnetic disks

7. A counter counts events with a sequence of binary states.

Section 5 Fixed-Function Integrated Circuits

1. An IC is an electronic circuit with all components integrated on a single silicon chip.

2. DIP—dual in-line package; SMT—surface-mount technology; SOIC—small-outline integrated circuit; SSI—small-scale integration; MSI—medium-scale integration; LSI—large-scale integration; VLSI—very large-scale integration; ULSI—ultra large-scale integration

3. (a) SSI   **(b)** MSI   **(c)** LSI   **(d)** VLSI   **(e)** ULSI

Section 6 **Test and Measurement Instruments**

1. The analog scope applies the measured waveform directly to the display circuits. The digital scope first converts the measured signal to digital form.

2. The logic analyzer has more channels than the oscilloscope and has more than one data display format.

3. The volts/div control sets the voltage for each division on the screen.

4. The sec/div control sets the time for each division on the screen.

5. The function generator produces various types of waveforms.

Section 7 **Introduction to Programmable Logic**

1. Simple programmable logic device (SPLD), complex programmable logic device (CPLD), and field-programmable gate array (FPGA)

2. A CPLD is made up of multiple SPLDs.

3. Design entry, functional simulation, synthesis, implementation, timing simulation, and download

4. *Design entry:* The logic design is entered using development software. *Functional simulation:* The design is software simulated to make sure it works logically. *Synthesis:* The design is translated into a netlist. *Implementation:* The logic developed by the netlist is mapped into the programmable device. *Timing simulation:* The design is software simulated to confirm that there are no timing problems. *Download:* The design is placed into the programmable device.

RELATED PROBLEMS FOR EXAMPLES

1 $f = 6.67$ kHz; Duty cycle = 16.7%

2 Serial transfer: 3.33 ns

3 Amplitude = 12 V; $T = 8$ ms

TRUE/FALSE QUIZ

1. T 2. F 3. T 4. T 5. F 6. F 7. T 8. F 9. T 10. T

SELF-TEST

1. (b) 2. (d) 3. (a) 4. (c) 5. (c) 6. (d) 7. (b) 8. (d)
9. (c) 10. (e) 11. (d) 12. (d) 13. (b) 14. (c) 15. (a)

ANSWERS TO ODD-NUMBERED PROBLEMS

1. Digital can be transmitted and stored more efficiently and reliably.

3. Clock
   Thermometer
   Speedometer

5. (a) 11010001   (b) 000101010

7. (a) 550 ns   (b) 600 ns   (c) 2.7 μs   (d) 10 V

9. 250 Hz

11. 50%

13. 8 μs; 1 μs

15. $L_{on} = $ SW1 + SW2 + SW1 $\cdot$ SW2

17. AND gate

19. (a) adder   (b) multiplier
    (c) multiplexer   (d) comparator

21. 01010000

23. DIP pins go through holes in a circuit board. SMT pins connect to surface pads.

25. 7 V

27. VHDL, AHDL

29. **(a)** Design entry: The step in a programmable logic design flow where a description of the circuit is entered in either schematic (graphic) form or in text form using an HDL.

  (b) Simulation: The step in a design flow where the entered design is simulated based on defined input waveforms.

  (c) Compilation: A program process that controls the design flow process and translates a design source code to object code for testing and downloading.

  (d) Download: The process in which the design is transferred from software to hardware.

NUMBER SYSTEMS, OPERATIONS, AND CODES

CHAPTER OBJECTIVES

- Review the decimal number system
- Count in the binary number system
- Convert from decimal to binary and from binary to decimal
- Apply arithmetic operations to binary numbers
- Determine the 1's and 2's complements of a binary number
- Express signed binary numbers in sign-magnitude, 1's complement, 2's complement, and floating-point format
- Carry out arithmetic operations with signed binary numbers
- Convert between the binary and hexadecimal number systems
- Add numbers in hexadecimal form
- Convert between the binary and octal number systems
- Express decimal numbers in binary coded decimal (BCD) form
- Add BCD numbers
- Convert between the binary system and the Gray code
- Interpret the American Standard Code for Information Interchange (ASCII)
- Explain how to detect code errors
- Discuss the cyclic redundancy check (CRC)

KEY TERMS

- LSB
- MSB
- Byte
- Floating-point number
- Hexadecimal
- Octal
- BCD
- Alphanumeric
- ASCII
- Parity
- Cyclic redundancy check (CRC)

INTRODUCTION

The binary number system and digital codes are fundamental to computers and to digital electronics in general. In this chapter, the binary number system and its relationship to other number systems such as decimal, hexadecimal, and octal is presented. Arithmetic operations with binary numbers are covered to provide a basis for understanding how computers and many other types of digital systems work. Also, digital codes such as binary coded decimal (BCD), the Gray code, and the ASCII are covered. The parity method for detecting errors in codes is introduced. The tutorials on the use of the calculator in certain operations are based on the TI-86 graphics calculator and the TI-36X calculator. The procedures shown may vary on other types.

From *Digital Fundamentals*, Tenth Edition, Thomas L. Floyd. Copyright © 2009 by Pearson Education, Inc. Published by Prentice Hall.

1 DECIMAL NUMBERS

You are familiar with the decimal number system because you use decimal numbers every day. Although decimal numbers are commonplace, their weighted structure is often not understood. In this section, the structure of decimal numbers is reviewed. This review will help you more easily understand the structure of the binary number system, which is important in computers and digital electronics.

After completing this section, you should be able to

- ◆ Explain why the decimal number system is a weighted system
- ◆ Explain how powers of ten are used in the decimal system
- ◆ Determine the weight of each digit in a decimal number

The decimal number system has ten digits.

In the **decimal** number system each of the ten digits, 0 through 9, represents a certain quantity. As you know, the ten symbols (**digits**) do not limit you to expressing only ten different quantities because you use the various digits in appropriate positions within a number to indicate the magnitude of the quantity. You can express quantities up through nine before running out of digits; if you wish to express a quantity greater than nine, you use two or more digits, and the position of each digit within the number tells you the magnitude it represents. If, for example, you wish to express the quantity twenty-three, you use (by their respective positions in the number) the digit 2 to represent the quantity twenty and the digit 3 to represent the quantity three, as illustrated below.

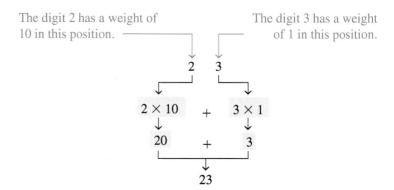

The decimal number system has a base of 10.

The position of each digit in a decimal number indicates the magnitude of the quantity represented and can be assigned a **weight.** The weights for whole numbers are positive powers of ten that increase from right to left, beginning with $10^0 = 1$.

$$\ldots 10^5 \ 10^4 \ 10^3 \ 10^2 \ 10^1 \ 10^0$$

For fractional numbers, the weights are negative powers of ten that decrease from left to right beginning with 10^{-1}.

$$10^2 \ 10^1 \ 10^0 . 10^{-1} \ 10^{-2} \ 10^{-3} \ldots$$
$$\uparrow\text{—— Decimal point}$$

The value of a digit is determined by its position in the number.

The value of a decimal number is the sum of the digits after each digit has been multiplied by its weight, as Examples 1 and 2 illustrate.

EXAMPLE 1

Express the decimal number 47 as a sum of the values of each digit.

Solution   The digit 4 has a weight of 10, which is 10^1, as indicated by its position. The digit 7 has a weight of 1, which is 10^0, as indicated by its position.

$$47 = (4 \times 10^1) + (7 \times 10^0)$$
$$= (4 \times 10) + (7 \times 1) = \mathbf{40 + 7}$$

*Related Problem**   Determine the value of each digit in 939.

_____
*Answers are at the end of the chapter.

EXAMPLE 2

Express the decimal number 568.23 as a sum of the values of each digit.

Solution   The whole number digit 5 has a weight of 100, which is 10^2, the digit 6 has a weight of 10, which is 10^1, the digit 8 has a weight of 1, which is 10^0, the fractional digit 2 has a weight of 0.1, which is 10^{-1}, and the fractional digit 3 has a weight of 0.01, which is 10^{-2}.

$$568.23 = (5 \times 10^2) + (6 \times 10^1) + (8 \times 10^0) + (2 \times 10^{-1}) + (3 \times 10^{-2})$$
$$= (5 \times 100) + (6 \times 10) + (8 \times 1) + (2 \times 0.1) + (3 \times 0.01)$$
$$= \mathbf{500} + \mathbf{60} + \mathbf{8} + \mathbf{0.2} + \mathbf{0.03}$$

Related Problem   Determine the value of each digit in 67.924.

**CALCULATOR
TUTORIAL**

Powers of Ten

Example   Find the value of 10^3.

10^x

TI-86   **Step 1:** [2nd] [LOG]

Step 2: [3]   10 ^ 3

Step 3: [ENTER]   1000

_____

TI-36X   **Step 1:** [1] [0] [y^x]

Step 2: [3] [=]   1000

**SECTION 1
CHECKUP**
Answers are at the end of the chapter.

1. What weight does the digit 7 have in each of the following numbers?
   (a) 1370   (b) 6725   (c) 7051   (d) 58.72
2. Express each of the following decimal numbers as a sum of the products obtained by multiplying each digit by its appropriate weight:
   (a) 51   (b) 137   (c) 1492   (d) 106.58

2 BINARY NUMBERS

The binary number system is another way to represent quantities. It is less complicated than the decimal system because it has only two digits. The decimal system with its ten digits is a base-ten system; the binary system with its two digits is a base-two system. The two binary digits (bits) are 1 and 0. The position of a 1 or 0 in a binary number indicates its weight, or value within the number, just as the position of a decimal digit determines the value of that digit. The weights in a binary number are based on powers of two.

After completing this section, you should be able to

+ Count in binary
+ Determine the largest decimal number that can be represented by a given number of bits
+ Convert a binary number to a decimal number

Counting in Binary

The binary number system has two digits (bits).

To learn to count in the binary system, first look at how you count in the decimal system. You start at zero and count up to nine before you run out of digits. You then start another digit position (to the left) and continue counting 10 through 99. At this point you have exhausted all two-digit combinations, so a third digit position is needed to count from 100 through 999.

A comparable situation occurs when you count in binary, except that you have only two digits, called *bits*. Begin counting: 0, 1. At this point you have used both digits, so include another digit position and continue: 10, 11. You have now exhausted all combinations of two digits, so a third position is required. With three digit positions you can continue to count: 100, 101, 110, and 111. Now you need a fourth digit position to continue, and so on. A binary count of zero through fifteen is shown in Table 1. Notice the patterns with which the 1s and 0s alternate in each column.

The binary number system has a base of 2.

COMPUTER NOTE

In computer operations, there are many cases where adding or subtracting 1 to a number stored in a counter is necessary. Computers have special instructions that use less time and generate less machine code than the ADD or SUB instructions. For the Intel processors, the INC (increment) instruction adds 1 to a number. For subtraction, the corresponding instruction is DEC (decrement), which subtracts 1 from a number.

▶ TABLE 1

DECIMAL NUMBER	BINARY NUMBER			
0	0	0	0	0
1	0	0	0	1
2	0	0	1	0
3	0	0	1	1
4	0	1	0	0
5	0	1	0	1
6	0	1	1	0
7	0	1	1	1
8	1	0	0	0
9	1	0	0	1
10	1	0	1	0
11	1	0	1	1
12	1	1	0	0
13	1	1	0	1
14	1	1	1	0
15	1	1	1	1

As you have seen in Table 1, four bits are required to count from zero to 15. In general, with n bits you can count up to a number equal to $2^n - 1$.

The value of a bit is determined by its position in the number.

$$\text{Largest decimal number} = 2^n - 1$$

For example, with five bits ($n = 5$) you can count from zero to thirty-one.

$$2^5 - 1 = 32 - 1 = 31$$

With six bits ($n = 6$) you can count from zero to sixty-three.

$$2^6 - 1 = 64 - 1 = 63$$

A table of powers of two is given in Appendix A.

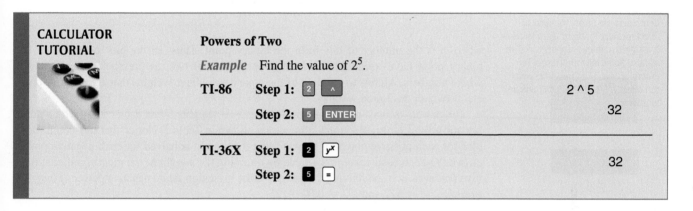

CALCULATOR TUTORIAL

Powers of Two

Example Find the value of 2^5.

TI-86   Step 1: [2] [^]

Step 2: [5] [ENTER]

$2 \wedge 5$

32

TI-36X   Step 1: [2] [y^x]

Step 2: [5] [=]

32

An Application

Learning to count in binary will help you to basically understand how digital circuits can be used to count events. This can be anything from counting items on an assembly line to counting operations in a computer. Let's take a simple example of counting tennis balls going into a box from a conveyor belt. Assume that nine balls are to go into each box.

The counter in Figure 1 counts the pulses from a sensor that detects the passing of a ball and produces a sequence of logic levels (digital waveforms) on each of its four parallel outputs. Each set of logic levels represents a 4-bit binary number (HIGH = 1 and LOW = 0), as indicated. As the decoder receives these waveforms, it decodes each set of four bits and converts it to the corresponding decimal number in the 7-segment display. When the counter gets to the binary state of 1001, it has counted nine tennis balls, the display shows decimal 9, and a new box is moved under the conveyor. Then the counter goes back to its zero state (0000), and the process starts over. (The number 9 was used only in the interest of single-digit simplicity.)

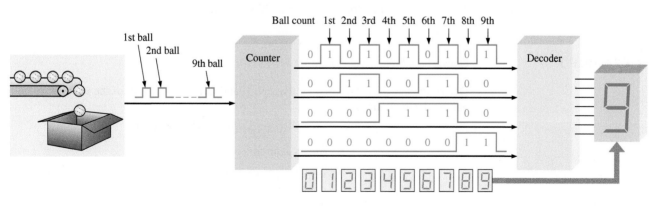

▲ FIGURE 1

Illustration of a simple binary counting application.

The Weighting Structure of Binary Numbers

The weight or value of a bit increases from right to left in a binary number.

A binary number is a weighted number. The right-most bit is the LSB (least significant bit) in a binary whole number and has a weight of $2^0 = 1$. The weights increase from right to left by a power of two for each bit. The left-most bit is the MSB (most significant bit); its weight depends on the size of the binary number.

Fractional numbers can also be represented in binary by placing bits to the right of the binary point, just as fractional decimal digits are placed to the right of the decimal point. The left-most bit is the MSB in a binary fractional number and has a weight of $2^{-1} = 0.5$. The fractional weights decrease from left to right by a negative power of two for each bit.

The weight structure of a binary number is

$$2^{n-1} \ldots 2^3\, 2^2\, 2^1\, 2^0 \,.\, 2^{-1}\, 2^{-2} \ldots 2^{-n}$$

↑—— Binary point

where n is the number of bits from the binary point. Thus, all the bits to the left of the binary point have weights that are positive powers of two, as previously discussed for whole numbers. All bits to the right of the binary point have weights that are negative powers of two, or fractional weights.

The powers of two and their equivalent decimal weights for an 8-bit binary whole number and a 6-bit binary fractional number are shown in Table 2. Notice that the weight doubles for each positive power of two and that the weight is halved for each negative power of two. You can easily extend the table by doubling the weight of the most significant positive power of two and halving the weight of the least significant negative power of two; for example, $2^9 = 512$ and $2^{-7} = 0.0078125$.

COMPUTER NOTE

Computers use binary numbers to select memory locations. Each location is assigned a unique number called an *address*. Some microprocessors, for example, have 32 address lines which can select 2^{32} (4,294,967,296) unique locations.

▼ TABLE 2

Binary weights.

POSITIVE POWERS OF TWO (WHOLE NUMBERS)									NEGATIVE POWERS OF TWO (FRACTIONAL NUMBER)					
2^8	2^7	2^6	2^5	2^4	2^3	2^2	2^1	2^0	2^{-1}	2^{-2}	2^{-3}	2^{-4}	2^{-5}	2^{-6}
256	128	64	32	16	8	4	2	1	1/2	1/4	1/8	1/16	1/32	1/64
									0.5	0.25	0.125	0.625	0.03125	0.015625

Binary-to-Decimal Conversion

Add the weights of all 1s in a binary number to get the decimal value.

The decimal value of any binary number can be found by adding the weights of all bits that are 1 and discarding the weights of all bits that are 0.

EXAMPLE 3

Convert the binary whole number 1101101 to decimal.

Solution   Determine the weight of each bit that is a 1, and then find the sum of the weights to get the decimal number.

Weight: $2^6\ 2^5\ 2^4\ 2^3\ 2^2\ 2^1\ 2^0$

Binary number: 1 1 0 1 1 0 1

$1101101 = 2^6 + 2^5 + 2^3 + 2^2 + 2^0$

$= 64 + 32 + 8 + 4 + 1 = \mathbf{109}$

Related Problem   Convert the binary number 10010001 to decimal.

EXAMPLE 4   Convert the fractional binary number 0.1011 to decimal.

Solution   Determine the weight of each bit that is a 1, and then sum the weights to get the decimal fraction.

$$\text{Weight:} \quad 2^{-1} \; 2^{-2} \; 2^{-3} \; 2^{-4}$$
$$\text{Binary number:} \; 0.1 \quad 0 \quad 1 \quad 1$$
$$0.1011 = 2^{-1} + 2^{-3} + 2^{-4}$$
$$= 0.5 + 0.125 + 0.0625 = \mathbf{0.6875}$$

Related Problem   Convert the binary number 10.111 to decimal.

**SECTION 2
CHECKUP**

1. What is the largest decimal number that can be represented in binary with eight bits?
2. Determine the weight of the 1 in the binary number 10000.
3. Convert the binary number 10111101.011 to decimal.

---

3   DECIMAL-TO-BINARY CONVERSION

In Section 2 you learned how to convert a binary number to the equivalent decimal number. Now you will learn two ways of converting from a decimal number to a binary number.

After completing this section, you should be able to

◆ Convert a decimal number to binary using the sum-of-weights method

◆ Convert a decimal whole number to binary using the repeated division-by-2 method

◆ Convert a decimal fraction to binary using the repeated multiplication-by-2 method

Sum-of-Weights Method

One way to find the binary number that is equivalent to a given decimal number is to determine the set of binary weights whose sum is equal to the decimal number. An easy way to remember binary weights is that the lowest is 1, which is 2^0, and that by doubling any weight, you get the next higher weight; thus, a list of seven binary weights would be 64, 32, 16, 8, 4, 2, 1 as you learned in the last section. The decimal number 9, for example, can be expressed as the sum of binary weights as follows:

To get the binary number for a given decimal number, find the binary weights that add up to the decimal number.

$$9 = 8 + 1 \quad \text{or} \quad 9 = 2^3 + 2^0$$

Placing 1s in the appropriate weight positions, 2^3 and 2^0, and 0s in the 2^2 and 2^1 positions determines the binary number for decimal 9.

$$2^3 \quad 2^2 \quad 2^1 \quad 2^0$$
$$1 \quad \;\; 0 \quad \;\; 0 \quad \;\; 1 \qquad \text{Binary number for decimal 9}$$

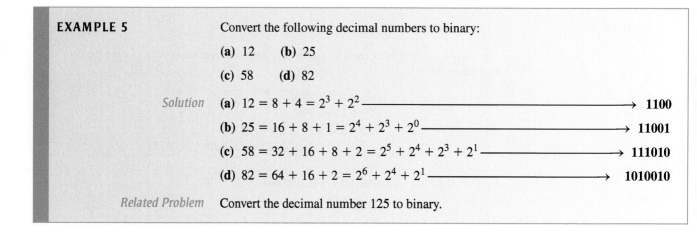

EXAMPLE 5

Convert the following decimal numbers to binary:

(a) 12   (b) 25

(c) 58   (d) 82

Solution

(a) $12 = 8 + 4 = 2^3 + 2^2$ $\longrightarrow$ **1100**

(b) $25 = 16 + 8 + 1 = 2^4 + 2^3 + 2^0$ $\longrightarrow$ **11001**

(c) $58 = 32 + 16 + 8 + 2 = 2^5 + 2^4 + 2^3 + 2^1$ $\longrightarrow$ **111010**

(d) $82 = 64 + 16 + 2 = 2^6 + 2^4 + 2^1$ $\longrightarrow$ **1010010**

Related Problem Convert the decimal number 125 to binary.

Repeated Division-by-2 Method

To get the binary number for a given decimal number, divide the decimal number by 2 until the quotient is 0. Remainders form the binary number.

A systematic method of converting whole numbers from decimal to binary is the *repeated division-by-2* process. For example, to convert the decimal number 12 to binary, begin by dividing 12 by 2. Then divide each resulting quotient by 2 until there is a 0 whole-number quotient. The **remainders** generated by each division form the binary number. The first remainder to be produced is the LSB (least significant bit) in the binary number, and the last remainder to be produced is the MSB (most significant bit). This procedure is illustrated as follows for converting the decimal number 12 to binary.

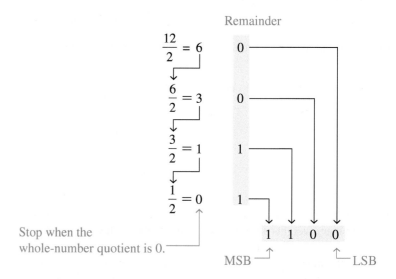

EXAMPLE 6

Convert the following decimal numbers to binary:

(a) 19   (b) 45

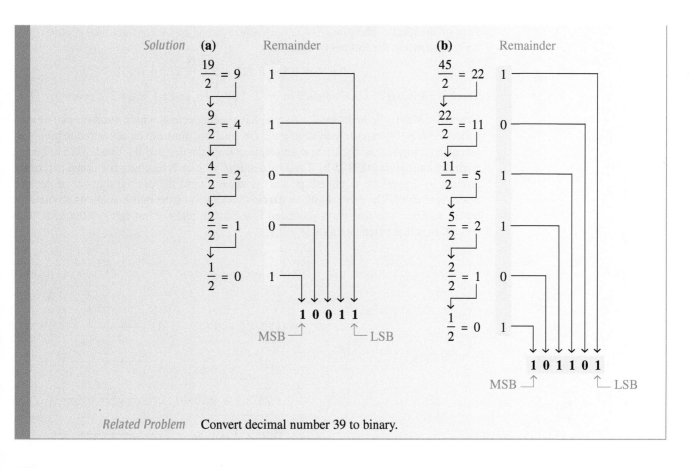

Solution

(a)

$$\frac{19}{2} = 9$$ Remainder 1

$$\frac{9}{2} = 4$$ 1

$$\frac{4}{2} = 2$$ 0

$$\frac{2}{2} = 1$$ 0

$$\frac{1}{2} = 0$$ 1

1 0 0 1 1

MSB ⌐ ⌐ LSB

(b)

$$\frac{45}{2} = 22$$ Remainder 1

$$\frac{22}{2} = 11$$ 0

$$\frac{11}{2} = 5$$ 1

$$\frac{5}{2} = 2$$ 1

$$\frac{2}{2} = 1$$ 0

$$\frac{1}{2} = 0$$ 1

1 0 1 1 0 1

MSB ⌐ ⌐ LSB

Related Problem   Convert decimal number 39 to binary.

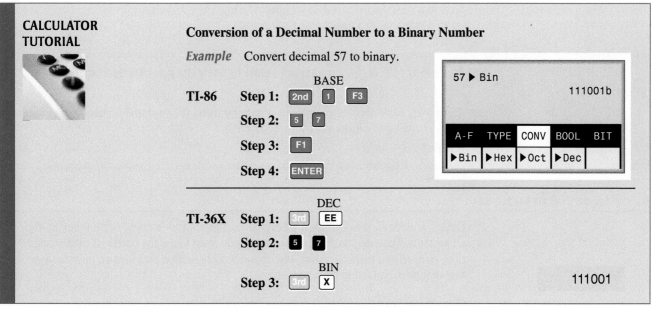

CALCULATOR TUTORIAL

Conversion of a Decimal Number to a Binary Number

Example   Convert decimal 57 to binary.

TI-86   **Step 1:** [2nd] [1] [F3]   BASE

Step 2: [5] [7]

Step 3: [F1]

Step 4: [ENTER]

57 ▶ Bin
111001b

| A-F | TYPE | CONV | BOOL | BIT |

▶Bin ▶Hex ▶Oct ▶Dec

TI-36X   **Step 1:** [3rd] [EE]   DEC

Step 2: [5] [7]

Step 3: [3rd] [X]   BIN

111001

Converting Decimal Fractions to Binary

Examples 5 and 6 demonstrated whole-number conversions. Now let's look at fractional conversions. An easy way to remember fractional binary weights is that the most significant weight is 0.5, which is 2^{-1}, and that by halving any weight, you get the next lower weight; thus a list of four fractional binary weights would be 0.5, 0.25, 0.125, 0.0625.

Sum-of-Weights The sum-of-weights method can be applied to fractional decimal numbers, as shown in the following example:

$$0.625 = 0.5 + 0.125 = 2^{-1} + 2^{-3} = 0.101$$

There is a 1 in the 2^{-1} position, a 0 in the 2^{-2} position, and a 1 in the 2^{-3} position.

Repeated Multiplication by 2 As you have seen, decimal whole numbers can be converted to binary by repeated division by 2. Decimal fractions can be converted to binary by repeated multiplication by 2. For example, to convert the decimal fraction 0.3125 to binary, begin by multiplying 0.3125 by 2 and then multiplying each resulting fractional part of the product by 2 until the fractional product is zero or until the desired number of decimal places is reached. The carry digits, or **carries,** generated by the multiplications produce the binary number. The first carry produced is the MSB, and the last carry is the LSB. This procedure is illustrated as follows:

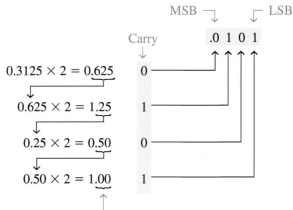

Continue to the desired number of decimal places or stop when the fractional part is all zeros.

SECTION 3 CHECKUP	1. Convert each decimal number to binary by using the sum-of-weights method: (a) 23 (b) 57 (c) 45.5 2. Convert each decimal number to binary by using the repeated division-by-2 method (repeated multiplication-by-2 for fractions): (a) 14 (b) 21 (c) 0.375

4   BINARY ARITHMETIC

Binary arithmetic is essential in all digital computers and in many other types of digital systems. To understand digital systems, you must know the basics of binary addition, subtraction, multiplication, and division. This section provides an introduction that will be expanded in later sections.

After completing this section, you should be able to

  ♦ Add binary numbers

  ♦ Subtract binary numbers

  ♦ Multiply binary numbers

  ♦ Divide binary numbers

Binary Addition

The four basic rules for adding binary digits (bits) are as follows:

In binary 1 + 1 = 10, not 2.

> 0 + 0 = 0   Sum of 0 with a carry of 0
> 0 + 1 = 1   Sum of 1 with a carry of 0
> 1 + 0 = 1   Sum of 1 with a carry of 0
> 1 + 1 = 10   Sum of 0 with a carry of 1

Notice that the first three rules result in a single bit and in the fourth rule the addition of two 1s yields a binary two (10). When binary numbers are added, the last condition creates a sum of 0 in a given column and a carry of 1 over to the next column to the left, as illustrated in the following addition of 11 + 1:

$$\begin{array}{ccc} \text{Carry} & \text{Carry} & \\ 1 \leftarrow & 1 \leftarrow & \\ 0 & 1 & 1 \\ +0 & 0 & 1 \\ \hline 1 & 0 & 0 \end{array}$$

In the right column, 1 + 1 = 0 with a carry of 1 to the next column to the left. In the middle column, 1 + 1 + 0 = 0 with a carry of 1 to the next column to the left. In the left column, 1 + 0 + 0 = 1.

When there is a carry of 1, you have a situation in which three bits are being added (a bit in each of the two numbers and a carry bit). This situation is illustrated as follows:

Carry bits

> 1 + 0 + 0 = 01   Sum of 1 with a carry of 0
> 1 + 1 + 0 = 10   Sum of 0 with a carry of 1
> 1 + 0 + 1 = 10   Sum of 0 with a carry of 1
> 1 + 1 + 1 = 11   Sum of 1 with a carry of 1

EXAMPLE 7

Add the following binary numbers:

(a) 11 + 11   **(b)** 100 + 10   **(c)** 111 + 11   **(d)** 110 + 100

Solution   The equivalent decimal addition is also shown for reference.

(a)	11	3	(b)	100	4	(c)	111	7	(d)	110	6
	+11	+3		+10	+2		+11	+3		+100	+4
	110	6		**110**	6		**1010**	10		**1010**	10

Related Problem   Add 1111 and 1100.

Binary Subtraction

The four basic rules for subtracting bits are as follows:

In binary 10 − 1 = 1, not 9.

> 0 − 0 = 0
> 1 − 1 = 0
> 1 − 0 = 1
> 10 − 1 = 1   0 − 1 with a borrow of 1

When subtracting numbers, you sometimes have to borrow from the next column to the left. A borrow is required in binary only when you try to subtract a 1 from a 0. In this case, when a 1 is borrowed from the next column to the left, a 10 is created in the column being subtracted, and the last of the four basic rules just listed must be applied. Examples 8 and 9 illustrate binary subtraction; the equivalent decimal subtractions are also shown.

EXAMPLE 8

Perform the following binary subtractions:

(a) $11 - 01$ (b) $11 - 10$

Solution

(a)
$$\begin{array}{cc} 11 & 3 \\ -\,01 & -\,1 \\ \hline 10 & 2 \end{array}$$

(b)
$$\begin{array}{cc} 11 & 3 \\ -\,10 & -\,2 \\ \hline 01 & 1 \end{array}$$

No borrows were required in this example. The binary number 01 is the same as 1.

Related Problem   Subtract 100 from 111.

EXAMPLE 9

Subtract 011 from 101.

Solution

$$\begin{array}{cc} 101 & 5 \\ -\,011 & -\,3 \\ \hline 010 & 2 \end{array}$$

Let's examine exactly what was done to subtract the two binary numbers since a borrow is required. Begin with the right column.

Left column:
When a 1 is borrowed, a 0 is left, so $0 - 0 = 0$.

Middle column:
Borrow 1 from next column to the left, making a 10 in this column, then $10 - 1 = 1$.

$$\begin{array}{c} \overset{0}{1}01 \\ -\,011 \\ \hline 010 \end{array}$$

Right column:
$1 - 1 = 0$

Related Problem   Subtract 101 from 110.

Binary Multiplication

Binary multiplication of two bits is the same as multiplication of the decimal digits 0 and 1.

The four basic rules for multiplying bits are as follows:

$$0 \times 0 = 0$$
$$0 \times 1 = 0$$
$$1 \times 0 = 0$$
$$1 \times 1 = 1$$

Multiplication is performed with binary numbers in the same manner as with decimal numbers. It involves forming partial products, shifting each successive partial product left one place, and then adding all the partial products. Example 10 illustrates the procedure; the equivalent decimal multiplications are shown for reference.

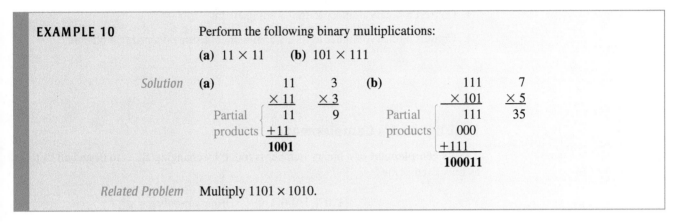

EXAMPLE 10

Perform the following binary multiplications:

(a) 11×11 **(b)** 101×111

Solution

(a)

$$\begin{array}{rr} & 11 \\ \times & 11 \\ \hline \end{array}$$

Partial products $\begin{cases} 11 \\ +11 \\ \hline 1001 \end{cases}$

$$\begin{array}{rr} & 3 \\ \times & 3 \\ \hline & 9 \end{array}$$

(b)

$$\begin{array}{rr} & 111 \\ \times & 101 \\ \hline \end{array}$$

Partial products $\begin{cases} 111 \\ 000 \\ +111 \\ \hline 100011 \end{cases}$

$$\begin{array}{rr} & 7 \\ \times & 5 \\ \hline & 35 \end{array}$$

Related Problem   Multiply 1101×1010.

Binary Division

Division in binary follows the same procedure as division in decimal, as Example 11 illustrates. The equivalent decimal divisions are also given.

A calculator can be used to perform arithmetic operations with binary numbers as long as the capacity of the calculator is not exceeded.

EXAMPLE 11

Perform the following binary divisions:

(a) $110 \div 11$ **(b)** $110 \div 10$

Solution

(a)

$$\begin{array}{r} 10 \\ 11 \overline{)110} \\ 11 \\ \hline 000 \end{array}$$

$$\begin{array}{r} 2 \\ 3 \overline{)6} \\ 6 \\ \hline 0 \end{array}$$

(b)

$$\begin{array}{r} 11 \\ 10 \overline{)110} \\ 10 \\ \hline 10 \\ 10 \\ \hline 00 \end{array}$$

$$\begin{array}{r} 3 \\ 2 \overline{)6} \\ 6 \\ \hline 0 \end{array}$$

Related Problem   Divide 1100 by 100.

SECTION 4 CHECKUP

1. Perform the following binary additions:
   (a) $1101 + 1010$ (b) $10111 + 01101$
2. Perform the following binary subtractions:
   (a) $1101 - 0100$ (b) $1001 - 0111$
3. Perform the indicated binary operations:
   (a) 110×111 (b) $1100 \div 011$

5   1's AND 2's COMPLEMENTS OF BINARY NUMBERS

The 1's complement and the 2's complement of a binary number are important because they permit the representation of negative numbers. The method of 2's complement arithmetic is commonly used in computers to handle negative numbers.

After completing this section, you should be able to

- ◆ Convert a binary number to its 1's complement
- ◆ Convert a binary number to its 2's complement using either of two methods

Finding the 1's Complement

Change each bit in a number to get the 1's complement.

The 1's **complement** of a binary number is found by changing all 1s to 0s and all 0s to 1s, as illustrated below:

$$1\ 0\ 1\ 1\ 0\ 0\ 1\ 0 \quad \text{Binary number}$$
$$\downarrow\downarrow\downarrow\downarrow\downarrow\downarrow\downarrow\downarrow$$
$$0\ 1\ 0\ 0\ 1\ 1\ 0\ 1 \quad \text{1's complement}$$

The simplest way to obtain the 1's complement of a binary number with a digital circuit is to use parallel inverters (NOT circuits), as shown in Figure 2 for an 8-bit binary number.

▶ FIGURE 2

Example of inverters used to obtain the 1's complement of a binary number.

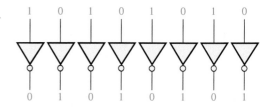

Finding the 2's Complement

Add 1 to the 1's complement to get the 2's complement.

The 2's complement of a binary number is found by adding 1 to the LSB of the 1's complement.

$$\text{2's complement} = (\text{1's complement}) + 1$$

EXAMPLE 12

Find the 2's complement of 10110010.

Solution

$$
\begin{array}{ll}
10110010 & \text{Binary number} \\
01001101 & \text{1's complement} \\
\underline{+\qquad 1} & \text{Add 1} \\
\mathbf{01001110} & \text{2's complement}
\end{array}
$$

Related Problem   Determine the 2's complement of 11001011.

An alternative method of finding the 2's complement of a binary number is as follows: Change all bits to the left of the least significant 1 to get 2's complement.

1. Start at the right with the LSB and write the bits as they are up to and including the first 1.

2. Take the 1's complements of the remaining bits.

EXAMPLE 13   Find the 2's complement of 10111000 using the alternative method.

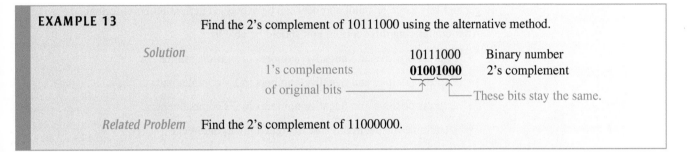

Solution

	10111000	Binary number
1's complements	**01001000**	2's complement
of original bits		These bits stay the same.

Related Problem   Find the 2's complement of 11000000.

The 2's complement of a negative binary number can be realized using inverters and an adder, as indicated in Figure 3. This illustrates how an 8-bit number can be converted to its 2's complement by first inverting each bit (taking the 1's complement) and then adding 1 to the 1's complement with an adder circuit.

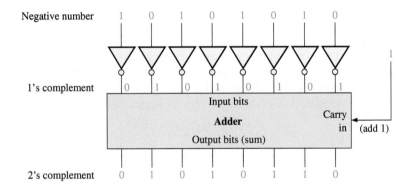

◀ **FIGURE 3**

Example of obtaining the 2's complement of a negative binary number.

To convert from a 1's or 2's complement back to the true (uncomplemented) binary form, use the same two procedures described previously. To go from the 1's complement back to true binary, reverse all the bits. To go from the 2's complement form back to true binary, take the 1's complement of the 2's complement number and add 1 to the least significant bit.

SECTION 5 CHECKUP

1. Determine the 1's complement of each binary number:
   (a) 00011010   (b) 11110111   (c) 10001101
2. Determine the 2's complement of each binary number:
   (a) 00010110   (b) 11111100   (c) 10010001

6 SIGNED NUMBERS

Digital systems, such as the computer, must be able to handle both positive and negative numbers. A signed binary number consists of both sign and magnitude information. The sign indicates whether a number is positive or negative, and the magnitude is the value of the number. There are three forms in which signed integer (whole) numbers can be represented in binary: sign-magnitude, 1's complement, and 2's complement. Of these, the 2's complement is the most important and the sign-magnitude is the least used. Noninteger and very large or small numbers can be expressed in floating-point format.

After completing this section, you should be able to

- ♦ Express positive and negative numbers in sign-magnitude
- ♦ Express positive and negative numbers in 1's complement
- ♦ Express positive and negative numbers in 2's complement
- ♦ Determine the decimal value of signed binary numbers
- ♦ Express a binary number in floating-point format

The Sign Bit

The left-most bit in a signed binary number is the **sign bit,** which tells you whether the number is positive or negative.

A 0 sign bit indicates a positive number, and a 1 sign bit indicates a negative number.

Sign-Magnitude Form

When a signed binary number is represented in sign-magnitude, the left-most bit is the sign bit and the remaining bits are the magnitude bits. The magnitude bits are in true (uncomplemented) binary for both positive and negative numbers. For example, the decimal number +25 is expressed as an 8-bit signed binary number using the sign-magnitude form as

$$00011001$$

Sign bit ⌐↑   ↑⌐ Magnitude bits

The decimal number −25 is expressed as

$$10011001$$

Notice that the only difference between +25 and −25 is the sign bit because the magnitude bits are in true binary for both positive and negative numbers.

In the sign-magnitude form, a negative number has the same magnitude bits as the corresponding positive number but the sign bit is a 1 rather than a zero.

1's Complement Form

Positive numbers in 1's complement form are represented the same way as the positive sign-magnitude numbers. Negative numbers, however, are the 1's complements of the corresponding positive numbers. For example, using eight bits, the decimal number −25 is expressed as the 1's complement of +25 (00011001) as

$$11100110$$

In the 1's complement form, a negative number is the 1's complement of the corresponding positive number.

COMPUTER NOTE

Computers use the 2's complement for negative integer numbers in arithmetic operations. The reason is that subtraction of a number is the same as adding the 2's complement of the number. Computers form the 2's complement by inverting the bits and adding 1, using special instructions that produce the same result as the adder in Figure 3.

2's Complement Form

Positive numbers in 2's complement form are represented the same way as in the sign-magnitude and 1's complement forms. Negative numbers are the 2's complements of the corresponding positive numbers. Again, using eight bits, let's take decimal number -25 and express it as the 2's complement of $+25$ (00011001). Inverting each bit and adding 1, you get

$$-25 = 11100111$$

In the 2's complement form, a negative number is the 2's complement of the corresponding positive number.

EXAMPLE 14

Express the decimal number -39 as an 8-bit number in the sign-magnitude, 1's complement, and 2's complement forms.

Solution First, write the 8-bit number for $+39$.

$$00100111$$

In the *sign-magnitude form,* -39 is produced by changing the sign bit to a 1 and leaving the magnitude bits as they are. The number is

10100111

In the *1's complement form,* -39 is produced by taking the 1's complement of $+39$ (00100111).

11011000

In the *2's complement form,* -39 is produced by taking the 2's complement of $+39$ (00100111) as follows:

$$
\begin{array}{ll}
11011000 & \text{1's complement} \\
\underline{+\quad\quad 1} & \\
\textbf{11011001} & \text{2's complement}
\end{array}
$$

Related Problem Express $+19$ and -19 as 8-bit numbers in sign-magnitude, 1's complement, and 2's complement.

The Decimal Value of Signed Numbers

Sign-magnitude Decimal values of positive and negative numbers in the sign-magnitude form are determined by summing the weights in all the magnitude bit positions where there are 1s and ignoring those positions where there are zeros. The sign is determined by examination of the sign bit.

EXAMPLE 15

Determine the decimal value of this signed binary number expressed in sign-magnitude: 10010101.

Solution The seven magnitude bits and their powers-of-two weights are as follows:

2^6	2^5	2^4	2^3	2^2	2^1	2^0
0	0	1	0	1	0	1

Summing the weights where there are 1s,

$$16 + 4 + 1 = 21$$

The sign bit is 1; therefore, the decimal number is **−21.**

Related Problem   Determine the decimal value of the sign-magnitude number 01110111.

1's Complement   Decimal values of positive numbers in the 1's complement form are determined by summing the weights in all bit positions where there are 1s and ignoring those positions where there are zeros. Decimal values of negative numbers are determined by assigning a negative value to the weight of the sign bit, summing all the weights where there are 1s, and adding 1 to the result.

EXAMPLE 16

Determine the decimal values of the signed binary numbers expressed in 1's complement:

(a) 00010111   **(b)** 11101000

Solution   **(a)** The bits and their powers-of-two weights for the positive number are as follows:

-2^7	2^6	2^5	2^4	2^3	2^2	2^1	2^0
0	0	0	1	0	1	1	1

Summing the weights where there are 1s,

$$16 + 4 + 2 + 1 = +23$$

(b) The bits and their powers-of-two weights for the negative number are as follows. Notice that the negative sign bit has a weight of -2^7 or -128.

-2^7	2^6	2^5	2^4	2^3	2^2	2^1	2^0
1	1	1	0	1	0	0	0

Summing the weights where there are 1s,

$$-128 + 64 + 32 + 8 = -24$$

Adding 1 to the result, the final decimal number is

$$-24 + 1 = -23$$

Related Problem   Determine the decimal value of the 1's complement number 11101011.

2's Complement   Decimal values of positive and negative numbers in the 2's complement form are determined by summing the weights in all bit positions where there are 1s and ignoring those positions where there are zeros. The weight of the sign bit in a negative number is given a negative value.

EXAMPLE 17

Determine the decimal values of the signed binary numbers expressed in 2's complement:

(a) 01010110   **(b)** 10101010

Solution **(a)** The bits and their powers-of-two weights for the positive number are as follows:

$$-2^7 \quad 2^6 \quad 2^5 \quad 2^4 \quad 2^3 \quad 2^2 \quad 2^1 \quad 2^0$$
$$0 \quad\;\; 1 \quad\;\; 0 \quad\;\; 1 \quad\;\; 0 \quad\;\; 1 \quad\;\; 1 \quad\;\; 0$$

Summing the weights where there are 1s,

$$64 + 16 + 4 + 2 = \mathbf{+86}$$

(b) The bits and their powers-of-two weights for the negative number are as follows. Notice that the negative sign bit has a weight of $-2^7 = -128$.

$$-2^7 \quad 2^6 \quad 2^5 \quad 2^4 \quad 2^3 \quad 2^2 \quad 2^1 \quad 2^0$$
$$1 \quad\;\; 0 \quad\;\; 1 \quad\;\; 0 \quad\;\; 1 \quad\;\; 0 \quad\;\; 1 \quad\;\; 0$$

Summing the weights where there are 1s,

$$-128 + 32 + 8 + 2 = \mathbf{-86}$$

Related Problem Determine the decimal value of the 2's complement number 11010111.

From these examples, you can see why the 2's complement form is preferred for representing signed integer numbers: To convert to decimal, it simply requires a summation of weights regardless of whether the number is positive or negative. The 1's complement system requires adding 1 to the summation of weights for negative numbers but not for positive numbers. Also, the 1's complement form is generally not used because two representations of zero (00000000 or 11111111) are possible.

Range of Signed Integer Numbers

We have used 8-bit numbers for illustration because the 8-bit grouping is common in most computers and has been given the special name **byte.** With one byte or eight bits, you can represent 256 different numbers. With two bytes or sixteen bits, you can represent 65,536 different numbers. With four bytes or 32 bits, you can represent 4.295×10^9 different numbers. The formula for finding the number of different combinations of n bits is

The range of magnitude of a binary number depends on the number of bits (n).

$$\text{Total combinations} = 2^n$$

For 2's complement signed numbers, the range of values for n-bit numbers is

$$\text{Range} = -(2^{n-1}) \text{ to } +(2^{n-1} - 1)$$

where in each case there is one sign bit and $n - 1$ magnitude bits. For example, with four bits you can represent numbers in 2's complement ranging from $-(2^3) = -8$ to $2^3 - 1 = +7$. Similarly, with eight bits you can go from -128 to $+127$, with sixteen bits you can go from $-32,768$ to $+32,767$, and so on. There is one less positive number than there are negative numbers because zero is represented as a positive number (all zeros).

Floating-Point Numbers

To represent very large **integer** (whole) numbers, many bits are required. There is also a problem when numbers with both integer and fractional parts, such as 23.5618, need to be represented. The floating-point number system, based on scientific notation, is capable of representing very large and very small numbers without an increase in the number of bits and also for representing numbers that have both integer and fractional components.

A **floating-point number** (also known as a *real number*) consists of two parts plus a sign. The **mantissa** is the part of a floating-point number that represents the magnitude of the number and is between 0 and 1. The **exponent** is the part of a floating-point number that represents the number of places that the decimal point (or binary point) is to be moved.

A decimal example will be helpful in understanding the basic concept of floating-point numbers. Let's consider a decimal number which, in integer form, is 241,506,800. The mantissa is .2415068 and the exponent is 9. When the integer is expressed as a floating-point number, it is normalized by moving the decimal point to the left of all the digits so that the mantissa is a fractional number and the exponent is the power of ten. The floating-point number is written as

$$0.2415068 \times 10^9$$

COMPUTER NOTE

In addition to the CPU (central processing unit), computers use *coprocessors* to perform complicated mathematical calculations using floating-point numbers. The purpose is to increase performance by freeing up the CPU for other tasks. The mathematical coprocessor is also known as the floating-point unit (FPU).

For binary floating-point numbers, the format is defined by ANSI/IEEE Standard 754-1985 in three forms: *single-precision, double-precision,* and *extended-precision.* These all have the same basic formats except for the number of bits. Single-precision floating-point numbers have 32 bits, double-precision numbers have 64 bits, and extended-precision numbers have 80 bits. We will restrict our discussion to the single-precision floating-point format.

Single-Precision Floating-Point Binary Numbers In the standard format for a single-precision binary number, the sign bit (S) is the left-most bit, the exponent (E) includes the next eight bits, and the mantissa or fractional part (F) includes the remaining 23 bits, as shown next.

	32 bits	
S	Exponent (E)	Mantissa (fraction, F)
1 bit	8 bits	23 bits

In the mantissa or fractional part, the binary point is understood to be to the left of the 23 bits. Effectively, there are 24 bits in the mantissa because in any binary number the left-most (most significant) bit is always a 1. Therefore, this 1 is understood to be there although it does not occupy an actual bit position.

The eight bits in the exponent represent a *biased exponent,* which is obtained by adding 127 to the actual exponent. The purpose of the bias is to allow very large or very small numbers without requiring a separate sign bit for the exponents. The biased exponent allows a range of actual exponent values from -126 to $+128$.

To illustrate how a binary number is expressed in floating-point format, let's use 1011010010001 as an example. First, it can be expressed as 1 plus a fractional binary number by moving the binary point 12 places to the left and then multiplying by the appropriate power of two.

$$1011010010001 = 1.011010010001 \times 2^{12}$$

Assuming that this is a positive number, the sign bit (S) is 0. The exponent, 12, is expressed as a biased exponent by adding it to 127 ($12 + 127 = 139$). The biased exponent (E) is expressed as the binary number 10001011. The mantissa is the fractional part (F) of the binary number, .011010010001. Because there is always a 1 to the left of the binary point in the power-of-two expression, it is not included in the mantissa. The complete floating-point number is

S	E	F
0	10001011	01101001000100000000000

Next, let's see how to evaluate a binary number that is already in floating-point format. The general approach to determining the value of a floating-point number is expressed by the following formula:

$$\text{Number} = (-1)^S (1 + F)(2^{E-127})$$

To illustrate, let's consider the following floating-point binary number:

S	E	F
1	10010001	10001110001000000000000

The sign bit is 1. The biased exponent is $10010001 = 145$. Applying the formula, we get

$$\text{Number} = (-1)^1 (1.10001110001)(2^{145-127})$$
$$= (-1)(1.10001110001)(2^{18}) = -1100011100010000000$$

This floating-point binary number is equivalent to $-407,688$ in decimal. Since the exponent can be any number between -126 and $+128$, extremely large and small numbers can be expressed. A 32-bit floating-point number can replace a binary integer number having 129 bits. Because the exponent determines the position of the binary point, numbers containing both integer and fractional parts can be represented.

There are two exceptions to the format for floating-point numbers: The number 0.0 is represented by all 0s, and infinity is represented by all 1s in the exponent and all 0s in the mantissa.

EXAMPLE 18

Convert the decimal number 3.248×10^4 to a single-precision floating-point binary number.

Solution   Convert the decimal number to binary.

$$3.248 \times 10^4 = 32480 = 111111011100000_2 = 1.11111011100000 \times 2^{14}$$

The MSB will not occupy a bit position because it is always a 1. Therefore, the mantissa is the fractional 23-bit binary number 11111011100000000000000 and the biased exponent is

$$14 + 127 = 141 = 10001101_2$$

The complete floating-point number is

0	10001101	11111011100000000000000

Related Problem   Determine the binary value of the following floating-point binary number:

0 10011000 10000100010100110000000

SECTION 6 CHECKUP

1. Express the decimal number $+9$ as an 8-bit binary number in the sign-magnitude system.
2. Express the decimal number -33 as an 8-bit binary number in the 1's complement system.
3. Express the decimal number -46 as an 8-bit binary number in the 2's complement system.
4. List the three parts of a signed, floating-point number.

7   Arithmetic Operations with Signed Numbers

In the last section, you learned how signed numbers are represented in three different forms. In this section, you will learn how signed numbers are added, subtracted, multiplied, and divided. Because the 2's complement form for representing signed numbers is the most widely used in computers and microprocessor-based systems, the coverage in this section is limited to 2's complement arithmetic. The processes covered can be extended to the other forms if necessary.

After completing this section, you should be able to

- Add signed binary numbers
- Define *overflow*
- Explain how computers add strings of numbers
- Subtract signed binary numbers
- Multiply signed binary numbers using the direct addition method
- Multiply signed binary numbers using the partial products method
- Divide signed binary numbers

Addition

The two numbers in an addition are the **addend** and the **augend.** The result is the **sum.** There are four cases that can occur when two signed binary numbers are added.

1. Both numbers positive
2. Positive number with magnitude larger than negative number
3. Negative number with magnitude larger than positive number
4. Both numbers negative

Let's take one case at a time using 8-bit signed numbers as examples. The equivalent decimal numbers are shown for reference.

Addition of two positive numbers yields a positive number.

Both numbers positive:

$$
\begin{array}{rr}
00000111 & 7 \\
+\ 00000100 & +\ 4 \\
\hline
00001011 & 11
\end{array}
$$

The sum is positive and is therefore in true (uncomplemented) binary.

Addition of a positive number and a smaller negative number yields a positive number.

Positive number with magnitude larger than negative number:

$$
\begin{array}{rr}
00001111 & 15 \\
+\ 11111010 & +\ -6 \\
\hline
\text{Discard carry} \longrightarrow \boxed{1}\ 00001001 & 9
\end{array}
$$

The final carry bit is discarded. The sum is positive and therefore in true (uncomplemented) binary.

Addition of a positive number and a larger negative number or two negative numbers yields a negative number in 2's complement.

Negative number with magnitude larger than positive number:

$$
\begin{array}{rr}
00010000 & 16 \\
+\ 11101000 & +\ -24 \\
\hline
11111000 & -8
\end{array}
$$

The sum is negative and therefore in 2's complement form.

Both numbers negative:

$$
\begin{array}{ccc}
& 11111011 & -5 \\
& +\ 11110111 & +\ -9 \\
\hline
\text{Discard carry} \longrightarrow\ 1 & 11110010 & -14
\end{array}
$$

The final carry bit is discarded. The sum is negative and therefore in 2's complement form.

In a computer, the negative numbers are stored in 2's complement form so, as you can see, the addition process is very simple: *Add the two numbers and discard any final carry bit.*

Overflow Condition   When two numbers are added and the number of bits required to represent the sum exceeds the number of bits in the two numbers, an **overflow** results as indicated by an incorrect sign bit. An overflow can occur only when both numbers are positive or both numbers are negative. If the sign bit of the result is different than the sign bit of the numbers that are added, overflow is indicated. The following 8-bit example will illustrate this condition.

$$
\begin{array}{cc}
01111101 & 125 \\
+\ 00111010 & +\ 58 \\
\hline
10110111 & 183
\end{array}
$$

Sign incorrect ⸻
Magnitude incorrect ⸻

In this example the sum of 183 requires eight magnitude bits. Since there are seven magnitude bits in the numbers (one bit is the sign), there is a carry into the sign bit which produces the overflow indication.

Numbers Added Two at a Time   Now let's look at the addition of a string of numbers, added two at a time. This can be accomplished by adding the first two numbers, then adding the third number to the sum of the first two, then adding the fourth number to this result, and so on. This is how computers add strings of numbers. The addition of numbers taken two at a time is illustrated in Example 19.

EXAMPLE 19

Add the signed numbers: 01000100, 00011011, 00001110, and 00010010.

Solution   The equivalent decimal additions are given for reference.

$$
\begin{array}{lll}
68 & 01000100 & \\
+\ 27 & +\ 00011011 & \text{Add 1st two numbers} \\
\hline
95 & 01011111 & \text{1st sum} \\
+\ 14 & +\ 00001110 & \text{Add 3rd number} \\
\hline
109 & 01101101 & \text{2nd sum} \\
+\ 18 & +\ 00010010 & \text{Add 4th number} \\
\hline
127 & \mathbf{01111111} & \text{Final sum}
\end{array}
$$

Related Problem   Add 00110011, 10111111, and 01100011. These are signed numbers.

Subtraction

Subtraction is a special case of addition. For example, subtracting +6 (the **subtrahend**) from +9 (the **minuend**) is equivalent to adding −6 to +9. Basically, *the subtraction operation changes the sign of the subtrahend and adds it to the minuend.* The result of a subtraction is called the **difference.**

Subtraction is addition with the sign of the subtrahend changed.

The sign of a positive or negative binary number is changed by taking its 2's complement.

For example, when you take the 2's complement of the positive number 00000100 (+4), you get 11111100, which is −4 as the following sum-of-weights evaluation shows:

$$-128 + 64 + 32 + 16 + 8 + 4 = -4$$

As another example, when you take the 2's complement of the negative number 11101101 (−19), you get 00010011, which is +19 as the following sum-of-weights evaluation shows:

$$16 + 2 + 1 = 19$$

Since subtraction is simply an addition with the sign of the subtrahend changed, the process is stated as follows:

To subtract two signed numbers, take the 2's complement of the subtrahend and add. Discard any final carry bit.

When doing binary subtraction with the 2's complement method, it is very important that both numbers have the same number of bits.

Example 20 illustrates the subtraction process.

EXAMPLE 20

Perform each of the following subtractions of the signed numbers:

(a) 00001000 − 00000011   (b) 00001100 − 11110111

(c) 11100111 − 00010011   (d) 10001000 − 11100010

Solution   Like in other examples, the equivalent decimal subtractions are given for reference.

(a) In this case, 8 − 3 = 8 + (−3) = 5.

$$
\begin{array}{ll}
00001000 & \text{Minuend } (+8) \\
+\ 11111101 & \text{2's complement of subtrahend } (-3) \\
\hline
\text{Discard carry} \longrightarrow \mathbf{1\ 00000101} & \text{Difference } (+5)
\end{array}
$$

(b) In this case, 12 − (−9) = 12 + 9 = 21.

$$
\begin{array}{ll}
00001100 & \text{Minuend } (+12) \\
+\ 00001001 & \text{2's complement of subtrahend } (+9) \\
\hline
00010101 & \text{Difference } (+21)
\end{array}
$$

(c) In this case, −25 − (+19) = −25 + (−19) = −44.

$$
\begin{array}{ll}
11100111 & \text{Minuend } (-25) \\
+\ 11101101 & \text{2's complement of subtrahend } (-19) \\
\hline
\text{Discard carry} \longrightarrow \mathbf{1\ 11010100} & \text{Difference } (-44)
\end{array}
$$

(d) In this case, −120 − (−30) = −120 + 30 = −90.

$$
\begin{array}{ll}
10001000 & \text{Minuend } (-120) \\
+\ 00011110 & \text{2's complement of subtrahend } (+30) \\
\hline
\mathbf{10100110} & \text{Difference } (-90)
\end{array}
$$

Related Problem   Subtract 01000111 from 01011000.

Multiplication

The numbers in a multiplication are the **multiplicand,** the **multiplier,** and the **product.** These are illustrated in the following decimal multiplication:

$$
\begin{array}{ll}
8 & \text{Multiplicand} \\
\times\ 3 & \text{Multiplier} \\
\hline
24 & \text{Product}
\end{array}
$$

The multiplication operation in most computers is accomplished using addition. As you have already seen, subtraction is done with an adder; now let's see how multiplication is done.

Direct addition and *partial products* are two basic methods for performing multiplication using addition. In the direct addition method, you add the multiplicand a number of times equal to the multiplier. In the previous decimal example (8×3), three multiplicands are added: $8 + 8 + 8 = 24$. The disadvantage of this approach is that it becomes very lengthy if the multiplier is a large number. For example, to multiply 350×75, you must add 350 to itself 75 times. Incidentally, this is why the term *times* is used to mean multiply.

When two binary numbers are multiplied, both numbers must be in true (uncomplemented) form. The direct addition method is illustrated in Example 21 adding two binary numbers at a time.

> Multiplication is equivalent to adding a number to itself a number of times equal to the multiplier.

EXAMPLE 21

Multiply the signed binary numbers: 01001101 (multiplicand) and 00000100 (multiplier) using the direct addition method.

Solution   Since both numbers are positive, they are in true form, and the product will be positive. The decimal value of the multiplier is 4, so the multiplicand is added to itself four times as follows:

01001101	1st time
+ 01001101	2nd time
10011010	Partial sum
+ 01001101	3rd time
11100111	Partial sum
+ 01001101	4th time
100110100	Product

Since the sign bit of the multiplicand is 0, it has no effect on the outcome. All of the bits in the product are magnitude bits.

Related Problem   Multiply 01100001 by 00000110 using the direct addition method.

The partial products method is perhaps the more common one because it reflects the way you multiply longhand. The multiplicand is multiplied by each multiplier digit beginning with the least significant digit. The result of the multiplication of the multiplicand by a multiplier digit is called a *partial product*. Each successive partial product is moved (shifted) one place to the left and when all the partial products have been produced, they are added to get the final product. Here is a decimal example.

239	Multiplicand
$\times$ 123	Multiplier
717	1st partial product (3×239)
478	2nd partial product (2×239)
+ 239	3rd partial product (1×239)
29,397	Final product

The sign of the product of a multiplication depends on the signs of the multiplicand and the multiplier according to the following two rules:

- **If the signs are the same, the product is positive.**

- **If the signs are different, the product is negative.**

The basic steps in the partial products method of binary multiplication are as follows:

Step 1: Determine if the signs of the multiplicand and multiplier are the same or different. This determines what the sign of the product will be.

Step 2: Change any negative number to true (uncomplemented) form. Because most computers store negative numbers in 2's complement, a 2's complement operation is required to get the negative number into true form.

Step 3: Starting with the least significant multiplier bit, generate the partial products. When the multiplier bit is 1, the partial product is the same as the multiplicand. When the multiplier bit is 0, the partial product is zero. Shift each successive partial product one bit to the left.

Step 4: Add each successive partial product to the sum of the previous partial products to get the final product.

Step 5: If the sign bit that was determined in step 1 is negative, take the 2's complement of the product. If positive, leave the product in true form. Attach the sign bit to the product.

EXAMPLE 22

Multiply the signed binary numbers: 01010011 (multiplicand) and 11000101 (multiplier).

Solution

Step 1: The sign bit of the multiplicand is 0 and the sign bit of the multiplier is 1. The sign bit of the product will be 1 (negative).

Step 2: Take the 2's complement of the multiplier to put it in true form.

$$11000101 \longrightarrow 00111011$$

Step 3 and 4: The multiplication proceeds as follows. Notice that only the magnitude bits are used in these steps.

```
      1010011      Multiplicand
   ×  0111011      Multiplier
      1010011      1st partial product
   +  1010011      2nd partial product
     11111001      Sum of 1st and 2nd
   +  0000000      3rd partial product
    011111001      Sum
   +  1010011      4th partial product
   1110010001      Sum
   + 1010011       5th partial product
  100011000001     Sum
   + 1010011       6th partial product
 1001100100001     Sum
   + 0000000       7th partial product
 1001100100001     Final product
```

Step 5: Since the sign of the product is a 1 as determined in step 1, take the 2's complement of the product.

$$1001100100001 \longrightarrow 0110011011111$$

Attach the sign bit ⟶

1 0110011011111

Related Problem

Verify the multiplication is correct by converting to decimal numbers and performing the multiplication.

Division

The numbers in a division are the **dividend,** the **divisor,** and the **quotient.** These are illustrated in the following standard division format.

$$\frac{\text{dividend}}{\text{divisor}} = \text{quotient}$$

The division operation in computers is accomplished using subtraction. Since subtraction is done with an adder, division can also be accomplished with an adder.

The result of a division is called the *quotient;* the quotient is the number of times that the divisor will go into the dividend. This means that the divisor can be subtracted from the dividend a number of times equal to the quotient, as illustrated by dividing 21 by 7.

21	Dividend
− 7	1st subtraction of divisor
14	1st partial remainder
− 7	2nd subtraction of divisor
7	2nd partial remainder
− 7	3rd subtraction of divisor
0	Zero remainder

In this simple example, the divisor was subtracted from the dividend three times before a remainder of zero was obtained. Therefore, the quotient is 3.

The sign of the quotient depends on the signs of the dividend and the divisor according to the following two rules:

♦ **If the signs are the same, the quotient is positive.**

♦ **If the signs are different, the quotient is negative.**

When two binary numbers are divided, both numbers must be in true (uncomplemented) form. The basic steps in a division process are as follows:

Step 1: Determine if the signs of the dividend and divisor are the same or different. This determines what the sign of the quotient will be. Initialize the quotient to zero.

Step 2: Subtract the divisor from the dividend using 2's complement addition to get the first partial remainder and add 1 to the quotient. If this partial remainder is positive, go to step 3. If the partial remainder is zero or negative, the division is complete.

Step 3: Subtract the divisor from the partial remainder and add 1 to the quotient. If the result is positive, repeat for the next partial remainder. If the result is zero or negative, the division is complete.

Continue to subtract the divisor from the dividend and the partial remainders until there is a zero or a negative result. Count the number of times that the divisor is subtracted and you have the quotient. Example 23 illustrates these steps using 8-bit signed binary numbers.

EXAMPLE 23

Divide 01100100 by 00011001.

Solution

Step 1: The signs of both numbers are positive, so the quotient will be positive. The quotient is initially zero: 00000000.

Step 2: Subtract the divisor from the dividend using 2's complement addition (remember that final carries are discarded).

01100100	Dividend
+ 11100111	2's complement of divisor
01001011	Positive 1st partial remainder

Add 1 to quotient: 00000000 + 00000001 = 00000001.

Step 3: Subtract the divisor from the 1st partial remainder using 2's complement addition.

01001011	1st partial remainder
+ 11100111	2's complement of divisor
00110010	Positive 2nd partial remainder

Add 1 to quotient: 00000001 + 00000001 = 00000010.

Step 4: Subtract the divisor from the 2nd partial remainder using 2's complement addition.

00110010	2nd partial remainder
+ 11100111	2's complement of divisor
00011001	Positive 3rd partial remainder

Add 1 to quotient: 00000010 + 00000001 = 00000011.

Step 5: Subtract the divisor from the 3rd partial remainder using 2's complement addition.

00011001	3rd partial remainder
+ 11100111	2's complement of divisor
00000000	Zero remainder

Add 1 to quotient: 00000011 + 00000001 = **00000100** (final quotient). The process is complete.

Related Problem Verify that the process is correct by converting to decimal numbers and performing the division.

SECTION 7 CHECKUP

1. List the four cases when numbers are added.
2. Add the signed numbers 00100001 and 10111100.
3. Subtract the signed numbers 00110010 from 01110111.
4. What is the sign of the product when two negative numbers are multiplied?
5. Multiply 01111111 by 00000101.
6. What is the sign of the quotient when a positive number is divided by a negative number?
7. Divide 00110000 by 00001100.

---

8 HEXADECIMAL NUMBERS

The hexadecimal number system has sixteen characters; it is used primarily as a compact way of displaying or writing binary numbers because it is very easy to convert between binary and hexadecimal. As you are probably aware, long binary numbers are difficult to read and write because it is easy to drop or transpose a bit. Since computers and microprocessors understand only 1s and 0s, it is necessary to use these digits when you program in "machine language." Imagine writing a sixteen bit instruction for a microprocessor system in 1s and 0s. It is much more efficient to use hexadecimal or octal; octal numbers are covered in Section 9. Hexadecimal is widely used in computer and microprocessor applications.

After completing this section, you should be able to

- List the hexadecimal characters
- Count in hexadecimal
- Convert from binary to hexadecimal
- Convert from hexadecimal to binary
- Convert from hexadecimal to decimal
- Convert from decimal to hexadecimal
- Add hexadecimal numbers
- Determine the 2's complement of a hexadecimal number
- Subtract hexadecimal numbers

The **hexadecimal** number system has a base of sixteen; that is, it is composed of 16 **numeric** and alphabetic **characters.** Most digital systems process binary data in groups that are multiples of four bits, making the hexadecimal number very convenient because each hexadecimal digit represents a 4-bit binary number (as listed in Table 3).

The hexadecimal number system consists of digits 0–9 and letters A–F.

DECIMAL	BINARY	HEXADECIMAL
0	0000	0
1	0001	1
2	0010	2
3	0011	3
4	0100	4
5	0101	5
6	0110	6
7	0111	7
8	1000	8
9	1001	9
10	1010	A
11	1011	B
12	1100	C
13	1101	D
14	1110	E
15	1111	F

◄ TABLE 3

Ten numeric digits and six alphabetic characters make up the hexadecimal number system. The use of letters A, B, C, D, E, and F to represent numbers may seem strange at first, but keep in mind that any number system is only a set of sequential symbols. If you understand what quantities these symbols represent, then the form of the symbols themselves is less important once you get accustomed to using them. We will use the subscript 16 to designate hexadecimal numbers to avoid confusion with decimal numbers. Sometimes you may see an "h" following a hexadecimal number.

With computer memories in the gigabyte (GB) range, specifying a memory address in binary is quite cumbersome. For example, it takes 32 bits to specify an address in a 4 GB memory. It is much easier to express a 32-bit code using 8 hexadecimal digits.

Counting in Hexadecimal

How do you count in hexadecimal once you get to F? Simply start over with another column and continue as follows:

$$\ldots, E, F, 10, 11, 12, 13, 14, 15, 16, 17, 18, 19, 1A, 1B, 1C, 1D, 1E, 1F,$$
$$20, 21, 22, 23, 24, 25, 26, 27, 28, 29, 2A, 2B, 2C, 2D, 2E, 2F, 30, 31, \ldots$$

With two hexadecimal digits, you can count up to FF_{16}, which is decimal 255. To count beyond this, three hexadecimal digits are needed. For instance, 100_{16} is decimal 256, 101_{16} is decimal 257, and so forth. The maximum 3-digit hexadecimal number is FFF_{16}, or decimal 4095. The maximum 4-digit hexadecimal number is $FFFF_{16}$, which is decimal 65,535.

Binary-to-Hexadecimal Conversion

Converting a binary number to hexadecimal is a straightforward procedure. Simply break the binary number into 4-bit groups, starting at the right-most bit and replace each 4-bit group with the equivalent hexadecimal symbol.

EXAMPLE 24

Convert the following binary numbers to hexadecimal:

(a) 1100101001010111   **(b)** 111111000101101001

Solution   **(a)** 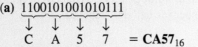   **(b)**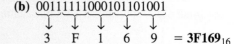

Two zeros have been added in part (b) to complete a 4-bit group at the left.

Related Problem   Convert the binary number 1001111011110011100 to hexadecimal.

Hexadecimal-to-Binary Conversion

Hexadecimal is a convenient way to represent binary numbers.

To convert from a hexadecimal number to a binary number, reverse the process and replace each hexadecimal symbol with the appropriate four bits.

EXAMPLE 25

Determine the binary numbers for the following hexadecimal numbers:

(a) $10A4_{16}$ **(b)** $CF8E_{16}$ **(c)** 9742_{16}

Solution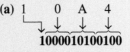

In part (a), the MSB is understood to have three zeros preceding it, thus forming a 4-bit group.

Related Problem   Convert the hexadecimal number 6BD3 to binary.

Conversion between hexadecimal and binary is direct and easy.

It should be clear that it is much easier to deal with a hexadecimal number than with the equivalent binary number. Since conversion is so easy, the hexadecimal system is widely used for representing binary numbers in programming, printouts, and displays.

Hexadecimal-to-Decimal Conversion

One way to find the decimal equivalent of a hexadecimal number is to first convert the hexadecimal number to binary and then convert from binary to decimal.

EXAMPLE 26

Convert the following hexadecimal numbers to decimal:

(a) $1C_{16}$ (b) $A85_{16}$

Solution   Remember, convert the hexadecimal number to binary first, then to decimal.

(a)   1   C
     ↓   ↓
     $\overline{0001}\,\overline{1100} = 2^4 + 2^3 + 2^2 = 16 + 8 + 4 = \mathbf{28}_{10}$

(b)   A   8   5
     ↓   ↓   ↓
     $\overline{1010}\,\overline{1000}\,\overline{0101} = 2^{11} + 2^9 + 2^7 + 2^2 + 2^0 = 2048 + 512 + 128 + 4 + 1 = \mathbf{2693}_{10}$

Related Problem   Convert the hexadecimal number 6BD to decimal.

Another way to convert a hexadecimal number to its decimal equivalent is to multiply the decimal value of each hexadecimal digit by its weight and then take the sum of these products. The weights of a hexadecimal number are increasing powers of 16 (from right to left). For a 4-digit hexadecimal number, the weights are

$$16^3 \quad 16^2 \quad 16^1 \quad 16^0$$
$$4096 \quad 256 \quad 16 \quad 1$$

A calculator can be used to perform arithmetic operations with hexadecimal numbers.

EXAMPLE 27

Convert the following hexadecimal numbers to decimal:

(a) $E5_{16}$ (b) $B2F8_{16}$

Solution   Recall from Table 3 that letters A through F represent decimal numbers 10 through 15, respectively.

(a) $E5_{16} = (E \times 16) + (5 \times 1) = (14 \times 16) + (5 \times 1) = 224 + 5 = \mathbf{229}_{10}$

(b) $B2F8_{16} = (B \times 4096) + (2 \times 256) + (F \times 16) + (8 \times 1)$
$$= (11 \times 4096) + (2 \times 256) + (15 \times 16) + (8 \times 1)$$
$$= \quad 45{,}056 \quad + \quad 512 \quad + \quad 240 \quad + \quad 8 \quad = \mathbf{45{,}816}_{10}$$

Related Problem   Convert $60A_{16}$ to decimal.

CALCULATOR TUTORIAL

Conversion of a Hexadecimal Number to a Decimal Number

Example   Convert hexadecimal 28A to decimal.

BASE

TI-86   **Step 1:** `2nd` `1` `F3`

       Step 2: `2` `8` `2nd` `M1` `2nd` `M1`

                 `2nd` `M2` `F2`

       Step 3: `2nd` `F3`

       Step 4: `F4`

       Step 5: `ENTER`

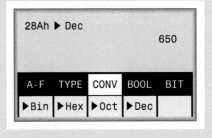

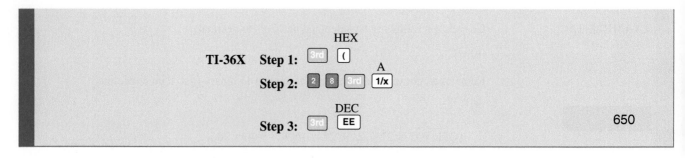

Decimal-to-Hexadecimal Conversion

Repeated division of a decimal number by 16 will produce the equivalent hexadecimal number, formed by the remainders of the divisions. The first remainder produced is the least significant digit (LSD). Each successive division by 16 yields a remainder that becomes a digit in the equivalent hexadecimal number. This procedure is similar to repeated division by 2 for decimal-to-binary conversion that was covered in Section 3. Example 28 illustrates the procedure. Note that when a quotient has a fractional part, the fractional part is multiplied by the divisor to get the remainder.

EXAMPLE 28

Convert the decimal number 650 to hexadecimal by repeated division by 16.

Solution

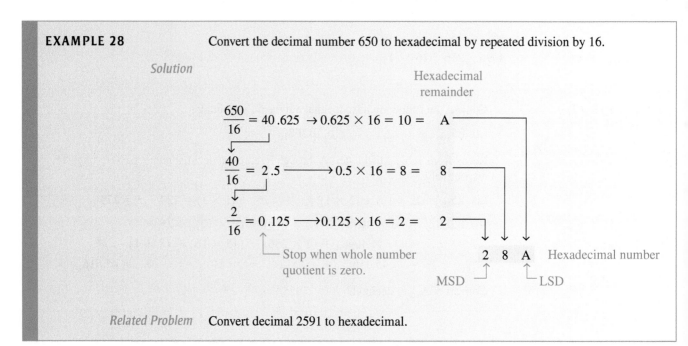

Related Problem   Convert decimal 2591 to hexadecimal.

Hexadecimal Addition

Addition can be done directly with hexadecimal numbers by remembering that the hexadecimal digits 0 through 9 are equivalent to decimal digits 0 through 9 and that hexadecimal digits A through F are equivalent to decimal numbers 10 through 15. When adding two hexadecimal numbers, use the following rules. (Decimal numbers are indicated by a subscript 10.)

1. In any given column of an addition problem, think of the two hexadecimal digits in terms of their decimal values. For instance, $5_{16} = 5_{10}$ and $C_{16} = 12_{10}$.

2. If the sum of these two digits is 15_{10} or less, bring down the corresponding hexadecimal digit.

3. If the sum of these two digits is greater than 15_{10}, bring down the amount of the sum that exceeds 16_{10} and carry a 1 to the next column.

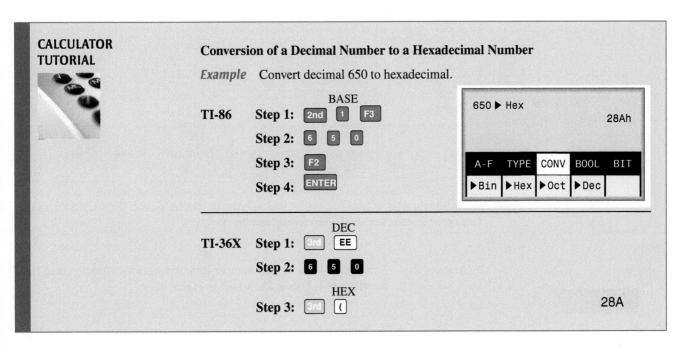

CALCULATOR TUTORIAL

Conversion of a Decimal Number to a Hexadecimal Number

Example   Convert decimal 650 to hexadecimal.

BASE

TI-86   Step 1: [2nd] [1] [F3]

Step 2: [6] [5] [0]

Step 3: [F2]

Step 4: [ENTER]

650 ▶ Hex
                                    28Ah

| A-F | TYPE | CONV | BOOL | BIT |
| ▶Bin | ▶Hex | ▶Oct | ▶Dec | |

DEC

TI-36X   Step 1: [3rd] [EE]

Step 2: [6] [5] [0]

HEX

Step 3: [3rd] [(]   28A

EXAMPLE 29

Add the following hexadecimal numbers:

(a) $23_{16} + 16_{16}$ **(b)** $58_{16} + 22_{16}$ **(c)** $2B_{16} + 84_{16}$ **(d)** $DF_{16} + AC_{16}$

Solution   **(a)** $\begin{array}{r} 23_{16} \\ +16_{16} \\ \hline \mathbf{39}_{16} \end{array}$ right column: $3_{16} + 6_{16} = 3_{10} + 6_{10} = 9_{10} = 9_{16}$
left column: $2_{16} + 1_{16} = 2_{10} + 1_{10} = 3_{10} = 3_{16}$

(b) $\begin{array}{r} 58_{16} \\ + 22_{16} \\ \hline \mathbf{7A}_{16} \end{array}$ right column: $8_{16} + 2_{16} = 8_{10} + 2_{10} = 10_{10} = A_{16}$
left column: $5_{16} + 2_{16} = 5_{10} + 2_{10} = 7_{10} = 7_{16}$

(c) $\begin{array}{r} 2B_{16} \\ + 84_{16} \\ \hline \mathbf{AF}_{16} \end{array}$ right column: $B_{16} + 4_{16} = 11_{10} + 4_{10} = 15_{10} = F_{16}$
left column: $2_{16} + 8_{16} = 2_{10} + 8_{10} = 10_{10} = A_{16}$

(d) $\begin{array}{r} DF_{16} \\ + AC_{16} \\ \hline \mathbf{18B}_{16} \end{array}$ right column: $F_{16} + C_{16} = 15_{10} + 12_{10} = 27_{10}$
$27_{10} - 16_{10} = 11_{10} = B_{16}$ with a 1 carry
left column: $D_{16} + A_{16} + 1_{16} = 13_{10} + 10_{10} + 1_{10} = 24_{10}$
$24_{10} - 16_{10} = 8_{10} = 8_{16}$ with a 1 carry

Related Problem   Add $4C_{16}$ and $3A_{16}$.

Hexadecimal Subtraction

As you have learned, the 2's complement allows you to subtract by adding binary numbers. Since a hexadecimal number can be used to represent a binary number, it can also be used to represent the 2's complement of a binary number.

There are three ways to get the 2's complement of a hexadecimal number. Method 1 is the most common and easiest to use. Methods 2 and 3 are alternate methods.

Method 1:   Convert the hexadecimal number to binary. Take the 2's complement of the binary number. Convert the result to hexadecimal. This is illustrated in Figure 4.

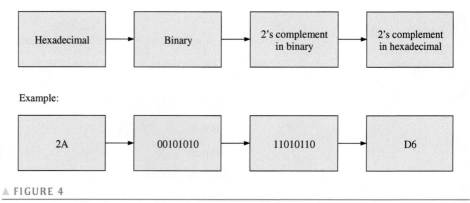

▲ FIGURE 4

Getting the 2's complement of a hexadecimal number, Method 1.

Method 2: Subtract the hexadecimal number from the maximum hexadecimal number and add 1. This is illustrated in Figure 5.

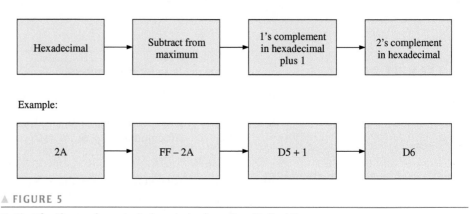

▲ FIGURE 5

Getting the 2's complement of a hexadecimal number, Method 2.

Method 3: Write the sequence of single hexadecimal digits. Write the sequence in reverse below the forward sequence. The 1's complement of each hex digit is the digit directly below it. Add 1 to the resulting number to get the 2's complement. This is illustrated in Figure 6.

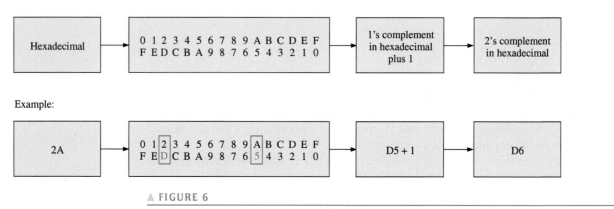

▲ FIGURE 6

Getting the 2's complement of a hexadecimal number, Method 3.

EXAMPLE 30

Subtract the following hexadecimal numbers:

(a) $84_{16} - 2A_{16}$ **(b)** $C3_{16} - 0B_{16}$

Solution **(a)** $2A_{16} = 00101010$

2's complement of $2A_{16} = 11010110 = D6_{16}$ (using Method 1)

$$84_{16}$$
$$\underline{+ D6_{16}} \quad \text{Add}$$
$$\cancel{1}5A_{16} \quad \text{Drop carry, as in 2's complement addition}$$

The difference is $\mathbf{5A}_{16}$.

(b) $0B_{16} = 00001011$

2's complement of $0B_{16} = 11110101 = F5_{16}$ (using Method 1)

$$C3_{16}$$
$$\underline{+ F5_{16}} \quad \text{Add}$$
$$\cancel{1}B8_{16} \quad \text{Drop carry}$$

The difference is $\mathbf{B8}_{16}$.

Related Problem Subtract 173_{16} from BCD_{16}.

SECTION 8 CHECKUP

1. Convert the following binary numbers to hexadecimal:
   (a) 10110011   (b) 110011101000
2. Convert the following hexadecimal numbers to binary:
   (a) 57_{16} (b) $3A5_{16}$ (c) $F80B_{16}$
3. Convert $9B30_{16}$ to decimal.
4. Convert the decimal number 573 to hexadecimal.
5. Add the following hexadecimal numbers directly:
   (a) $18_{16} + 34_{16}$ (b) $3F_{16} + 2A_{16}$
6. Subtract the following hexadecimal numbers:
   (a) $75_{16} - 21_{16}$ (b) $94_{16} - 5C_{16}$

---

9 OCTAL NUMBERS

Like the hexadecimal number system, the octal number system provides a convenient way to express binary numbers and codes. However, it is used less frequently than hexadecimal in conjunction with computers and microprocessors to express binary quantities for input and output purposes.

After completing this section, you should be able to

◆ Write the digits of the octal number system

◆ Convert from octal to decimal

+ Convert from decimal to octal

+ Convert from octal to binary

+ Convert from binary to octal

The **octal** number system is composed of eight digits, which are

$$0, 1, 2, 3, 4, 5, 6, 7$$

To count above 7, begin another column and start over:

$$10, 11, 12, 13, 14, 15, 16, 17, 20, 21, \ldots$$

The octal number system has a base of 8.

Counting in octal is similar to counting in decimal, except that the digits 8 and 9 are not used. To distinguish octal numbers from decimal numbers or hexadecimal numbers, we will use the subscript 8 to indicate an octal number. For instance, 15_8 in octal is equivalent to 13_{10} in decimal and D in hexadecimal. Sometimes you may see an "o" or a "Q" following an octal number.

Octal-to-Decimal Conversion

Since the octal number system has a base of eight, each successive digit position is an increasing power of eight, beginning in the right-most column with 8^0. The evaluation of an octal number in terms of its decimal equivalent is accomplished by multiplying each digit by its weight and summing the products, as illustrated here for 2374_8.

$$\text{Weight:} \quad 8^3 \; 8^2 \; 8^1 \; 8^0$$
$$\text{Octal number:} \quad 2 \;\; 3 \;\; 7 \;\; 4$$
$$2374_8 = (2 \times 8^3) \;\; + (3 \times 8^2) + (7 \times 8^1) + (4 \times 8^0)$$
$$= (2 \times 512) + (3 \times 64) + (7 \times 8) \;\; + (4 \times 1)$$
$$= \quad 1024 \quad + \quad 192 \quad + \quad 56 \quad + \quad 4 \quad = 1276_{10}$$

Decimal-to-Octal Conversion

A method of converting a decimal number to an octal number is the repeated division-by-8 method, which is similar to the method used in the conversion of decimal numbers to binary or to hexadecimal. To show how it works, let's convert the decimal number 359 to octal. Each successive division by 8 yields a remainder that becomes a digit in the equivalent octal number. The first remainder generated is the least significant digit (LSD).

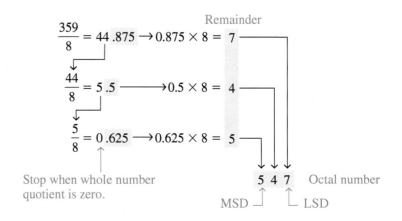

82

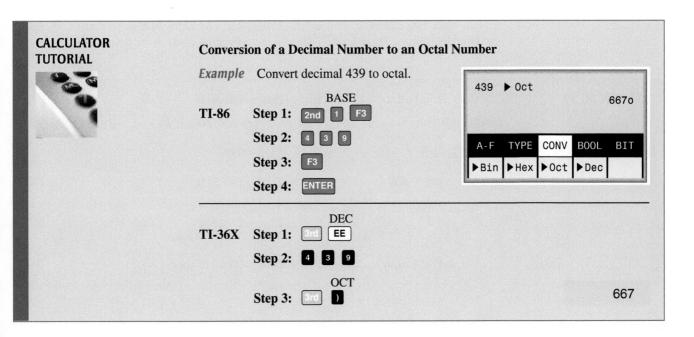

CALCULATOR TUTORIAL

Conversion of a Decimal Number to an Octal Number

Example   Convert decimal 439 to octal.

BASE
TI-86   Step 1: `2nd` `1` `F3`

Step 2: `4` `3` `9`

Step 3: `F3`

Step 4: `ENTER`

```
439 ▶ Oct
                    667o

A-F   TYPE  CONV  BOOL  BIT
▶Bin ▶Hex ▶Oct ▶Dec
```

DEC
TI-36X   Step 1: `3rd` `EE`

Step 2: `4` `3` `9`

OCT
Step 3: `3rd` `)`

667

Octal-to-Binary Conversion

Because each octal digit can be represented by a 3-bit binary number, it is very easy to convert from octal to binary. Each octal digit is represented by three bits as shown in Table 4.

Octal is a convenient way to represent binary numbers, but it is not as commonly used as hexadecimal.

▼ TABLE 4

Octal/binary conversion.

OCTAL DIGIT	0	1	2	3	4	5	6	7
BINARY	000	001	010	011	100	101	110	111

To convert an octal number to a binary number, simply replace each octal digit with the appropriate three bits.

EXAMPLE 31

Convert each of the following octal numbers to binary:

(a) 13_8 (b) 25_8 (c) 140_8 (d) 7526_8

Solution

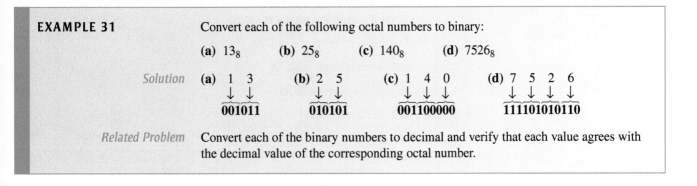

(a) 1 3
    ↓ ↓
    001011

(b) 2 5
    ↓ ↓
    010101

(c) 1 4 0
    ↓ ↓ ↓
    001100000

(d) 7 5 2 6
    ↓ ↓ ↓ ↓
    111101010110

Related Problem   Convert each of the binary numbers to decimal and verify that each value agrees with the decimal value of the corresponding octal number.

Binary-to-Octal Conversion

Conversion of a binary number to an octal number is the reverse of the octal-to-binary conversion. The procedure is as follows: Start with the right-most group of three bits and, moving from right to left, convert each 3-bit group to the equivalent octal digit. If there are not three bits available for the left-most group, add either one or two zeros to make a complete group. These leading zeros do not affect the value of the binary number.

EXAMPLE 32

Convert each of the following binary numbers to octal:

(a) 110101   (b) 101111001   (c) 100110011010   (d) 11010000100

Solution

(a) $\underline{110}\underline{101}$
    ↓ ↓
    6 5 $= \mathbf{65_8}$

(b) $\underline{101}\underline{111}\underline{001}$
    ↓ ↓ ↓
    5 7 1 $= \mathbf{571_8}$

(c) $\underline{100}\underline{110}\underline{011}\underline{010}$
    ↓ ↓ ↓ ↓
    4 6 3 2 $= \mathbf{4632_8}$

(d) $\underline{011}\underline{010}\underline{000}\underline{100}$
    ↓ ↓ ↓ ↓
    3 2 0 4 $= \mathbf{3204_8}$

Related Problem

Convert the binary number 1010101000111110010 to octal.

SECTION 9 CHECKUP

1. Convert the following octal numbers to decimal:
   (a) 73_8 (b) 125_8

2. Convert the following decimal numbers to octal:
   (a) 98_{10} (b) 163_{10}

3. Convert the following octal numbers to binary:
   (a) 46_8 (b) 723_8 (c) 5624_8

4. Convert the following binary numbers to octal:
   (a) 110101111   (b) 1001100010   (c) 10111111001

---

10   BINARY CODED DECIMAL (BCD)

Binary coded decimal (BCD) is a way to express each of the decimal digits with a binary code. There are only ten code groups in the BCD system, so it is very easy to convert between decimal and BCD. Because we like to read and write in decimal, the BCD code provides an excellent interface to binary systems. Examples of such interfaces are keypad inputs and digital readouts.

After completing this section, you should be able to

♦ Convert each decimal digit to BCD

♦ Express decimal numbers in BCD

♦ Convert from BCD to decimal

♦ Add BCD numbers

The 8421 BCD Code

In BCD, 4 bits represent each decimal digit.

The 8421 code is a type of **BCD** (binary coded decimal) code. Binary coded decimal means that each decimal digit, 0 through 9, is represented by a binary code of four bits. The designation 8421 indicates the binary weights of the four bits (2^3, 2^2, 2^1, 2^0). The ease of conversion between 8421 code numbers and the familiar decimal numbers is the main advantage of this code. All you have to remember are the ten binary combinations that represent the ten decimal digits as shown in Table 5. The 8421 code is the predominant BCD code, and when we refer to BCD, we always mean the 8421 code unless otherwise stated.

◀ TABLE 5

Decimal/BCD conversion.

DECIMAL DIGIT	0	1	2	3	4	5	6	7	8	9
BCD	0000	0001	0010	0011	0100	0101	0110	0111	1000	1001

Invalid Codes You should realize that, with four bits, sixteen numbers (0000 through 1111) can be represented but that, in the 8421 code, only ten of these are used. The six code combinations that are not used—1010, 1011, 1100, 1101, 1110, and 1111—are invalid in the 8421 BCD code.

To express any decimal number in BCD, simply replace each decimal digit with the appropriate 4-bit code, as shown by Example 33.

EXAMPLE 33

Convert each of the following decimal numbers to BCD:

(a) 35   (b) 98   (c) 170   (d) 2469

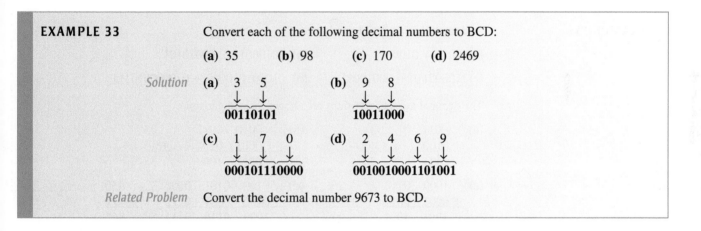

Related Problem Convert the decimal number 9673 to BCD.

It is equally easy to determine a decimal number from a BCD number. Start at the rightmost bit and break the code into groups of four bits. Then write the decimal digit represented by each 4-bit group.

EXAMPLE 34

Convert each of the following BCD codes to decimal:

(a) 10000110   (b) 001101010001   (c) 1001010001110000

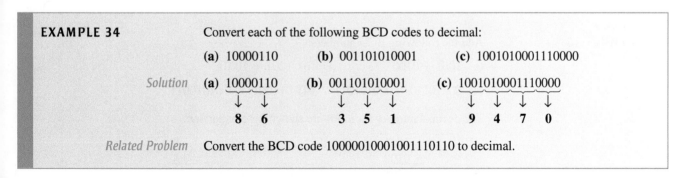

Related Problem Convert the BCD code 10000010001001110110 to decimal.

Applications Digital clocks, digital thermometers, digital meters, and other devices with seven-segment displays typically use BCD code to simplify the displaying of decimal numbers. BCD is not as efficient as straight binary for calculations, but it is particularly useful if only limited processing is required, such as in a digital thermometer.

BCD Addition

BCD is a numerical code and can be used in arithmetic operations. Addition is the most important operation because the other three operations (subtraction, multiplication, and division) can be accomplished by the use of addition. Here is how to add two BCD numbers:

Step 1: Add the two BCD numbers, using the rules for binary addition in Section 4.

Step 2: If a 4-bit sum is equal to or less than 9, it is a valid BCD number.

Step 3: If a 4-bit sum is greater than 9, or if a carry out of the 4-bit group is generated, it is an invalid result. Add 6 (0110) to the 4-bit sum in order to skip the six invalid states and return the code to 8421. If a carry results when 6 is added, simply add the carry to the next 4-bit group.

Example 35 illustrates BCD additions in which the sum in each 4-bit column is equal to or less than 9, and the 4-bit sums are therefore valid BCD numbers. Example 36 illustrates the procedure in the case of invalid sums (greater than 9 or a carry).

An alternative method to add BCD numbers is to convert them to decimal, perform the addition, and then convert the answer back to BCD.

EXAMPLE 35

Add the following BCD numbers:

(a) 0011 + 0100   (b) 00100011 + 00010101

(c) 10000110 + 00010011   (d) 010001010000 + 010000010111

Solution   The decimal number additions are shown for comparison.

(a)
```
   0011        3
 + 0100      + 4
  -----       --
   0111        7
```

(b)
```
   0010  0011       23
 + 0001  0101     + 15
  ----------        --
   0011  1000       38
```

(c)
```
   1000  0110       86
 + 0001  0011     + 13
  ----------        --
   1001  1001       99
```

(d)
```
   0100  0101  0000       450
 + 0100  0001  0111     + 417
  ----------------        ---
   1000  0110  0111       867
```

Note that in each case the sum in any 4-bit column does not exceed 9, and the results are valid BCD numbers.

Related Problem   Add the BCD numbers: 1001000001000011 + 0000100100100101.

EXAMPLE 36

Add the following BCD numbers:

(a) 1001 + 0100   (b) 1001 + 1001

(c) 00010110 + 00010101   (d) 01100111 + 01010011

Solution   The decimal number additions are shown for comparison.

(a)
```
        1001                              9
      + 0100                            + 4
       -----                             --
        1101    Invalid BCD number (>9)  13
      + 0110    Add 6
  -----------
   0001  0011   Valid BCD number
     ↓     ↓
     1     3
```

(b)

	1001			9
	+ 1001			+ 9
1	0010	Invalid because of carry		18
	+ 0110	Add 6		
0001	**1000**	Valid BCD number		
↓	↓			
1	8			

(c)

	0001	0110		16
	+ 0001	0101		+ 15
	0010	1011	Right group is invalid (>9),	31
			left group is valid.	
		+ 0110	Add 6 to invalid code. Add	
			carry, 0001, to next group.	
	0011	**0001**	Valid BCD number	
	↓	↓		
	3	1		

(d)

	0110	0111		67
	+ 0101	0011		+ 53
	1011	1010	Both groups are invalid (>9)	120
	+ 0110	+ 0110	Add 6 to both groups	
0001	**0010**	**0000**	Valid BCD number	
↓	↓	↓		
1	2	0		

Related Problem Add the BCD numbers: 01001000 + 00110100.

SECTION 10 CHECKUP

1. What is the binary weight of each 1 in the following BCD numbers?
   (a) 0010   (b) 1000   (c) 0001   (d) 0100
2. Convert the following decimal numbers to BCD:
   (a) 6   (b) 15   (c) 273   (d) 849
3. What decimal numbers are represented by each BCD code?
   (a) 10001001   (b) 001001111000   (c) 000101010111
4. In BCD addition, when is a 4-bit sum invalid?

---

11   DIGITAL CODES

Many specialized codes are used in digital systems. You have just learned about the BCD code; now let's look at a few others. Some codes are strictly numeric, like BCD, and others are alphanumeric; that is, they are used to represent numbers, letters, symbols, and instructions. The codes introduced in this section are the Gray code, the ASCII code, and the Unicode.

After completing this section, you should be able to

- ◆ Explain the advantage of the Gray code
- ◆ Convert between Gray code and binary

- Use the ASCII code
- Discuss the Unicode

The Gray Code

The single bit change characteristic of the Gray code minimizes the chance for error.

The **Gray code** is unweighted and is not an arithmetic code; that is, there are no specific weights assigned to the bit positions. The important feature of the Gray code is that *it exhibits only a single bit change from one code word to the next in sequence.* This property is important in many applications, such as shaft position encoders, where error susceptibility increases with the number of bit changes between adjacent numbers in a sequence.

Table 6 is a listing of the 4-bit Gray code for decimal numbers 0 through 15. Binary numbers are shown in the table for reference. Like binary numbers, *the Gray code can have any number of bits.* Notice the single-bit change between successive Gray code words. For instance, in going from decimal 3 to decimal 4, the Gray code changes from 0010 to 0110, while the binary code changes from 0011 to 0100, a change of three bits. The only bit change in the Gray code is in the third bit from the right: the other bits remain the same.

▶ TABLE 6

Four-bit Gray code.

DECIMAL	BINARY	GRAY CODE	DECIMAL	BINARY	GRAY CODE
0	0000	0000	8	1000	1100
1	0001	0001	9	1001	1101
2	0010	0011	10	1010	1111
3	0011	0010	11	1011	1110
4	0100	0110	12	1100	1010
5	0101	0111	13	1101	1011
6	0110	0101	14	1110	1001
7	0111	0100	15	1111	1000

Binary-to-Gray Code Conversion   Conversion between binary code and Gray code is sometimes useful. The following rules explain how to convert from a binary number to a Gray code word:

1. The most significant bit (left-most) in the Gray code is the same as the corresponding MSB in the binary number.

2. Going from left to right, add each adjacent pair of binary code bits to get the next Gray code bit. Discard carries.

For example, the conversion of the binary number 10110 to Gray code is as follows:

$$1 - + \rightarrow 0 - + \rightarrow 1 - + \rightarrow 1 - + \rightarrow 0 \qquad \text{Binary}$$
$$\downarrow \qquad\quad \downarrow \qquad\quad \downarrow \qquad\quad \downarrow \qquad\quad \downarrow$$
$$1 \qquad\quad 1 \qquad\quad 1 \qquad\quad 0 \qquad\quad 1 \qquad \text{Gray}$$

The Gray code is 11101.

Gray-to-Binary Code Conversion   To convert from Gray code to binary, use a similar method; however, there are some differences. The following rules apply:

1. The most significant bit (left-most) in the binary code is the same as the corresponding bit in the Gray code.

2. Add each binary code bit generated to the Gray code bit in the next adjacent position. Discard carries.

88

For example, the conversion of the Gray code word 11011 to binary is as follows:

$$\begin{array}{ccccccccc} 1 & & 1 & & 0 & & 1 & & 1 \\ \downarrow & +\nearrow & \downarrow & +\nearrow & \downarrow & +\nearrow & \downarrow & +\nearrow & \downarrow \\ 1 & & 0 & & 0 & & 1 & & 0 \end{array}$$

The binary number is 10010.

EXAMPLE 37

(a) Convert the binary number 11000110 to Gray code.

(b) Convert the Gray code 10101111 to binary.

Solution (a) Binary to Gray code:

$$\begin{array}{cccccccc} 1- & +\rightarrow 1- & +\rightarrow 0- & +\rightarrow 0- & +\rightarrow 0- & +\rightarrow 1- & +\rightarrow 1- & +\rightarrow 0 \\ \downarrow & \downarrow & \downarrow & \downarrow & \downarrow & \downarrow & \downarrow & \downarrow \\ 1 & 0 & 1 & 0 & 0 & 1 & 0 & 1 \end{array}$$

(b) Gray code to binary:

$$\begin{array}{cccccccc} 1 & 0 & 1 & 0 & 1 & 1 & 1 & 1 \\ \downarrow +\nearrow & \downarrow +\nearrow & \downarrow +\nearrow & \downarrow +\nearrow & \downarrow +\nearrow & \downarrow +\nearrow & \downarrow +\nearrow & \downarrow \\ 1 & 1 & 0 & 0 & 1 & 0 & 1 & 0 \end{array}$$

Related Problem (a) Convert binary 101101 to Gray code.   (b) Convert Gray code 100111 to binary.

An Application The concept of a 3-bit shaft position encoder is shown in Figure 7. Basically, there are three concentric rings that are segmented into eight sectors. The more sectors there are, the more accurately the position can be represented, but we are using only eight to illustrate. Each sector of each ring is either reflective or nonreflective. As the rings rotate with the shaft, they come under an IR emitter that produces three separate IR beams. A 1 is indicated where there is a reflected beam, and a 0 is indicated where there is no reflected beam. The IR detector senses the presence or absence of reflected beams and produces a corresponding 3-bit code. The IR emitter/detector is in a fixed position. As the shaft rotates counterclockwise through 360°, the eight sectors move under the

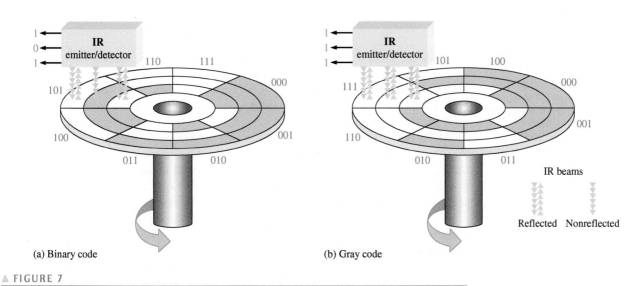

(a) Binary code   (b) Gray code

▲ FIGURE 7

A simplified illustration of how the Gray code solves the error problem in shaft position encoders. Three bits are shown to illustrate the concept, although most shaft encoders use more than 10 bits to achieve a higher resolution.

three beams. Each beam is either reflected or absorbed by the sector surface to represent a binary or Gray code number that indicates the shaft position.

In Figure 7(a), the sectors are arranged in a straight binary pattern, so that the detector output goes from 000 to 001 to 010 to 011 and so on. When a beam is aligned over a reflective sector, the output is 1; when a beam is aligned over a nonreflective sector, the output is 0. If one beam is slightly ahead of the others during the transition from one sector to the next, an erroneous output can occur. Consider what happens when the beams are on the 111 sector and about to enter the 000 sector. If the MSB beam is slightly ahead, the position would be incorrectly indicated by a transitional 011 instead of a 111 or a 000. In this type of application, it is virtually impossible to maintain precise mechanical alignment of the IR emitter/detector beams; therefore, some error will usually occur at many of the transitions between sectors.

The Gray code is used to eliminate the error problem which is inherent in the binary code. As shown in Figure 7(b), the Gray code assures that only one bit will change between adjacent sectors. This means that even though the beams may not be in precise alignment, there will never be a transitional error. For example, let's again consider what happens when the beams are on the 111 sector and about to move into the next sector, 101. The only two possible outputs during the transition are 111 and 101, no matter how the beams are aligned. A similar situation occurs at the transitions between each of the other sectors.

Alphanumeric Codes

In order to communicate, you need not only numbers, but also letters and other symbols. In the strictest sense, alphanumeric codes are codes that represent numbers and alphabetic characters (letters). Most such codes, however, also represent other characters such as symbols and various instructions necessary for conveying information.

At a minimum, an alphanumeric code must represent 10 decimal digits and 26 letters of the alphabet, for a total of 36 items. This number requires six bits in each code combination because five bits are insufficient ($2^5 = 32$). There are 64 total combinations of six bits, so there are 28 unused code combinations. Obviously, in many applications, symbols other than just numbers and letters are necessary to communicate completely. You need spaces, periods, colons, semicolons, question marks, etc. You also need instructions to tell the receiving system what to do with the information. With codes that are six bits long, you can handle decimal numbers, the alphabet, and 28 other symbols. This should give you an idea of the requirements for a basic alphanumeric code. The ASCII is the most common alphanumeric code and is covered next.

ASCII

ASCII is the abbreviation for American Standard Code for Information Interchange. Pronounced "askee," ASCII is a universally accepted alphanumeric code used in most computers and other electronic equipment. Most computer keyboards are standardized with the ASCII. When you enter a letter, a number, or control command, the corresponding ASCII code goes into the computer.

ASCII has 128 characters and symbols represented by a 7-bit binary code. Actually, ASCII can be considered an 8-bit code with the MSB always 0. This 8-bit code is 00 through 7F in hexadecimal. The first thirty-two ASCII characters are nongraphic commands that are never printed or displayed and are used only for control purposes. Examples of the control characters are "null," "line feed," "start of text," and "escape." The other characters are graphic symbols that can be printed or displayed and include the letters of the alphabet (lowercase and uppercase), the ten decimal digits, punctuation signs, and other commonly used symbols.

Table 7 is a listing of the ASCII code showing the decimal, hexadecimal, and binary representations for each character and symbol. The left section of the table lists the names of the 32 control characters (00 through 1F hexadecimal). The graphic symbols are listed in the rest of the table (20 through 7F hexadecimal).

American Standard Code for Information Interchange (ASCII).

CONTROL CHARACTERS

NAME	DEC	BINARY	HEX
NUL	0	0000000	00
SOH	1	0000001	01
STX	2	0000010	02
ETX	3	0000011	03
EOT	4	0000100	04
ENQ	5	0000101	05
ACK	6	0000110	06
BEL	7	0000111	07
BS	8	0001000	08
HT	9	0001001	09
LF	10	0001010	0A
VT	11	0001011	0B
FF	12	0001100	0C
CR	13	0001101	0D
SO	14	0001110	0E
SI	15	0001111	0F
DLE	16	0010000	10
DC1	17	0010001	11
DC2	18	0010010	12
DC3	19	0010011	13
DC4	20	0010100	14
NAK	21	0010101	15
SYN	22	0010110	16
ETB	23	0010111	17
CAN	24	0011000	18
EM	25	0011001	19
SUB	26	0011010	1A
ESC	27	0011011	1B
FS	28	0011100	1C
GS	29	0011101	1D
RS	30	0011110	1E
US	31	0011111	1F

GRAPHIC SYMBOLS

SYMBOL	DEC	BINARY	HEX	SYMBOL	DEC	BINARY	HEX	SYMBOL	DEC	BINARY	HEX
space	32	0100000	20	@	64	1000000	40	`	96	1100000	60
!	33	0100001	21	A	65	1000001	41	a	97	1100001	61
"	34	0100010	22	B	66	1000010	42	b	98	1100010	62
#	35	0100011	23	C	67	1000011	43	c	99	1100011	63
$	36	0100100	24	D	68	1000100	44	d	100	1100100	64
%	37	0100101	25	E	69	1000101	45	e	101	1100101	65
&	38	0100110	26	F	70	1000110	46	f	102	1100110	66
'	39	0100111	27	G	71	1000111	47	g	103	1100111	67
(	40	0101000	28	H	72	1001000	48	h	104	1101000	68
)	41	0101001	29	I	73	1001001	49	i	105	1101001	69
*	42	0101010	2A	J	74	1001010	4A	j	106	1101010	6A
+	43	0101011	2B	K	75	1001011	4B	k	107	1101011	6B
,	44	0101100	2C	L	76	1001100	4C	l	108	1101100	6C
-	45	0101101	2D	M	77	1001101	4D	m	109	1101101	6D
.	46	0101110	2E	N	78	1001110	4E	n	110	1101110	6E
/	47	0101111	2F	O	79	1001111	4F	o	111	1101111	6F
0	48	0110000	30	P	80	1010000	50	p	112	1110000	70
1	49	0110001	31	Q	81	1010001	51	q	113	1110001	71
2	50	0110010	32	R	82	1010010	52	r	114	1110010	72
3	51	0110011	33	S	83	1010011	53	s	115	1110011	73
4	52	0110100	34	T	84	1010100	54	t	116	1110100	74
5	53	0110101	35	U	85	1010101	55	u	117	1110101	75
6	54	0110110	36	V	86	1010110	56	v	118	1110110	76
7	55	0110111	37	W	87	1010111	57	w	119	1110111	77
8	56	0111000	38	X	88	1011000	58	x	120	1111000	78
9	57	0111001	39	Y	89	1011001	59	y	121	1111001	79
:	58	0111010	3A	Z	90	1011010	5A	z	122	1111010	7A
;	59	0111011	3B	[	91	1011011	5B	{	123	1111011	7B
<	60	0111100	3C	\	92	1011100	5C			124	1111100	7C
=	61	0111101	3D	]	93	1011101	5D	}	125	1111101	7D
>	62	0111110	3E	^	94	1011110	5E	~	126	1111110	7E
?	63	0111111	3F	_	95	1011111	5F	Del	127	1111111	7F

EXAMPLE 38

Determine the binary ASCII codes that are entered from the computer's keyboard when the following C language program statement is typed in. Also express each code in hexadecimal.

$$\text{if } (x > 5)$$

Solution The ASCII code for each symbol is found in Table 7.

Symbol	Binary	Hexadecimal
i	1101001	69_{16}
f	1100110	66_{16}
Space	0100000	20_{16}
(	0101000	28_{16}
x	1111000	78_{16}
>	0111110	$3E_{16}$
5	0110101	35_{16}
)	0101001	29_{16}

Related Problem Determine the sequence of ASCII codes required for the following C program statement and express them in hexadecimal:

$$\text{if } (y < 8)$$

The ASCII Control Characters   The first thirty-two codes in the ASCII table (Table 7) represent the control characters. These are used to allow devices such as a computer and printer to communicate with each other when passing information and data. Table 8 lists the control characters and the control key function that allows them to be entered directly from an ASCII keyboard by pressing the control key (CTRL) and the corresponding symbol. A brief description of each control character is also given. The descriptions are based on obsolete teletype requirements, and the codes are generally used for different purposes than the description implies.

Extended ASCII Characters

In addition to the 128 standard ASCII characters, there are an additional 128 characters that were adopted by IBM for use in their PCs (personal computers). Because of the popularity of the PC, these particular extended ASCII characters are also used in applications other than PCs and have become essentially an unofficial standard.

The extended ASCII characters are represented by an 8-bit code series from hexadecimal 80 to hexadecimal FF and can be grouped into the following general categories: foreign (non-English) alphabetic characters, foreign currency symbols, Greek letters, mathematical symbols, drawing characters, bar graphing characters, and shading characters.

Unicode

Unicode provides the ability to encode all of the characters used for the written languages of the world by assigning each character a unique numeric value and name utilizing the universal character set (UCS). It is applicable in computer applications dealing with multilingual text, mathematical symbols, or other technical characters.

NAME	DECIMAL	HEX	KEYS	DESCRIPTION
NUL	0	00	CTRL @	null character
SOH	1	01	CTRL A	start of header
STX	2	02	CTRL B	start of text
ETX	3	03	CTRL C	end of text
EOT	4	04	CTRL D	end of transmission
ENQ	5	05	CTRL E	enquire
ACK	6	06	CTRL F	acknowledge
BEL	7	07	CTRL G	bell
BS	8	08	CTRL H	backspace
HT	9	09	CTRL I	horizontal tab
LF	10	0A	CTRL J	line feed
VT	11	0B	CTRL K	vertical tab
FF	12	0C	CTRL L	form feed (new page)
CR	13	0D	CTRL M	carriage return
SO	14	0E	CTRL N	shift out
SI	15	0F	CTRL O	shift in
DLE	16	10	CTRL P	data link escape
DC1	17	11	CTRL Q	device control 1
DC2	18	12	CTRL R	device control 2
DC3	19	13	CTRL S	device control 3
DC4	20	14	CTRL T	device control 4
NAK	21	15	CTRL U	negative acknowledge
SYN	22	16	CTRL V	synchronize
ETB	23	17	CTRL W	end of transmission block
CAN	24	18	CTRL X	cancel
EM	25	19	CTRL Y	end of medium
SUB	26	1A	CTRL Z	substitute
ESC	27	1B	CTRL [	escape
FS	28	1C	CTRL /	file separator
GS	29	1D	CTRL]	group separator
RS	30	1E	CTRL ^	record separator
US	31	1F	CTRL _	unit separator

◄ TABLE 8

ASCII control characters.

Unicode has a wide array of characters, and their various encoding forms have begun to supplant ASCII in many environments. While ASCII basically uses 7-bit codes, Unicode uses relatively abstract "code points"—non-negative integer numbers—that map sequences of one or more bytes, using different encoding forms and schemes. To permit compatibility, Unicode assigns the first 128 code points to the same characters as ASCII. One can, therefore, think of ASCII as a 7-bit encoding scheme for a very small subset of Unicode and of the UCS.

Unicode consists of about 100,000 characters, a set of code charts for visual reference, an encoding methodology and set of standard character encodings, and an enumeration of character properties such as uppercase and lowercase. It also consists of a number of related items, such as character properties, rules for text normalization, decomposition, collation, rendering, and bidirectional display order (for the correct display of text containing both right-to-left scripts, such as Arabic or Hebrew, and left-to-right scripts).

1. Convert the following binary numbers to the Gray code:

   (a) 1100   (b) 1010   (c) 11010

2. Convert the following Gray codes to binary:

   (a) 1000   (b) 1010   (c) 11101

3. What is the ASCII representation for each of the following characters? Express each as a bit pattern and in hexadecimal notation.

   (a) K   (b) r   (c) $ (d) +

12 ERROR DETECTION CODES

In this section, two methods for adding bits to codes to detect a single-bit error are discussed. The parity method of error detection is introduced, and the cyclic redundancy check is discussed.

After completing this section, you should be able to

♦ Determine if there is an error in a code based on the parity bit

♦ Assign the proper parity bit to a code

♦ Explain the cyclic redundancy (CRC) check

Parity Method for Error Detection

A parity bit tells if the number of 1s is odd or even.

Many systems use a parity bit as a means for bit **error detection.** Any group of bits contain either an even or an odd number of 1s. A parity bit is attached to a group of bits to make the total number of 1s in a group always even or always odd. An even parity bit makes the total number of 1s even, and an odd parity bit makes the total odd.

A given system operates with even or odd **parity,** but not both. For instance, if a system operates with even parity, a check is made on each group of bits received to make sure the total number of 1s in that group is even. If there is an odd number of 1s, an error has occurred.

As an illustration of how parity bits are attached to a code, Table 9 lists the parity bits for each BCD number for both even and odd parity. The parity bit for each BCD number is in the *P* column.

▶ TABLE 9

The BCD code with parity bits.

EVEN PARITY		ODD PARITY	
P	BCD	*P*	BCD
0	0000	1	0000
1	0001	0	0001
1	0010	0	0010
0	0011	1	0011
1	0100	0	0100
0	0101	1	0101
0	0110	1	0110
1	0111	0	0111
1	1000	0	1000
0	1001	1	1001

The parity bit can be attached to the code at either the beginning or the end, depending on system design. Notice that the total number of 1s, including the parity bit, is always even for even parity and always odd for odd parity.

Detecting an Error A parity bit provides for the detection of a single bit error (or any odd number of errors, which is very unlikely) but cannot check for two errors in one group. For instance, let's assume that we wish to transmit the BCD code 0101. (Parity can be used with any number of bits; we are using four for illustration.) The total code transmitted, including the even parity bit, is

Now let's assume that an error occurs in the third bit from the left (the 1 becomes a 0).

```
        ┌──────Even parity bit
        ↓
00001
        ↑
        └─ Bit errror
```

When this code is received, the parity check circuitry determines that there is only a single 1 (odd number), when there should be an even number of 1s. Because an even number of 1s does not appear in the code when it is received, an error is indicated.

An odd parity bit also provides in a similar manner for the detection of a single error in a given group of bits.

EXAMPLE 39

Assign the proper even parity bit to the following code groups:

(a) 1010   **(b)** 111000   **(c)** 101101

(d) 1000111001001   **(e)** 101101011111

Solution   Make the parity bit either 1 or 0 as necessary to make the total number of 1s even. The parity bit will be the left-most bit (color).

(a) 01010   **(b)** 1111000   **(c)** 0101101

(d) 0100011100101   **(e)** 1101101011111

Related Problem   Add an even parity bit to the 7-bit ASCII code for the letter K.

EXAMPLE 40

An odd parity system receives the following code groups: 10110, 11010, 110011, 110101110100, and 1100010101010. Determine which groups, if any, are in error.

Solution   Since odd parity is required, any group with an even number of 1s is incorrect. The following groups are in error: **110011** and **1100010101010**.

Related Problem   The following ASCII character is received by an odd parity system: 00110111. Is it correct?

Cyclic Redundancy Check

The **cyclic redundancy check (CRC)** is a widely used code used for detecting one- and two-bit transmission errors when digital data is transferred on a communication link. The communication link can be between two computers that are connected to a network or between a digital storage device (such as a CD, DVD, or a hard drive) and a PC. If it is properly designed, the CRC can also detect multiple errors for a number of bits in sequence (burst errors). In CRC, a certain number of check bits, sometimes called a *checksum,* are appended to the data bits (added to end) that are being transmitted. The transmitted data is tested by the receiver for errors using the CRC. Not every possible error can be identified, but the CRC is much more efficient than just a simple parity check.

CRC is often described mathematically as the division of two polynomials to generate a remainder. A polynomial is a mathematical expression that is a sum of terms with positive exponents. When the coefficients are limited to 1s and 0s, it is called a *univariate polynomial.* An example of a univariate polynomial is $1x^3 + 0x^2 + 1x^1 + 1x^0$ or simply $x^3 + x^1 + x^0$, which can be fully described by the 4-bit binary number 1011. Most cyclic redundancy checks use a 16-bit or larger polynomial, but for simplicity the process is illustrated here with four bits.

Modulo-2 Operations Simply put, CRC is based on the division of two binary numbers; and, as you know, division is just a series of subtractions and shifts. To do subtraction, a method called *modulo-2* addition can be used. Modulo-2 addition (or subtraction) is the same as binary addition with the carries discarded, as shown in the truth table in Table 10. **Truth tables** are widely used to describe the operation of logic circuits, as you will learn in Chapter 3. With two bits, there is a total of four possible combinations, as shown in the table. This particular table describes the modulo-2 operation also known as *exclusive-OR* and can be implemented with a logic gate that will be introduced in Chapter 3. A simple rule for modulo-2 is that the output is 1 if the inputs are different; otherwise, it is 0.

▶ TABLE 10

Modulo-2 operation.

INPUT BITS	OUTPUT BIT
0 0	0
0 1	1
1 0	1
1 1	0

CRC Process The process is as follows:

1. Select a fixed generator code; it can have fewer bits than the data bits to be checked. This code is understood in advance by both the sending and receiving devices and must be the same for both.

2. Append a number of 0s equal to the number of bits in the generator code to the data bits.

3. Divide the data bits including the appended bits by the generator code bits using modulo-2.

4. If the remainder is 0, the data and appended bits are sent as is.

5. If the remainder is not 0, the appended bits are made equal to the remainder bits in order to get a 0 remainder before data is sent.

6. At the receiving end, the receiver divides the incoming appended data bit code by the same generator code as used by the sender.

7. If the remainder is 0, there is no error detected (it is possible in rare cases for multiple errors to cancel). If the remainder is not 0, an error has been detected in the transmission and a retransmission is requested by the receiver.

Figure 8 illustrates the CRC process.

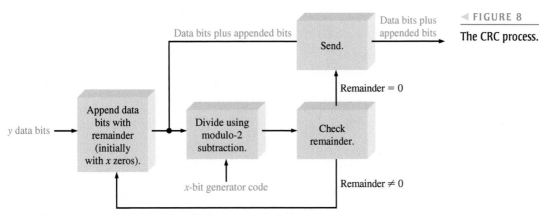

(a) Transmitting end of communication link

◀ **FIGURE 8**

The CRC process.

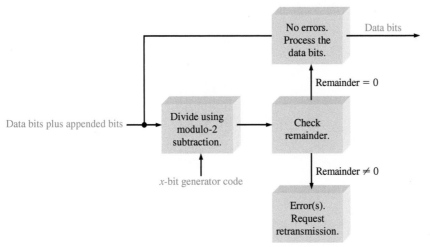

(b) Receiving end of communication link

EXAMPLE 41

Determine the transmitted CRC for the following byte of data (D) and generator code (G). Verify that the remainder is 0.

$$D: \quad 11010011$$

$$G: \quad 1010$$

Solution Since the generator code has four data bits, add four 0s (blue) to the data byte. The appended data (D′) is

$$D' = 110100110000$$

Divide the appended data by the generator code (red) using the modulo-2 operation until all bits have been used.

$$\frac{D'}{G} = \frac{110100110000}{1010}$$

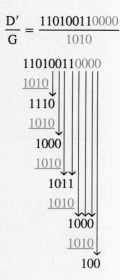

Remainder = 0100. Since the remainder is not 0, append the data with the four remainder bits (blue). Then divide by the generator code (red). The transmitted CRC is **110100110100**.

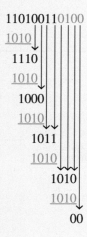

Remainder = 0

Related Problem   Change the generator code to 1100 and verify that a 0 remainder results when the CRC process is applied to the data byte (11010011).

EXAMPLE 42

During transmission, an error occurs in the second bit from the left in the appended data byte generated in Example 41. The received data is

$$D' = 100100110100$$

Apply the CRC process to the received data to detect the error using the same generator code (1010).

Solution

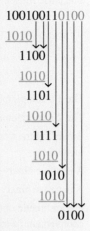

Remainder = 0100. Since it is not zero, an error is indicated.

Related Problem Assume two errors in the data byte as follows: 10011011. Apply the CRC process to check for the errors using the same received data and the same generator code.

SECTION 12 CHECKUP

1. Which odd-parity code is in error?
   (a) 1011   (b) 1110   (c) 0101   (d) 1000
2. Which even-parity code is in error?
   (a) 11000110   (b) 00101000   (c) 10101010   (d) 11111011
3. Add an even parity bit to the end of each of the following codes.
   (a) 1010100   (b) 0100000   (c) 1110111   (d) 1000110
4. What does CRC stand for?
5. Apply modulo-2 operations to determine the following:
   (a) 1 + 1   (b) 1 − 1   (c) 1 − 0   (d) 0 + 1

SUMMARY

◆ A binary number is a weighted number in which the weight of each whole number digit is a positive power of two and the weight of each fractional digit is a negative power of two. The whole number weights increase from right to left—from least significant digit to most significant.

◆ A binary number can be converted to a decimal number by summing the decimal values of the weights of all the 1s in the binary number.

◆ A decimal whole number can be converted to binary by using the sum-of-weights or the repeated division-by-2 method.

◆ A decimal fraction can be converted to binary by using the sum-of-weights or the repeated multiplication-by-2 method.

◆ The basic rules for binary addition are as follows:

$$0 + 0 = 0$$
$$0 + 1 = 1$$
$$1 + 0 = 1$$
$$1 + 1 = 10$$

◆ The basic rules for binary subtraction are as follows:

$$0 - 0 = 0$$
$$1 - 1 = 0$$
$$1 - 0 = 1$$
$$10 - 1 = 1$$

◆ The 1's complement of a binary number is derived by changing 1s to 0s and 0s to 1s.

◆ The 2's complement of a binary number can be derived by adding 1 to the 1's complement.

◆ Binary subtraction can be accomplished with addition by using the 1's or 2's complement method.

◆ A positive binary number is represented by a 0 sign bit.

◆ A negative binary number is represented by a 1 sign bit.

◆ For arithmetic operations, negative binary numbers are represented in 1's complement or 2's complement form.

◆ In an addition operation, an overflow is possible when both numbers are positive or when both numbers are negative. An incorrect sign bit in the sum indicates the occurrence of an overflow.

◆ The hexadecimal number system consists of 16 digits and characters, 0 through 9 followed by A through F.

◆ One hexadecimal digit represents a 4-bit binary number, and its primary usefulness is in simplifying bit patterns and making them easier to read.

◆ A decimal number can be converted to hexadecimal by the repeated division-by-16 method.

◆ The octal number system consists of eight digits, 0 through 7.

◆ A decimal number can be converted to octal by using the repeated division-by-8 method.

◆ Octal-to-binary conversion is accomplished by simply replacing each octal digit with its 3-bit binary equivalent. The process is reversed for binary-to-octal conversion.

◆ A decimal number is converted to BCD by replacing each decimal digit with the appropriate 4-bit binary code.

◆ The ASCII is a 7-bit alphanumeric code that is widely used in computer systems for input and output of information.

◆ A parity bit is used to detect an error in a code.

◆ The CRC (cyclic redundancy check) is based on polynomial division using modulo-2 operations.

KEY TERMS

Alphanumeric   Consisting of numerals, letters, and other characters.

ASCII   American Standard Code for Information Interchange; the most widely used alphanumeric code.

BCD   Binary coded decimal; a digital code in which each of the decimal digits, 0 through 9, is represented by a group of four bits.

Byte   A group of eight bits.

Cyclic redundancy check (CRC)   A type of error detection code.

Floating-point number   A number representation based on scientific notation in which the number consists of an exponent and a mantissa.

Hexadecimal   Describes a number system with a base of 16.

LSB   Least significant bit; the right-most bit in a binary whole number or code.

MSB   Most significant bit; the left-most bit in a binary whole number or code.

Octal   Describes a number system with a base of eight.

Parity   In relation to binary codes, the condition of evenness or oddness of the number of 1s in a code group.

TRUE/FALSE QUIZ

Answers are at the end of the chapter.

1. The decimal number system is a weighted system with ten digits.
2. The binary number system is a weighted system with two digits.
3. LSB stands for lowest single bit.
4. In binary, $1 + 1 = 2$.
5. The 1's complement of the binary number 1010 is 0101.
6. The 2's complement of the binary number 0001 is 1110.
7. The right-most bit in a signed binary number is the sign bit.
8. The hexadecimal number system has 16 characters, six of which are alphabetic characters.
9. BCD stands for binary coded decimal.
10. ASCII stands for American standard code for information indication.
11. CRC stands for cyclic redundancy check.
12. The modulo-2 sum of 11 and 10 is 100.

SELF-TEST

Answers are at the end of the chapter.

1. $2 \times 10^1 + 8 \times 10^0$ is equal to
   (a) 10   (b) 280   (c) 2.8   (d) 28
2. The binary number 1101 is equal to the decimal number
   (a) 13   (b) 49   (c) 11   (d) 3
3. The binary number 11011101 is equal to the decimal number
   (a) 121   (b) 221   (c) 441   (d) 256
4. The decimal number 17 is equal to the binary number
   (a) 10010   (b) 11000   (c) 10001   (d) 01001
5. The decimal number 175 is equal to the binary number
   (a) 11001111   (b) 10101110   (c) 10101111   (d) 11101111
6. The sum of $11010 + 01111$ equals
   (a) 101001   (b) 101010   (c) 110101   (d) 101000
7. The difference of $110 - 010$ equals
   (a) 001   (b) 010   (c) 101   (d) 100
8. The 1's complement of 10111001 is
   (a) 01000111   (b) 01000110   (c) 11000110   (d) 10101010
9. The 2's complement of 11001000 is
   (a) 00110111   (b) 00110001   (c) 01001000   (d) 00111000
10. The decimal number $+122$ is expressed in the 2's complement form as
    (a) 01111010   (b) 11111010   (c) 01000101   (d) 10000101
11. The decimal number -34 is expressed in the 2's complement form as
    (a) 01011110   (b) 10100010   (c) 11011110   (d) 01011101
12. A single-precision floating-point binary number has a total of
    (a) 8 bits   (b) 16 bits   (c) 24 bits   (d) 32 bits
13. In the 2's complement form, the binary number 10010011 is equal to the decimal number
    (a) -19 (b) $+109$ (c) $+91$ (d) -109
14. The binary number 101100111001010100001 can be written in octal as
    (a) 5471230_8 (b) 5471241_8 (c) 2634521_8 (d) 23162501_8
15. The binary number 10001101010001101111 can be written in hexadecimal as
    (a) $AD467_{16}$ (b) $8C46F_{16}$ (c) $8D46F_{16}$ (d) $AE46F_{16}$

16. The binary number for $F7A9_{16}$ is
    (a) 1111011110101001   (b) 1110111110101001
    (c) 1111111010110001   (d) 1111011010101001
17. The BCD number for decimal 473 is
    (a) 111011010   (b) 110001110011   (c) 010001110011   (d) 010011110011
18. Refer to Table 7. The command STOP in ASCII is
    (a) 1010011101010010011111010000   (b) 1010010100110010011101010000
    (c) 1001010110110110011101010001   (d) 1010011101010010011101100100
19. The code that has an even-parity error is
    (a) 1010011   (b) 1101000   (c) 1001000   (d) 1110111
20. In the cyclic redundancy check, the absence of errors is indicated by
    (a) Remainder = generator code   (b) Remainder = 0
    (c) Remainder = 1   (d) Quotient = 0

PROBLEMS

Answers to odd-numbered problems are at the end of the chapter.

Section 1 Decimal Numbers

1. What is the weight of the digit 6 in each of the following decimal numbers?
   (a) 1386   (b) 54,692   (c) 671,920
2. Express each of the following decimal numbers as a power of ten:
   (a) 10   (b) 100   (c) 10,000   (d) 1,000,000
3. Give the value of each digit in the following decimal numbers:
   (a) 471   (b) 9356   (c) 125,000
4. How high can you count with four decimal digits?

Section 2 Binary Numbers

5. Convert the following binary numbers to decimal:
   (a) 11   (b) 100   (c) 111   (d) 1000
   (e) 1001   (f) 1100   (g) 1011   (h) 1111
6. Convert the following binary numbers to decimal:
   (a) 1110   (b) 1010   (c) 11100   (d) 10000
   (e) 10101   (f) 11101   (g) 10111   (h) 11111
7. Convert each binary number to decimal:
   (a) 110011.11   (b) 101010.01   (c) 1000001.111
   (d) 1111000.101   (e) 1011100.10101   (f) 1110001.0001
   (g) 1011010.1010   (h) 1111111.11111
8. What is the highest decimal number that can be represented by each of the following numbers of binary digits (bits)?
   (a) two   (b) three   (c) four   (d) five   (e) six
   (f) seven   (g) eight   (h) nine   (i) ten   (j) eleven
9. How many bits are required to represent the following decimal numbers?
   (a) 17   (b) 35   (c) 49   (d) 68
   (e) 81   (f) 114   (g) 132   (h) 205
10. Generate the binary sequence for each decimal sequence:
    (a) 0 through 7   (b) 8 through 15   (c) 16 through 31
    (d) 32 through 63   (e) 64 through 75

Section 3 Decimal-to-Binary Conversion

11. Convert each decimal number to binary by using the sum-of-weights method:
    (a) 10   (b) 17   (c) 24   (d) 48
    (e) 61   (f) 93   (g) 125   (h) 186

12. Convert each decimal fraction to binary using the sum-of-weights method:
    (a) 0.32   (b) 0.246   (c) 0.0981

13. Convert each decimal number to binary using repeated division by 2:
    (a) 15   (b) 21   (c) 28   (d) 34
    (e) 40   (f) 59   (g) 65   (h) 73

14. Convert each decimal fraction to binary using repeated multiplication by 2:
    (a) 0.98   (b) 0.347   (c) 0.9028

Section 4   **Binary Arithmetic**

15. Add the binary numbers:
    (a) $11 + 01$ (b) $10 + 10$ (c) $101 + 11$
    (d) $111 + 110$ (e) $1001 + 101$ (f) $1101 + 1011$

16. Use direct subtraction on the following binary numbers:
    (a) $11 - 1$ (b) $101 - 100$ (c) $110 - 101$
    (d) $1110 - 11$ (e) $1100 - 1001$ (f) $11010 - 10111$

17. Perform the following binary multiplications:
    (a) 11×11 (b) 100×10 (c) 111×101
    (d) 1001×110 (e) 1101×1101 (f) 1110×1101

18. Divide the binary numbers as indicated:
    (a) $100 \div 10$ (b) $1001 \div 11$ (c) $1100 \div 100$

Section 5   **1's and 2's Complements of Binary Numbers**

19. What are two ways of representing zero in 1's complement form?

20. How is zero represented in 2's complement form?

21. Determine the 1's complement of each binary number:
    (a) 101   (b) 110   (c) 1010
    (d) 11010111   (e) 1110101   (f) 00001

22. Determine the 2's complement of each binary number using either method:
    (a) 10   (b) 111   (c) 1001   (d) 1101
    (e) 11100   (f) 10011   (g) 10110000   (h) 00111101

Section 6   **Signed Numbers**

23. Express each decimal number in binary as an 8-bit sign-magnitude number:
    (a) $+29$ (b) -85 (c) $+100$ (d) -123

24. Express each decimal number as an 8-bit number in the 1's complement form:
    (a) -34 (b) $+57$ (c) -99 (d) $+115$

25. Express each decimal number as an 8-bit number in the 2's complement form:
    (a) $+12$ (b) -68 (c) $+101$ (d) -125

26. Determine the decimal value of each signed binary number in the sign-magnitude form:
    (a) 10011001   (b) 01110100   (c) 10111111

27. Determine the decimal value of each signed binary number in the 1's complement form:
    (a) 10011001   (b) 01110100   (c) 10111111

28. Determine the decimal value of each signed binary number in the 2's complement form:
    (a) 10011001   (b) 01110100   (c) 10111111

29. Express each of the following sign-magnitude binary numbers in single-precision floating-point format:
    (a) 0111110000101011   (b) 100110000011000

30. Determine the values of the following single-precision floating-point numbers:
    (a) 1 10000001 01001001110001000000000
    (b) 0 11001100 10000111110100100000000

Section 7   **Arithmetic Operations with Signed Numbers**

31. Convert each pair of decimal numbers to binary and add using the 2's complement form:

(a) 33 and 15   (b) 56 and -27 (c) -46 and 25   (d) -110 and -84

32. Perform each addition in the 2's complement form:

(a) 00010110 + 00110011   (b) 01110000 + 10101111

33. Perform each addition in the 2's complement form:

(a) 10001100 + 00111001   (b) 11011001 + 11100111

34. Perform each subtraction in the 2's complement form:

(a) 00110011 − 00010000   (b) 01100101 − 11101000

35. Multiply 01101010 by 11110001 in the 2's complement form.

36. Divide 01000100 by 00011001 in the 2's complement form.

Section 8   **Hexadecimal Numbers**

37. Convert each hexadecimal number to binary:

(a) 38_{16} (b) 59_{16} (c) $A14_{16}$ (d) $5C8_{16}$

(e) 4100_{16} (f) $FB17_{16}$ (g) $8A9D_{16}$

38. Convert each binary number to hexadecimal:

(a) 1110   (b) 10   (c) 10111

(d) 10100110   (e) 1111110000   (f) 100110000010

39. Convert each hexadecimal number to decimal:

(a) 23_{16} (b) 92_{16} (c) $1A_{16}$ (d) $8D_{16}$

(e) $F3_{16}$ (f) EB_{16} (g) $5C2_{16}$ (h) 700_{16}

40. Convert each decimal number to hexadecimal:

(a) 8   (b) 14   (c) 33   (d) 52

(e) 284   (f) 2890   (g) 4019   (h) 6500

41. Perform the following additions:

(a) $37_{16} + 29_{16}$ (b) $A0_{16} + 6B_{16}$ (c) $FF_{16} + BB_{16}$

42. Perform the following subtractions:

(a) $51_{16} - 40_{16}$ (b) $C8_{16} - 3A_{16}$ (c) $FD_{16} - 88_{16}$

Section 9   **Octal Numbers**

43. Convert each octal number to decimal:

(a) 12_8 (b) 27_8 (c) 56_8 (d) 64_8 (e) 103_8

(f) 557_8 (g) 163_8 (h) 1024_8 (i) 7765_8

44. Convert each decimal number to octal by repeated division by 8:

(a) 15   (b) 27   (c) 46   (d) 70

(e) 100   (f) 142   (g) 219   (h) 435

45. Convert each octal number to binary:

(a) 13_8 (b) 57_8 (c) 101_8 (d) 321_8 (e) 540_8

(f) 4653_8 (g) 13271_8 (h) 45600_8 (i) 100213_8

46. Convert each binary number to octal:

(a) 111   (b) 10   (c) 110111

(d) 101010   (e) 1100   (f) 1011110

(g) 101100011001   (h) 10110000011   (i) 111111101111000

Section 10   **Binary Coded Decimal (BCD)**

47. Convert each of the following decimal numbers to 8421 BCD:

(a) 10   (b) 13   (c) 18   (d) 21   (e) 25   (f) 36

(g) 44   (h) 57   (i) 69   (j) 98   (k) 125   (l) 156

48. Convert each of the decimal numbers in Problem 47 to straight binary, and compare the number of bits required with that required for BCD.

49. Convert the following decimal numbers to BCD:

(a) 104   **(b)** 128   **(c)** 132   **(d)** 150   **(e)** 186

(f) 210   **(g)** 359   **(h)** 547   **(i)** 1051

50. Convert each of the BCD numbers to decimal:

(a) 0001   **(b)** 0110   **(c)** 1001

(d) 00011000   **(e)** 00011001   **(f)** 00110010

(g) 01000101   **(h)** 10011000   **(i)** 100001110000

51. Convert each of the BCD numbers to decimal:

(a) 10000000   **(b)** 001000110111

(c) 001101000110   **(d)** 010000100001

(e) 011101010100   **(f)** 100000000000

(g) 100101111000   **(h)** 0001011010000011

(i) 1001000000011000   **(j)** 0110011001100111

52. Add the following BCD numbers:

(a) 0010 + 0001   **(b)** 0101 + 0011

(c) 0111 + 0010   **(d)** 1000 + 0001

(e) 00011000 + 00010001   **(f)** 01100100 + 00110011

(g) 01000000 + 01000111   **(h)** 10000101 + 00010011

53. Add the following BCD numbers:

(a) 1000 + 0110   **(b)** 0111 + 0101

(c) 1001 + 1000   **(d)** 1001 + 0111

(e) 00100101 + 00100111   **(f)** 01010001 + 01011000

(g) 10011000 + 10010111   **(h)** 010101100001 + 011100001000

54. Convert each pair of decimal numbers to BCD, and add as indicated:

(a) 4 + 3   **(b)** 5 + 2   **(c)** 6 + 4   **(d)** 17 + 12

(e) 28 + 23   **(f)** 65 + 58   **(g)** 113 + 101   **(h)** 295 + 157

Section 11   **Digital Codes**

55. In a certain application a 4-bit binary sequence cycles from 1111 to 0000 periodically. There are four bit changes, and because of circuit delays, these changes may not occur at the same instant. For example, if the LSB changes first, the number will appear as 1110 during the transition from 1111 to 0000 and may be misinterpreted by the system. Illustrate how the Gray code avoids this problem.

56. Convert each binary number to Gray code:

(a) 11011   **(b)** 1001010   **(c)** 1111011101110

57. Convert each Gray code to binary:

(a) 1010   **(b)** 00010   **(c)** 11000010001

58. Convert each of the following decimal numbers to ASCII. Refer to Table 7.

(a) 1   **(b)** 3   **(c)** 6   **(d)** 10   **(e)** 18

(f) 29   **(g)** 56   **(h)** 75   **(i)** 107

59. Determine each ASCII character. Refer to Table 7.

(a) 0011000   **(b)** 1001010   **(c)** 0111101

(d) 0100011   **(e)** 0111110   **(f)** 1000010

60. Decode the following ASCII coded message:

```
1001000 1100101 1101100 1101100 1101111 0101110
0100000 1001000 1101111 1110111 0100000 1100001
1110010 1100101 0100000 1111001 1101111 1110101
0111111
```

61. Write the message in Problem 60 in hexadecimal.

62. Convert the following statement to ASCII:

$$30 \text{ INPUT A, B}$$

Section 12 **Error Detection Codes**

63. Determine which of the following even parity codes are in error:

(a) 100110010   (b) 011101010   (c) 10111111010001010

64. Determine which of the following odd parity codes are in error:

(a) 11110110   (b) 00110001   (c) 01010101010101010

65. Attach the proper even parity bit to each of the following bytes of data:

(a) 10100100   (b) 00001001   (c) 11111110

66. Apply modulo-2 to the following:

(a) 1100 + 1011   (b) 1111 + 0100   (c) 10011001 + 100011100

67. Verify that modulo-2 subtraction is the same as modulo-2 addition by adding the result of each operation in problem 66 to either of the original numbers to get the other number. This will show that the result is the same as the difference of the two numbers.

68. Apply CRC to the data bits 10110010 using the generator code 1010 to produce the transmitted CRC code.

69. Assume that the code produced in problem 68 incurs an error in the most significant bit during transmission. Apply CRC to detect the error.

ANSWERS

SECTION CHECKUPS

Section 1 **Decimal Numbers**

1. (a) 1370: 10   (b) 6725: 100   (c) 7051: 1000   (d) 58.72: 0.1

2. (a) $51 = (5 \times 10) + (1 \times 1)$ (b) $137 = (1 \times 100) + (3 \times 10) + (7 \times 1)$

(c) $1492 = (1 \times 1000) + (4 \times 100) + (9 \times 10) + (2 \times 1)$

(d) $106.58 = (1 \times 100) + (0 \times 10) + (6 \times 1) + (5 \times 0.1) + (8 \times 0.01)$

Section 2 **Binary Numbers**

1. $2^8 - 1 = 255$

2. Weight is 16.

3. $10111101.011 = 189.375$

Section 3 **Decimal-to-Binary Conversion**

1. (a) $23 = 10111$ (b) $57 = 111001$ (c) $45.5 = 101101.1$

2. (a) $14 = 1110$ (b) $21 = 10101$ (c) $0.375 = 0.011$

Section 4 **Binary Arithmetic**

1. (a) $1101 + 1010 = 10111$ (b) $10111 + 01101 = 100100$

2. (a) $1101 - 0100 = 1001$ (b) $1001 - 0111 = 0010$

3. (a) $110 \times 111 = 101010$ (b) $1100 \div 011 = 100$

Section 5 **1's and 2's Complements of Binary Numbers**

1. (a) 1's comp of 00011010 = 11100101   (b) 1's comp of 11110111 = 00001000

(c) 1's comp of 10001101 = 01110010

2. (a) 2's comp of 00010110 = 11101010   (b) 2's comp of 11111100 = 00000100

(c) 2's comp of 10010001 = 01101111

Section 6   **Signed Numbers**

1. Sign-magnitude: $+9 = 00001001$

2. 1's comp: $-33 = 11011110$

3. 2's comp: $-46 = 11010010$

4. Sign bit, exponent, and mantissa

Section 7   **Arithmetic Operations with Signed Numbers**

1. Cases of addition: positive number is larger, negative number is larger, both are positive, both are negative

2. $00100001 + 10111100 = 11011101$

3. $01110111 - 00110010 = 01000101$

4. Sign of product is positive.

5. $00000101 \times 01111111 = 01001111011$

6. Sign of quotient is negative.

7. $00110000 \div 00001100 = 00000100$

Section 8   **Hexadecimal Numbers**

1. (a) $10110011 = B3_{16}$ (b) $110011101000 = CE8_{16}$

2. (a) $57_{16} = 01010111$ (b) $3A5_{16} = 001110100101$

   (c) $F8OB_{16} = 1111100000001011$

3. $9B30_{16} = 39,728_{10}$

4. $573_{10} = 23D_{16}$

5. (a) $18_{16} + 34_{16} = 4C_{16}$ (b) $3F_{16} + 2A_{16} = 69_{16}$

6. (a) $75_{16} - 21_{16} = 54_{16}$ (b) $94_{16} - 5C_{16} = 38_{16}$

Section 9   **Octal Numbers**

1. (a) $73_8 = 59_{10}$ (b) $125_8 = 85_{10}$

2. (a) $98_{10} = 142_8$ (b) $163_{10} = 243_8$

3. (a) $46_8 = 100110$ (b) $723_8 = 111010011$ (c) $5624_8 = 101110010100$

4. (a) $110101111 = 657_8$ (b) $1001100010 = 1142_8$ (c) $10111111001 = 2771_8$

Section 10   **Binary Coded Decimal (BCD)**

1. (a) 0010: 2   (b) 1000: 8   (c) 0001: 1   (d) 0100: 4

2. (a) $6_{10} = 0110$ (b) $15_{10} = 00010101$ (c) $273_{10} = 001001110011$

   (d) $849_{10} = 100001001001$

3. (a) $10001001 = 89_{10}$ (b) $001001111000 = 278_{10}$ (c) $000101010111 = 157_{10}$

4. A 4-bit sum is invalid when it is greater than 9_{10}.

Section 11   **Digital Codes**

1. (a) $1100_2 = 1010$ Gray   (b) $1010_2 = 1111$ Gray   (c) $11010_2 = 10111$ Gray

2. (a) 1000 Gray $= 1111_2$ (b) 1010 Gray $= 1100_2$ (c) 11101 Gray $= 10110_2$

3. (a) K: $1001011 \rightarrow 4B_{16}$ (b) r: $1110010 \rightarrow 72_{16}$

   (c) \$: $0100100 \rightarrow 24_{16}$ (d) +: $0101011 \rightarrow 2B_{16}$

Section 12   **Error Detection Codes**

1. (c) 0101 has an error.

2. (d) 11111011 has an error.

3. (a) 10101001   (b) 01000001   (c) 11101110   (d) 10001101

4. Cyclic redundancy check

5. (a) 0   (b) 0   (c) 1   (d) 1

RELATED PROBLEMS FOR EXAMPLES

1 9 has a value of 900, 3 has a value of 30, 9 has a value of 9.

2 6 has a value of 60, 7 has a value of 7, 9 has a value of 9/10 (0.9), 2 has a value of 2/100 (0.02), 4 has a value of 4/1000 (0.004).

3 $10010001 = 128 + 16 + 1 = 145$ **4** $10.111 = 2 + 0.5 + 0.25 + 0.125 = 2.875$

5 $125 = 64 + 32 + 16 + 8 + 4 + 1 = 1111101$ **6** $39 = 100111$

7 $1111 + 1100 = 11011$ **8** $111 - 100 = 011$ **9** $110 - 101 = 001$

10 $1101 \times 1010 = 10000010$ **11** $1100 \div 100 = 11$ **12** 00110101

13 01000000 **14** See Table 11.   **15** $01110111 = +119_{10}$

▶ TABLE 11

	SIGN-MAGNITUDE	1'S COMP	2'S COMP
+19	00010011	00010011	00010011
−19	10010011	11101100	11101101

16 $11101011 = -20_{10}$ **17** $11010111 = -41_{10}$

18 $11000010001010011000000000$ **19** 01010101 **20** 00010001

21 1001000110 **22** $(83)(-59) = -4897$ (10110011011111 in 2's comp)

23 $100 \div 25 = 4$ (0100) **24** $4F79C_{16}$ **25** 0110101111010011_2

26 $6BD_{16} = 011010111101 = 2^{10} + 2^9 + 2^7 + 2^5 + 2^4 + 2^3 + 2^2 + 2^0$
$= 1024 + 512 + 128 + 32 + 16 + 8 + 4 + 1 = 1725_{10}$

27 $60A_{16} = (6 \times 256) + (0 \times 16) + (10 \times 1) = 1546_{10}$

28 $2591_{10} = A1F_{16}$ **29** $4C_{16} + 3A_{16} = 86_{16}$

30 $BCD_{16} - 173_{16} = A5A_{16}$

31 **(a)** $001011_2 = 11_{10} = 13_8$ **(b)** $010101_2 = 21_{10} = 25_8$
     (c) $001100000_2 = 96_{10} = 140_8$ **(d)** $111101010110_2 = 3926_{10} = 7526_8$

32 1250762_8 **33** 1001011001110011 **34** $82{,}276_{10}$

35 1001100101101000 **36** 10000010 **37** **(a)** 111011 (Gray)   **(b)** 111010_2

38 The sequence of codes for if $(y < 8)$ is $69_{16} 66_{16} 20_{16} 28_{16} 79_{16} 3C_{16} 38_{16} 29_{16}$

39 01001011 **40** Yes   **41** A 0 remainder results   **42** Errors are indicated.

TRUE/FALSE QUIZ

1. T   **2.** T   **3.** F   **4.** F   **5.** T   **6.** F   **7.** F   **8.** T   **9.** T   **10.** F   **11.** T   **12.** F

SELF-TEST

1. (d)   **2.** (a)   **3.** (b)   **4.** (c)   **5.** (c)   **6.** (a)   **7.** (d)   **8.** (b)

9. (d)   **10.** (a)   **11.** (c)   **12.** (d)   **13.** (d)   **14.** (b)   **15.** (c)   **16.** (a)

17. (c)   **18.** (a)   **19.** (b)   **20.** (b)

ANSWERS TO ODD-NUMBERED PROBLEMS

1. (a) 1   (b) 100   (c) 100,000
3. (a) 400; 70; 1   (b) 9000; 300; 50; 6
   (c) 100,000; 20,000; 5000; 0; 0; 0
5. (a) 3   (b) 4   (c) 7   (d) 8   (e) 9
   (f) 12   (g) 11   (h) 15
7. (a) 51.75   (b) 42.25   (c) 65.875
   (d) 120.625   (e) 92.65625   (f) 113.0625
   (g) 90.625   (h) 127.96875
9. (a) 5 bits   (b) 6 bits   (c) 6 bits
   (d) 7 bits   (e) 7 bits   (f) 7 bits
   (g) 8 bits   (h) 8 bits
11. (a) 1010   (b) 10001   (c) 11000
   (d) 110000   (e) 111101   (f) 1011101
   (g) 1111101   (h) 10111010
13. (a) 1111   (b) 10101   (c) 11100
   (d) 100010   (e) 101000   (f) 111011
   (g) 1000001   (h) 1001001
15. (a) 100   (b) 100   (c) 1000
   (d) 1101   (e) 1110   (f) 11000
17. (a) 1001   (b) 1000   (c) 100011
   (d) 110110   (e) 10101001   (f) 10110110
19. all 0s or all 1s
21. (a) 010   (b) 001   (c) 0101
   (d) 00101000   (e) 0001010   (f) 11110
23. (a) 00011101   (b) 11010101
   (c) 01100100   (d) 11111011
25. (a) 00001100   (b) 10111100
   (c) 01100101   (d) 10000011
27. (a) −102   (b) +116   (c) −64
29. (a) 0 10001101 11110000101011000000000
   (b) 1 10001010 11000001100000000000000
31. (a) 00110000   (b) 00011101
   (c) 11101011   (d) 100111110
33. (a) 11000101   (b) 11000000
35. 100111001010
37. (a) 00111000   (b) 01011001   (c) 101000010100
   (d) 010111001000   (e) 0100000100000000
   (f) 1111101100010111   (g) 1000101010011101

39. (a) 35   (b) 146   (c) 26   (d) 141
   (e) 243   (f) 235   (g) 1474   (h) 1792
41. (a) 60_{16} (b) $10B_{16}$ (c) $1BA_{16}$
43. (a) 10   (b) 23   (c) 46   (d) 52   (e) 67
   (f) 367   (g) 115   (h) 532   (i) 4085
45. (a) 001011   (b) 101111   (c) 001000001
   (d) 011010001   (e) 101100000
   (f) 100110101011   (g) 001011010111001
   (h) 100101110000000   (i) 0010000000010001011
47. (a) 00010000   (b) 00010011
   (c) 00011000   (d) 00100001
   (e) 00100101   (f) 00110110
   (g) 01000100   (h) 01010111
   (i) 01101001   (j) 10011000
   (k) 000100100101   (l) 000101010110
49. (a) 000100000100   (b) 000100101000
   (c) 000100110010   (d) 000101010000
   (e) 000110000110   (f) 001000010000
   (g) 001101011001   (h) 010101000111
   (i) 0001000001010001
51. (a) 80   (b) 237   (c) 346   (d) 421   (e) 754
   (f) 800   (g) 978   (h) 1683   (i) 9018   (j) 6667
53. (a) 00010100   (b) 00010010
   (c) 00010111   (d) 00010110
   (e) 01010010   (f) 000100001001
   (g) 000110010101   (h) 0001001001101001
55. The Gray code makes only one bit change at a time when going from one number in the sequence to the next.
57. (a) 1100   (b) 00011   (c) 10000011110
59. (a) CAN   (b) J   (c) =
   (d) #   (e) >   (f) B
61. 48 65 6C 6C 6F 2E 20 48 6F 77 20 61 72 65 20 79 6F 75 3F
63. (b) is incorrect.
65. (a) 110100100   (b) 000001001   (c) 111111110
67. In each case, you get the other number.
69. The remainder is 0100, indicating an error.

LOGIC GATES

CHAPTER OBJECTIVES

◆ Describe the operation of the inverter, the AND gate, and the OR gate

◆ Describe the operation of the NAND gate and the NOR gate

◆ Express the operation of NOT, AND, OR, NAND, and NOR gates with Boolean algebra

◆ Describe the operation of the exclusive-OR and exclusive-NOR gates

◆ Recognize and use both the distinctive shape logic gate symbols and the rectangular outline logic gate symbols of ANSI/IEEE Standard 91-1984

◆ Construct timing diagrams showing the proper time relationships of inputs and outputs for the various logic gates

◆ Make basic comparisons between the major IC technologies—CMOS and bipolar (TTL)

◆ Explain how the different series within the CMOS and bipolar (TTL) families differ from each other

◆ Define *propagation delay time, power dissipation, speed-power product,* and *fan-out* in relation to logic gates

◆ List specific fixed-function integrated circuit devices that contain the various logic gates

◆ Use each logic gate in simple applications

◆ Troubleshoot logic gates for opens and shorts by using the oscilloscope

◆ Discuss the basic concepts of programmable logic

KEY TERMS

◆ Inverter
◆ Truth table
◆ Timing diagram
◆ Boolean algebra
◆ Complement
◆ AND gate
◆ Enable
◆ OR gate

◆ NAND gate
◆ NOR gate
◆ Exclusive-OR gate
◆ Exclusive-NOR gate
◆ CMOS
◆ Bipolar
◆ Propagation delay time
◆ Fan-out
◆ Unit load

◆ AND array
◆ Fuse
◆ Antifuse
◆ EPROM
◆ EEPROM
◆ Flash
◆ SRAM
◆ Target device
◆ JTAG

INTRODUCTION

The emphasis in this chapter is on the operation, application, and troubleshooting of logic gates. The relationship of input and output waveforms of a gate using timing diagrams is thoroughly covered.

Logic symbols used to represent the logic gates are in accordance with ANSI/IEEE Standard 91-1984. This standard has been adopted by private industry and the military for use in internal documentation as well as published literature.

Both fixed-function logic and programmable logic are discussed in this chapter. Because integrated circuits (ICs) are used in all applications, the logic function of a device is generally of greater importance to the technician or technologist than the details of the component-level circuit operation within the IC package. Therefore, detailed coverage of the devices at the component level can be treated as an optional topic.

FIXED-FUNCTION LOGIC DEVICES

(CMOS AND BIPOLAR SERIES)

74XX00	74XX02	74XX04
74XX08	74XX10	74XX11
74XX20	74XX21	74XX27
74XX30	74XX32	74XX86
74XX266		

From *Digital Fundamentals*, Tenth Edition, Thomas L. Floyd. Copyright © 2009 by Pearson Education, Inc. Published by Prentice Hall.

1 THE INVERTER

The inverter (NOT circuit) performs the operation called *inversion* or *complementation*. The inverter changes one logic level to the opposite level. In terms of bits, it changes a 1 to a 0 and a 0 to a 1.

After completing this section, you should be able to

- ◆ Identify negation and polarity indicators
- ◆ Identify an inverter by either its distinctive shape symbol or its rectangular outline symbol
- ◆ Produce the truth table for an inverter
- ◆ Describe the logical operation of an inverter

Standard logic symbols for the **inverter** are shown in Figure 1. Part (a) shows the *distinctive shape* symbols, and part (b) shows the *rectangular outline* symbols. In this textbook, distinctive shape symbols are generally used; however, the rectangular outline symbols are found in many industry publications, and you should become familiar with them as well. (Logic symbols are in accordance with **ANSI/IEEE** Standard 91-1984.)

▶ FIGURE 1

Standard logic symbols for the inverter (ANSI/IEEE Std. 91-1984).

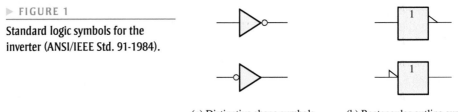

(a) Distinctive shape symbols with negation indicators

(b) Rectangular outline symbols with polarity indicators

The Negation and Polarity Indicators

The negation indicator is a "bubble" (○) that indicates **inversion** or *complementation* when it appears on the input or output of any logic element, as shown in Figure 1(a) for the inverter. Generally, inputs are on the left of a logic symbol and the output is on the right. When appearing on the input, the bubble means that a 0 is the active or *asserted* input state, and the input is called an active-LOW input. When appearing on the output, the bubble means that a 0 is the active or asserted output state, and the output is called an active-LOW output. The absence of a bubble on the input or output means that a 1 is the active or asserted state, and in this case, the input or output is called active-HIGH.

The polarity or level indicator is a "triangle" (◣) that indicates inversion when it appears on the input or output of a logic element, as shown in Figure 1(b). When appearing on the input, it means that a LOW level is the active or asserted input state. When appearing on the output, it means that a LOW level is the active or asserted output state.

Either indicator (bubble or triangle) can be used both on distinctive shape symbols and on rectangular outline symbols. Figure 1(a) indicates the principal inverter symbols used in this text. Note that a change in the placement of the negation or polarity indicator does not imply a change in the way an inverter operates.

Inverter Truth Table

When a HIGH level is applied to an inverter input, a LOW level will appear on its output. When a LOW level is applied to its input, a HIGH will appear on its output. This operation is summarized in Table 1, which shows the output for each possible input in terms of levels and corresponding bits. A table such as this is called a **truth table**.

Inverter Operation

Figure 2 shows the output of an inverter for a pulse input, where t_1 and t_2 indicate the corresponding points on the input and output pulse waveforms.

When the input is LOW, the output is HIGH; when the input is HIGH, the output is LOW, thereby producing an inverted output pulse.

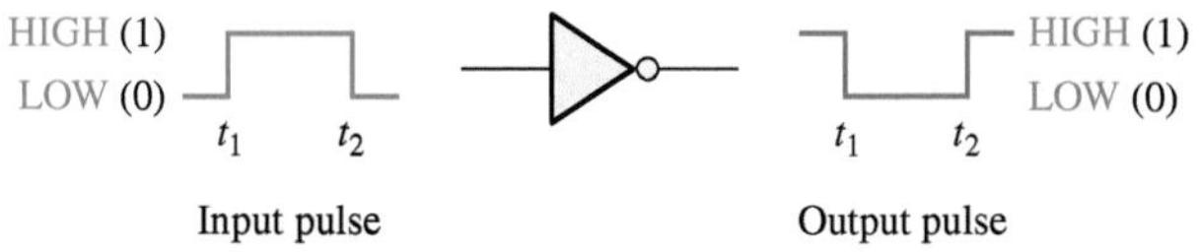

◄ TABLE 1

Inverter truth table.

INPUT	OUTPUT
LOW (0)	HIGH (1)
HIGH (1)	LOW (0)

HIGH (1)
LOW (0)

t_1 t_2

Input pulse

HIGH (1)
LOW (0)

t_1 t_2

Output pulse

◄ **FIGURE 2**

Inverter operation with a pulse input. Open file F03-02 on www.pearsoned.com/electronics to verify inverter operation.

Timing Diagrams

A **timing diagram** is basically a graph that accurately displays the relationship of two or more waveforms with respect to each other on a time basis. For example, the time relationship of the output pulse to the input pulse in Figure 2 can be shown with a simple timing diagram by aligning the two pulses so that the occurrences of the pulse edges appear in the proper time relationship. The rising edge of the input pulse and the falling edge of the output pulse occur at the same time (ideally). Similarly, the falling edge of the input pulse and the rising edge of the output pulse occur at the same time (ideally). This timing relationship is shown in Figure 3. In practice, there is a very small delay from the input transition until the corresponding output transition. Timing diagrams are especially useful for illustrating the time relationship of digital waveforms with multiple pulses.

A timing diagram shows how two or more waveforms relate in time.

Input

Output

t_1 t_2

▲ **FIGURE 3**

Timing diagram for the case in Figure 2.

EXAMPLE 1

A waveform is applied to an inverter in Figure 4. Determine the output waveform corresponding to the input and show the timing diagram. According to the placement of the bubble, what is the active output state?

▶ **FIGURE 4**

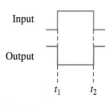

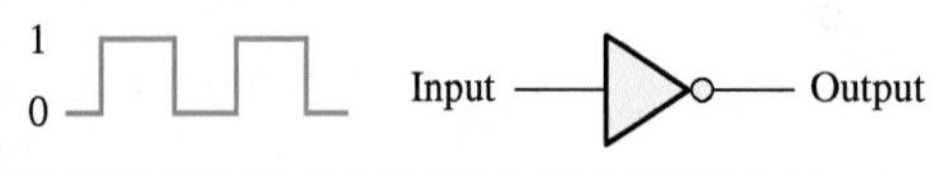

1
0   Input ——▷o— Output

Solution   The output waveform is exactly opposite to the input (inverted), as shown in Figure 5, which is the basic timing diagram. The active or asserted output state is **0.**

▶ **FIGURE 5**

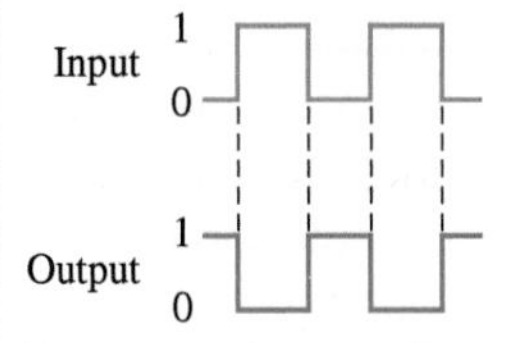

Input   1
         0

Output   1
         0

Related Problem*   If the inverter is shown with the negative indicator (bubble) on the input instead of the output, how is the timing diagram affected?

---

*Answers are at the end of the chapter.

Logic Expression for an Inverter

Boolean algebra uses variables and operators to describe a logic circuit.

In **Boolean algebra,** which is the mathematics of logic circuits, a variable is generally designated by one or two letters although there can be more. Letters near the beginning of the alphabet usually designate inputs, while letters near the end of the alphabet usually designate outputs. The **complement** of a variable is designated by a bar over the letter. A variable can take on a value of either 1 or 0. If a given variable is 1, its complement is 0 and vice versa.

The operation of an inverter (NOT circuit) can be expressed as follows: If the input variable is called A and the output variable is called X, then

$$X = \overline{A}$$

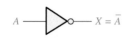

▲ FIGURE 6

The inverter complements an input variable.

This expression states that the output is the complement of the input, so if $A = 0$, then $X = 1$, and if $A = 1$, then $X = 0$. Figure 6 illustrates this. The complemented variable $\overline{A}$ can be read as "A bar" or "not A."

An Application

Figure 7 shows a circuit for producing the 1's complement of an 8-bit binary number. The bits of the binary number are applied to the inverter inputs and the 1's complement of the number appears on the outputs.

▶ FIGURE 7

Example of a 1's complement circuit using inverters.

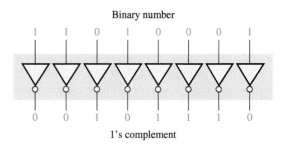

Binary number

1's complement

**SECTION 1
CHECKUP**
Answers are at the end of the chapter.

1. When a 1 is on the input of an inverter, what is the output?
2. An active-HIGH pulse (HIGH level when asserted, LOW level when not) is required on an inverter input.
   (a) Draw the appropriate logic symbol, using the distinctive shape and the negation indicator, for the inverter in this application.
   (b) Describe the output when a positive-going pulse is applied to the input of an inverter.

---

2   THE AND GATE

The AND gate is one of the basic gates that can be combined to form any logic function. An AND gate can have two or more inputs and performs what is known as logical multiplication.

After completing this section, you should be able to

♦ Identify an AND gate by its distinctive shape symbol or by its rectangular outline symbol

♦ Describe the operation of an AND gate

♦ Generate the truth table for an AND gate with any number of inputs

+ Produce a timing diagram for an AND gate with any specified input wave-forms

+ Write the logic expression for an AND gate with any number of inputs

+ Discuss examples of AND gate applications

The term *gate* is used to describe a circuit that performs a basic logic operation. The AND gate is composed of two or more inputs and a single output, as indicated by the standard logic symbols shown in Figure 8. Inputs are on the left, and the output is on the right in each symbol. Gates with two inputs are shown; however, an AND gate can have any number of inputs greater than one. Although examples of both distinctive shape symbols and rectangular outline symbols are shown, the distinctive shape symbol, shown in part (a), is used predominantly in this book.

COMPUTER NOTE

Logic gates are one of the fundamental building blocks of computers. Most of the functions in a computer, with the exception of certain types of memory, are implemented with logic gates used on a very large scale. For example, a microprocessor, which is the main part of a computer, is made up of hundreds of thousands or even millions of logic gates.

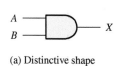

(a) Distinctive shape

(b) Rectangular outline with the AND (&) qualifying symbol

◀ **FIGURE 8**

Standard logic symbols for the AND gate showing two inputs (ANSI/IEEE Std. 91-1984).

Operation of an AND Gate

An **AND gate** produces a HIGH output *only* when *all* of the inputs are HIGH. When any of the inputs is LOW, the output is LOW. Therefore, the basic purpose of an AND gate is to determine when certain conditions are simultaneously true, as indicated by HIGH levels on all of its inputs, and to produce a HIGH on its output to indicate that all these conditions are true. The inputs of the 2-input AND gate in Figure 8 are labeled A and B, and the output is labeled X. The gate operation can be stated as follows:

An AND gate can have more than two inputs.

For a 2-input AND gate, output X is HIGH only when inputs A and B are HIGH; X is LOW when either A or B is LOW, or when both A and B are LOW.

Figure 9 illustrates a 2-input AND gate with all four possibilities of input combinations and the resulting output for each.

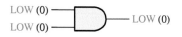

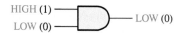

▲ **FIGURE 9**

All possible logic levels for a 2-input AND gate. Open file F03-09 to verify AND gate operation.

AND Gate Truth Table

The logical operation of a gate can be expressed with a truth table that lists all input combinations with the corresponding outputs, as illustrated in Table 2 for a 2-input AND gate. The truth table can be expanded to any number of inputs. Although the terms HIGH and LOW tend to give a "physical" sense to the input and output states, the truth table is

▼ **TABLE 2**

Truth table for a 2-input AND gate.

INPUTS		OUTPUT
A	*B*	*X*
0	0	0
0	1	0
1	0	0
1	1	1

1 = HIGH, 0 = LOW

For an AND gate, all HIGH inputs produce a HIGH output.

shown with 1s and 0s; a HIGH is equivalent to a 1 and a LOW is equivalent to a 0 in positive logic. For any AND gate, regardless of the number of inputs, the output is HIGH *only* when *all* inputs are HIGH.

The total number of possible combinations of binary inputs to a gate is determined by the following formula:

Equation 1

$$N = 2^n$$

where N is the number of possible input combinations and n is the number of input variables. To illustrate,

For two input variables: $N = 2^2 = 4$ combinations

For three input variables: $N = 2^3 = 8$ combinations

For four input variables: $N = 2^4 = 16$ combinations

You can determine the number of input bit combinations for gates with any number of inputs by using Equation 1.

EXAMPLE 2

(a) Develop the truth table for a 3-input AND gate.

(b) Determine the total number of possible input combinations for a 4-input AND gate.

Solution

(a) There are eight possible input combinations ($2^3 = 8$) for a 3-input AND gate. The input side of the truth table (Table 3) shows all eight combinations of three bits. The output side is all 0s except when all three input bits are 1s.

▶ TABLE 3

INPUTS			OUTPUT
A	B	C	X
0	0	0	0
0	0	1	0
0	1	0	0
0	1	1	0
1	0	0	0
1	0	1	0
1	1	0	0
1	1	1	1

(b) $N = 2^4 = $ **16.** There are 16 possible combinations of input bits for a 4-input AND gate.

Related Problem Develop the truth table for a 4-input AND gate.

Operation with Waveform Inputs

In most applications, the inputs to a gate are not stationary levels but are voltage waveforms that change frequently between HIGH and LOW logic levels. Now let's look at the operation of AND gates with pulse waveform inputs, keeping in mind that an AND gate obeys the truth table operation regardless of whether its inputs are constant levels or levels that change back and forth.

Let's examine the waveform operation of an AND gate by looking at the inputs with respect to each other in order to determine the output level at any given time. In Figure 10, inputs A and B are both HIGH (1) during the time interval, t_1, making output X HIGH (1) during this interval. During time interval t_2, input A is LOW (0) and input B is HIGH (1), so the output is LOW (0). During time interval t_3, both inputs are HIGH (1) again, and therefore the output is HIGH (1). During time interval t_4, input A is HIGH (1) and input B is LOW (0), resulting in a LOW (0) output. Finally, during time interval t_5, input A is LOW (0), input B is LOW (0), and the output is therefore LOW (0). As you know, a diagram of input and output waveforms showing time relationships is called a *timing diagram*.

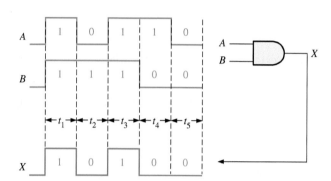

◄ FIGURE 10

Example of AND gate operation with a timing diagram showing input and output relationships.

EXAMPLE 3

If two waveforms, A and B, are applied to the AND gate inputs as in Figure 11, what is the resulting output waveform?

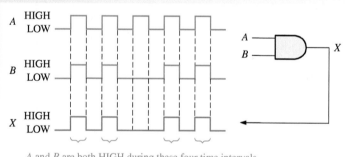

A and B are both HIGH during these four time intervals. Therefore X is HIGH.

▲ FIGURE 11

Solution   The output waveform X is HIGH only when both A and B waveforms are HIGH as shown in the timing diagram in Figure 11.

Related Problem   Determine the output waveform and show a timing diagram if the second and fourth pulses in waveform A of Figure 11 are replaced by LOW levels.

Remember, when analyzing the waveform operation of logic gates, it is important to pay careful attention to the time relationships of all the inputs with respect to each other and to the output.

EXAMPLE 4

For the two input waveforms, A and B, in Figure 12, show the output waveform with its proper relation to the inputs.

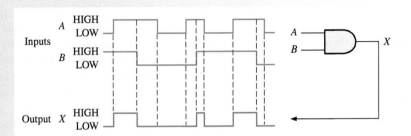

▲ FIGURE 12

Solution   The output waveform is HIGH only when both of the input waveforms are HIGH as shown in the timing diagram.

Related Problem   Show the output waveform if the B input to the AND gate in Figure 12 is always HIGH.

EXAMPLE 5

For the 3-input AND gate in Figure 13, determine the output waveform in relation to the inputs.

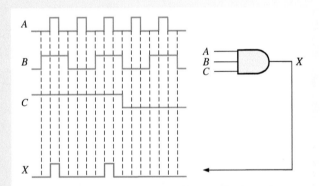

▲ FIGURE 13

Solution   The output waveform X of the 3-input AND gate is HIGH only when all three input waveforms A, B, and C are HIGH.

Related Problem   What is the output waveform of the AND gate in Figure 13 if the C input is always HIGH?

EXAMPLE 6

Use Multisim to simulate a 3-input AND gate with input waveforms that cycle through binary numbers 0 through 9.

Solution   Use the Multisim word generator in the up counter mode to provide the combination of waveforms representing the binary sequence, as shown in Figure 14. The first three waveforms on the oscilloscope display are the inputs, and the bottom waveform is the output.

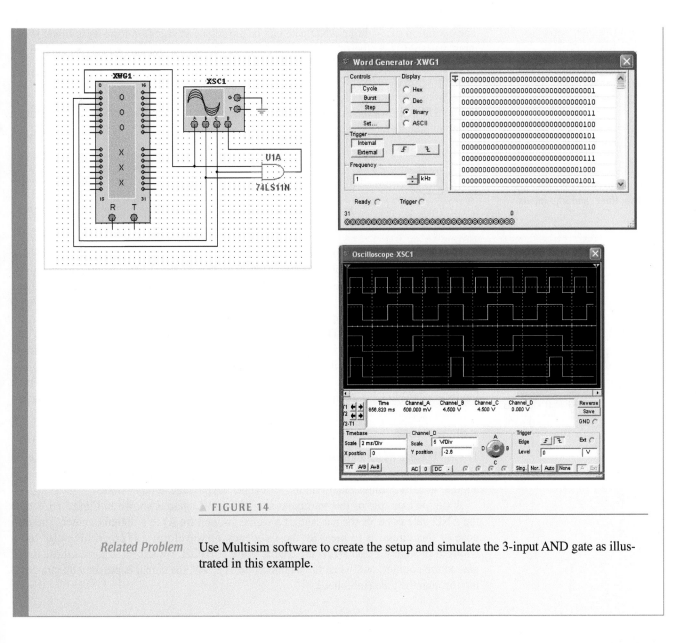

▲ FIGURE 14

Related Problem   Use Multisim software to create the setup and simulate the 3-input AND gate as illustrated in this example.

Logic Expressions for an AND Gate

The logical AND function of two variables is represented mathematically either by placing a dot between the two variables, as $A \cdot B,$ or by simply writing the adjacent letters without the dot, as AB. We will normally use the latter notation because it is easier to write.

Boolean multiplication follows the same basic rules governing binary multiplication, are as follows:

$$0 \cdot 0 = 0$$
$$0 \cdot 1 = 0$$
$$1 \cdot 0 = 0$$
$$1 \cdot 1 = 1$$

Boolean multiplication is the same as the AND function.

COMPUTER NOTE

Computers can utilize all of the basic logic operations when it is necessary to selectively manipulate certain bits in one or more bytes of data. Selective bit manipulations are done with a *mask*. For example, to clear (make all 0s) the right four bits in a data byte but keep the left four bits, ANDing the data byte with 11110000 will do the job. Notice that any bit ANDed with zero will be 0 and any bit ANDed with 1 will remain the same. If 10101010 is ANDed with the mask 11110000, the result is 10100000.

When variables are shown together like *ABC*, they are ANDed.

The operation of a 2-input AND gate can be expressed in equation form as follows: If one input variable is *A*, the other input variable is *B*, and the output variable is *X*, then the Boolean expression is

$$X = AB$$

Figure 15(a) shows the AND gate logic symbol with two input variables and the output variable indicated.

FIGURE 15

Boolean expressions for AND gates with two, three, and four inputs.

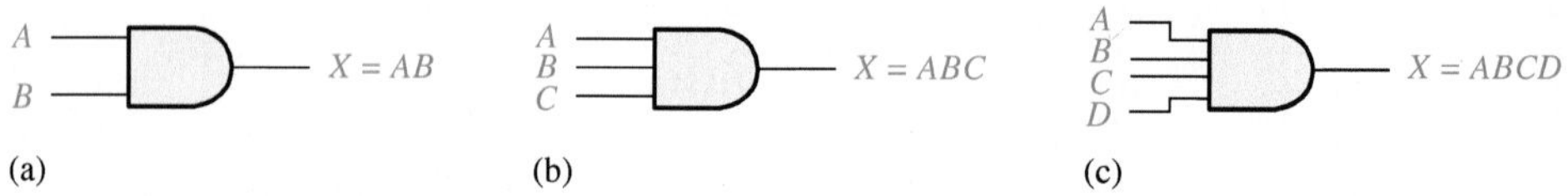

To extend the AND expression to more than two input variables, simply use a new letter for each input variable. The function of a 3-input AND gate, for example, can be expressed as $X = ABC$, where *A*, *B*, and *C* are the input variables. The expression for a 4-input AND gate can be $X = ABCD$, and so on. Parts (b) and (c) of Figure 15 show AND gates with three and four input variables, respectively.

You can evaluate an AND gate operation by using the Boolean expressions for the output. For example, each variable on the inputs can be either a 1 or a 0; so for the 2-input AND gate, make substitutions in the equation for the output, $X = AB$, as shown in Table 4. This evaluation shows that the output *X* of an AND gate is a 1 (HIGH) only when both inputs are 1s (HIGHs). A similar analysis can be made for any number of input variables.

TABLE 4

A	*B*	*AB* = *X*
0	0	$0 \cdot 0 = 0$
0	1	$0 \cdot 1 = 0$
1	0	$1 \cdot 0 = 0$
1	1	$1 \cdot 1 = 1$

Applications

The AND Gate as an Enable/Inhibit Device A common application of the AND gate is to **enable** (that is, to allow) the passage of a signal (pulse waveform) from one point to another at certain times and to inhibit (prevent) the passage at other times.

A simple example of this particular use of an AND gate is shown in Figure 16, where the AND gate controls the passage of a signal (waveform *A*) to a digital counter. The purpose of this circuit is to measure the frequency of waveform *A*. The enable pulse has a width of precisely 1 ms. When the enable pulse is HIGH, waveform *A* passes through the gate to the counter; and when the enable pulse is LOW, the signal is prevented from passing through the gate (inhibited).

FIGURE 16

An AND gate performing an enable/inhibit function for a frequency counter.

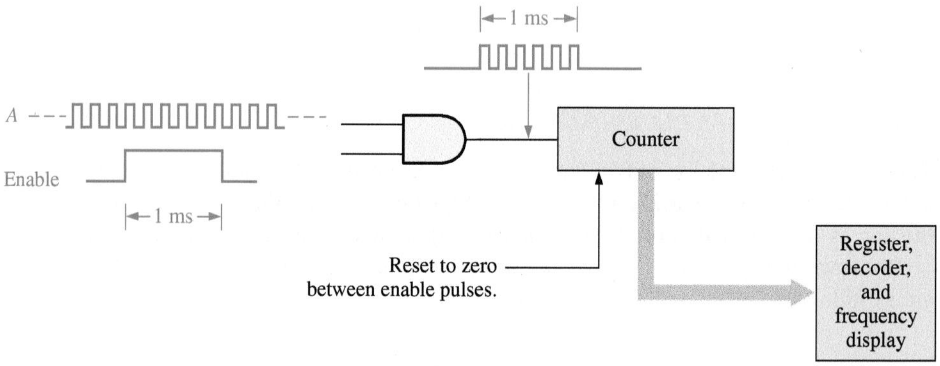

During the 1 millisecond (1 ms) interval of the enable pulse, pulses in waveform *A* pass through the AND gate to the counter. The number of pulses passing through during the 1 ms interval is equal to the frequency of waveform *A*. For example, Figure 16 shows six pulses in one millisecond, which is a frequency of 6 kHz. If 1000 pulses pass through the gate in the 1 ms interval of the enable pulse, there are 1000 pulses/ms, or a frequency of 1 MHz.

The counter counts the number of pulses per second and produces a binary output that goes to a decoding and display circuit to produce a readout of the frequency. The enable pulse repeats at certain intervals and a new updated count is made so that if the frequency changes, the new value will be displayed. Between enable pulses, the counter is reset so that it starts at zero each time an enable pulse occurs. The current frequency count is stored in a register so that the display is unaffected by the resetting of the counter.

A Seat Belt Alarm System   In Figure 17, an AND gate is used in a simple automobile seat belt alarm system to detect when the ignition switch is on *and* the seat belt is unbuckled. If the ignition switch is on, a HIGH is produced on input *A* of the AND gate. If the seat belt is not properly buckled, a HIGH is produced on input *B* of the AND gate. Also, when the ignition switch is turned on, a timer is started that produces a HIGH on input *C* for 30 s. If all three conditions exist—that is, if the ignition is on *and* the seat belt is unbuckled *and* the timer is running—the output of the AND gate is HIGH, and an audible alarm is energized to remind the driver.

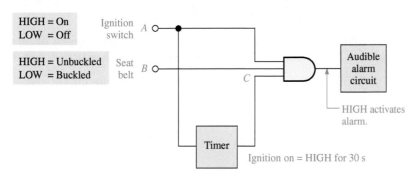

◄ FIGURE 17

A simple seat belt alarm circuit using an AND gate.

SECTION 2 CHECKUP	1. When is the output of an AND gate HIGH?
	2. When is the output of an AND gate LOW?
	3. Describe the truth table for a 5-input AND gate.

3 THE OR GATE

The OR gate is another of the basic gates from which all logic functions are constructed. An OR gate can have two or more inputs and performs what is known as logical addition.

After completing this section, you should be able to

- ◆ Identify an OR gate by its distinctive shape symbol or by its rectangular outline symbol
- ◆ Describe the operation of an OR gate
- ◆ Generate the truth table for an OR gate with any number of inputs
- ◆ Produce a timing diagram for an OR gate with any specified input waveforms
- ◆ Write the logic expression for an OR gate with any number of inputs
- ◆ Discuss an OR gate application

An **OR gate** has two or more inputs and one output, as indicated by the standard logic symbols in Figure 18, where OR gates with two inputs are illustrated. An OR gate can have

An OR gate can have more than two inputs.

any number of inputs greater than one. Although both distinctive shape and rectangular outline symbols are shown, the distinctive shape OR gate symbol is used in this textbook.

▶ FIGURE 18

Standard logic symbols for the OR gate showing two inputs (ANSI/IEEE Std. 91-1984).

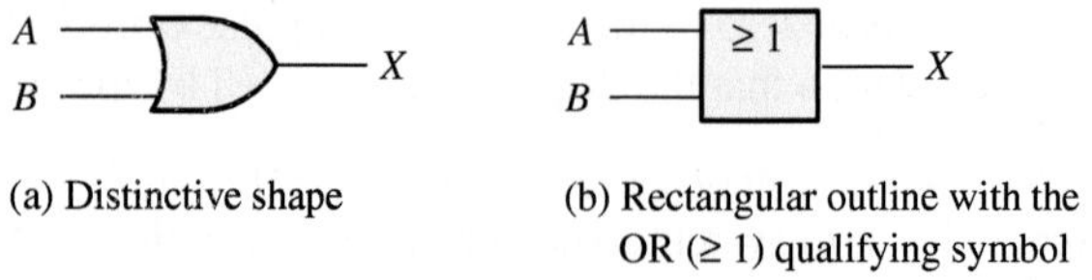

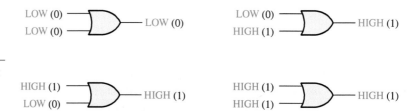

(a) Distinctive shape

(b) Rectangular outline with the OR (≥ 1) qualifying symbol

Operation of an OR Gate

For an OR gate, at least one HIGH input produces a HIGH output.

An OR gate produces a HIGH on the output when *any* of the inputs is HIGH. The output is LOW only when all of the inputs are LOW. Therefore, an OR gate determines when one or more of its inputs are HIGH and produces a HIGH on its output to indicate this condition. The inputs of the 2-input OR gate in Figure 18 are labeled A and B, and the output is labeled X. The operation of the gate can be stated as follows:

For a 2-input OR gate, output X is HIGH when either input A or input B is HIGH, or when both A and B are HIGH; X is LOW only when both A and B are LOW.

The HIGH level is the active or asserted output level for the OR gate. Figure 19 illustrates the operation for a 2-input OR gate for all four possible input combinations.

▶ FIGURE 19

All possible logic levels for a 2-input OR gate. Open file F03-19 to verify OR gate operation.

OR Gate Truth Table

▼ TABLE 5

Truth table for a 2-input OR gate.

INPUTS		OUTPUT
A	*B*	*X*
0	0	0
0	1	1
1	0	1
1	1	1

1 = HIGH, 0 = LOW

The operation of a 2-input OR gate is described in Table 5. This truth table can be expanded for any number of inputs; but regardless of the number of inputs, the output is HIGH when one or more of the inputs are HIGH.

Operation with Waveform Inputs

Now let's look at the operation of an OR gate with pulse waveform inputs, keeping in mind its logical operation. Again, the important thing in the analysis of gate operation with pulse waveforms is the time relationship of all the waveforms involved. For example, in Figure 20,

▶ FIGURE 20

Example of OR gate operation with a timing diagram showing input and output time relationships.

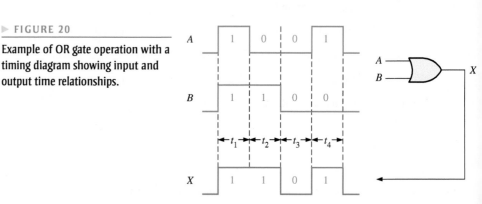

inputs A and B are both HIGH (1) during time interval t_1, making output X HIGH (1). During time interval t_2, input A is LOW (0), but because input B is HIGH (1), the output is HIGH (1). Both inputs are LOW (0) during time interval t_3, so there is a LOW (0) output during this time. During time interval t_4, the output is HIGH (1) because input A is HIGH (1).

In this illustration, we have applied the truth table operation of the OR gate to each of the time intervals during which the levels are nonchanging. Examples 7 through 9 further illustrate OR gate operation with waveforms on the inputs.

EXAMPLE 7

If the two input waveforms, A and B, in Figure 21 are applied to the OR gate, what is the resulting output waveform?

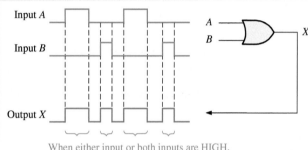

When either input or both inputs are HIGH, the output is HIGH.

▲ FIGURE 21

Solution The output waveform X of a 2-input OR gate is HIGH when either or both input waveforms are HIGH as shown in the timing diagram. In this case, both input waveforms are never HIGH at the same time.

Related Problem Determine the output waveform and show the timing diagram if input A is changed such that it is HIGH from the beginning of the existing first pulse to the end of the existing second pulse.

EXAMPLE 8

For the two input waveforms, A and B, in Figure 22, show the output waveform with its proper relation to the inputs.

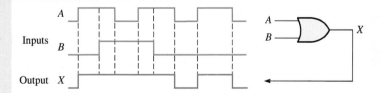

▲ FIGURE 22

Solution When either or both input waveforms are HIGH, the output is HIGH as shown by the output waveform X in the timing diagram.

Related Problem Determine the output waveform and show the timing diagram if the middle pulse of input A is replaced by a LOW level.

123

EXAMPLE 9

For the 3-input OR gate in Figure 23, determine the output waveform in proper time relation to the inputs.

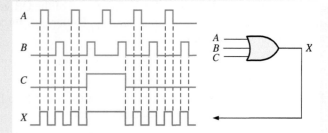

▲ FIGURE 23

Solution   The output is HIGH when one or more of the input waveforms are HIGH as indicated by the output waveform X in the timing diagram.

Related Problem   Determine the output waveform and show the timing diagram if input C is always LOW.

Logic Expressions for an OR Gate

When variables are separated by +, they are ORed.

The logical OR function of two variables is represented mathematically by a + between the two variables, for example, $A + B$. The plus sign is read as "OR."

Addition in Boolean algebra involves variables whose values are either binary 1 or binary 0. The basic rules for **Boolean addition** are as follows:

$$0 + 0 = 0$$
$$0 + 1 = 1$$
$$1 + 0 = 1$$
$$1 + 1 = 1$$

Boolean addition is the same as the OR function.

Notice that Boolean addition differs from binary addition in the case where two 1s are added. There is no carry in Boolean addition.

The operation of a 2-input OR gate can be expressed as follows: If one input variable is A, if the other input variable is B, and if the output variable is X, then the Boolean expression is

$$X = A + B$$

Figure 24(a) shows the OR gate logic symbol with two input variables and the output variable labeled.

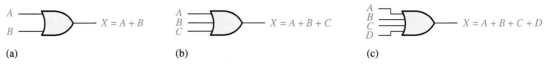

(a)   (b)   (c)

▲ FIGURE 24

Boolean expressions for OR gates with two, three, and four inputs.

To extend the OR expression to more than two input variables, a new letter is used for each additional variable. For instance, the function of a 3-input OR gate can be expressed as $X = A + B + C$. The expression for a 4-input OR gate can be written as $X = A + B + C + D$, and so on. Parts (b) and (c) of Figure 24 show OR gates with three and four input variables, respectively.

OR gate operation can be evaluated by using the Boolean expressions for the output X by substituting all possible combinations of 1 and 0 values for the input variables, as shown in Table 6 for a 2-input OR gate. This evaluation shows that the output X of an OR gate is a 1 (HIGH) when any one or more of the inputs are 1 (HIGH). A similar analysis can be extended to OR gates with any number of input variables.

An Application

A simplified portion of an intrusion detection and alarm system is shown in Figure 25. This system could be used for one room in a home—a room with two windows and a door. The sensors are magnetic switches that produce a HIGH output when open and a LOW output when closed. As long as the windows and the door are secured, the switches are closed and all three of the OR gate inputs are LOW. When one of the windows or the door is opened, a HIGH is produced on that input to the OR gate and the gate output goes HIGH. It then activates and latches an alarm circuit to warn of the intrusion.

COMPUTER NOTE

Another mask operation that is used in computer programming to selectively make certain bits in a data byte equal to 1 (called setting) while not affecting any other bit is done with the OR operation. A mask is used that contains a 1 in any position where a data bit is to be set. For example, if you want to force the sign bit in an 8-bit signed number to equal 1, but leave all other bits unchanged, you can OR the data byte with the mask 10000000.

▼ TABLE 6

A	B	A + B = X
0	0	0 + 0 = 0
0	1	0 + 1 = 1
1	0	1 + 0 = 1
1	1	1 + 1 = 1

Open door/window sensors

HIGH = Open
LOW = Closed

◄ FIGURE 25

A simplified intrusion detection system using an OR gate.

HIGH activates alarm.

Alarm circuit

SECTION 3 CHECKUP

1. When is the output of an OR gate HIGH?
2. When is the output of an OR gate LOW?
3. Describe the truth table for a 3-input OR gate.

4 THE NAND GATE

The NAND gate is a popular logic element because it can be used as a universal gate; that is, NAND gates can be used in combination to perform the AND, OR, and inverter operations.

After completing this section, you should be able to

- Identify a NAND gate by its distinctive shape symbol or by its rectangular outline symbol
- Describe the operation of a NAND gate

- ◆ Develop the truth table for a NAND gate with any number of inputs
- ◆ Produce a timing diagram for a NAND gate with any specified input waveforms
- ◆ Write the logic expression for a NAND gate with any number of inputs
- ◆ Describe NAND gate operation in terms of its negative-OR equivalent
- ◆ Discuss examples of NAND gate applications

The NAND gate is the same as the AND gate except the output is inverted.

The term *NAND* is a contraction of NOT-AND and implies an AND function with a complemented (inverted) output. The standard logic symbol for a 2-input NAND gate and its equivalency to an AND gate followed by an inverter are shown in Figure 26(a), where the symbol ≡ means equivalent to. A rectangular outline symbol is shown in part (b).

▶ FIGURE 26

Standard NAND gate logic symbols (ANSI/IEEE Std. 91-1984).

(a) Distinctive shape, 2-input NAND gate and its NOT/AND equivalent

(b) Rectangular outline, 2-input NAND gate with polarity indicator

Operation of a NAND Gate

A **NAND gate** produces a LOW output only when all the inputs are HIGH. When any of the inputs is LOW, the output will be HIGH. For the specific case of a 2-input NAND gate, as shown in Figure 26 with the inputs labeled A and B and the output labeled X, the operation can be stated as follows:

▼ TABLE 7

Truth table for a 2-input NAND gate.

INPUTS		OUTPUT
A	B	X
0	0	1
0	1	1
1	0	1
1	1	0

1 = HIGH, 0 = LOW.

For a 2-input NAND gate, output X is LOW only when inputs A and B are HIGH; X is HIGH when either A or B is LOW, or when both A and B are LOW.

This operation is opposite that of the AND in terms of the output level. In a NAND gate, the LOW level (0) is the active or asserted output level, as indicated by the bubble on the output. Figure 27 illustrates the operation of a 2-input NAND gate for all four input combinations, and Table 7 is the truth table summarizing the logical operation of the 2-input NAND gate.

▲ FIGURE 27

Operation of a 2-input NAND gate. Open file F03-27 to verify NAND gate operation.

Operation with Waveform Inputs

Now let's look at the pulse waveform operation of a NAND gate. Remember from the truth table that the only time a LOW output occurs is when all of the inputs are HIGH.

126

EXAMPLE 10

If the two waveforms A and B shown in Figure 28 are applied to the NAND gate inputs, determine the resulting output waveform.

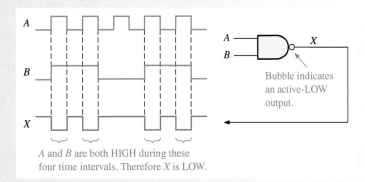

A and B are both HIGH during these four time intervals. Therefore X is LOW.

▲ FIGURE 28

Solution   Output waveform X is LOW only during the four time intervals when both input waveforms A and B are HIGH as shown in the timing diagram.

Related Problem   Determine the output waveform and show the timing diagram if input waveform B is inverted.

EXAMPLE 11

Show the output waveform for the 3-input NAND gate in Figure 29 with its proper time relationship to the inputs.

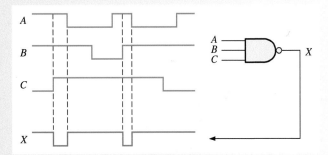

▲ FIGURE 29

Solution   The output waveform X is LOW only when all three input waveforms are HIGH as shown in the timing diagram.

Related Problem   Determine the output waveform and show the timing diagram if input waveform A is inverted.

Negative-OR Equivalent Operation of a NAND Gate   Inherent in a NAND gate's operation is the fact that one or more LOW inputs produce a HIGH output. Table 7 shows that output X is HIGH (1) when any of the inputs, A and B, is LOW (0). From this viewpoint, a NAND gate can be used for an OR operation that requires one or more LOW inputs to produce a HIGH output. This aspect of NAND operation is referred to as **negative-OR.**

127

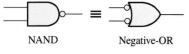

NAND   Negative-OR

▲ FIGURE 30

Standard symbols representing the two equivalent operations of a NAND gate.

The term *negative* in this context means that the inputs are defined to be in the active or asserted state when LOW.

For a 2-input NAND gate performing a negative-OR operation, output X is HIGH when either input A or input B is LOW, or when both A and B are LOW.

When a NAND gate is used to detect one or more LOWs on its inputs rather than all HIGHs, it is performing the negative-OR operation and is represented by the standard logic symbol shown in Figure 30. Although the two symbols in Figure 30 represent the same physical gate, they serve to define its role or mode of operation in a particular application, as illustrated by Examples 12 and 13.

EXAMPLE 12

A manufacturing plant uses two tanks to store certain liquid chemicals that are required in a manufacturing process. Each tank has a sensor that detects when the chemical level drops to 25% of full. The sensors produce a HIGH level of 5 V when the tanks are more than one-quarter full. When the volume of chemical in a tank drops to one-quarter full, the sensor puts out a LOW level of 0 V.

It is required that a single green light-emitting diode (LED) on an indicator panel show when both tanks are more than one-quarter full. Show how a NAND gate can be used to implement this function.

Solution   Figure 31 shows a NAND gate with its two inputs connected to the tank level sensors and its output connected to the indicator panel. The operation can be stated as follows: If tank A *and* tank B are above one-quarter full, the LED is on.

▶ FIGURE 31

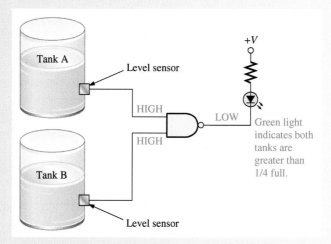

As long as both sensor outputs are HIGH (5 V), indicating that both tanks are more than one-quarter full, the NAND gate output is LOW (0 V). The green LED circuit is arranged so that a LOW voltage turns it on. The resistor limits the LED current.

Related Problem   How can the circuit of Figure 31 be modified to monitor the levels in three tanks rather than two?

EXAMPLE 13

The supervisor of the manufacturing process described in Example 12 has decided that he would prefer to have a red LED display come on when at least one of the tanks falls to the quarter-full level rather than have the green LED display indicate when both are above one quarter. Show how this requirement can be implemented.

Solution   Figure 32 shows a NAND gate operating as a negative-OR gate to detect the occurrence of at least one LOW on its inputs. A sensor puts out a LOW voltage if the volume in its tank goes to one-quarter full or less. When this happens, the gate output goes HIGH. The red LED circuit in the panel is arranged so that a HIGH voltage turns it on. The operation can be stated as follows: If tank *A or* tank *B or* both are below one-quarter full, the LED is on.

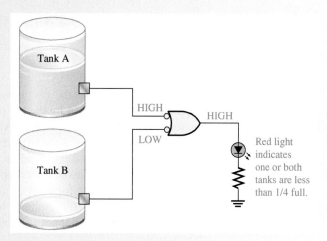

▲ FIGURE 32

Notice that, in this example and in Example 12, the same 2-input NAND gate is used, but a different gate symbol is used in the schematic, illustrating the different way in which the NAND and equivalent negative-OR operations are used.

Related Problem   How can the circuit in Figure 32 be modified to monitor four tanks rather than two?

EXAMPLE 14

For the 4-input NAND gate in Figure 33, operating as a negative-OR gate, determine the output with respect to the inputs.

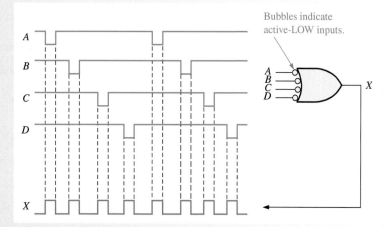

▲ FIGURE 33

The output waveform X is HIGH any time an input waveform is LOW as shown in the timing diagram.

Related Problem Determine the output waveform if input waveform A is inverted before it is applied to the gate.

Logic Expressions for a NAND Gate

A bar over a variable or variables indicates an inversion.

The Boolean expression for the output of a 2-input NAND gate is

$$X = \overline{AB}$$

This expression says that the two input variables, A and B, are first ANDed and then complemented, as indicated by the bar over the AND expression. This is a description in equation form of the operation of a NAND gate with two inputs. Evaluating this expression for all possible values of the two input variables, you get the results shown in Table 8.

Once an expression is determined for a given logic function, that function can be evaluated for all possible values of the variables. The evaluation tells you exactly what the output of the logic circuit is for each of the input conditions, and it therefore gives you a complete description of the circuit's logic operation. The NAND expression can be extended to more than two input variables by including additional letters to represent the other variables.

▽ TABLE 8

A	B	$\overline{AB} = X$
0	0	$\overline{0 \cdot 0} = \overline{0} = 1$
0	1	$\overline{0 \cdot 1} = \overline{0} = 1$
1	0	$\overline{1 \cdot 0} = \overline{0} = 1$
1	1	$\overline{1 \cdot 1} = \overline{1} = 0$

SECTION 4 CHECKUP

1. When is the output of a NAND gate LOW?
2. When is the output of a NAND gate HIGH?
3. Describe the functional differences between a NAND gate and a negative-OR gate. Do they both have the same truth table?
4. Write the output expression for a NAND gate with inputs A, B, and C.

5   THE NOR GATE

The NOR gate, like the NAND gate, is a useful logic element because it can also be used as a universal gate; that is, NOR gates can be used in combination to perform the AND, OR, and inverter operations.

After completing this section, you should be able to

♦ Identify a NOR gate by its distinctive shape symbol or by its rectangular outline symbol

♦ Describe the operation of a NOR gate

♦ Develop the truth table for a NOR gate with any number of inputs

♦ Produce a timing diagram for a NOR gate with any specified input waveforms

♦ Write the logic expression for a NOR gate with any number of inputs

♦ Describe NOR gate operation in terms of its negative-AND equivalent

♦ Discuss examples of NOR gate applications

The term *NOR* is a contraction of NOT-OR and implies an OR function with an inverted (complemented) output. The standard logic symbol for a 2-input NOR gate and its equivalent OR gate followed by an inverter are shown in Figure 34(a). A rectangular outline symbol is shown in part (b).

The NOR is the same as the OR except the output is inverted.

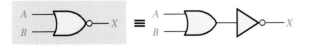 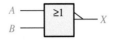

◀ FIGURE 34

Standard NOR gate logic symbols (ANSI/IEEE Std. 91-1984).

(a) Distinctive shape, 2-input NOR gate and its NOT/OR equivalent

(b) Rectangular outline, 2-input NOR gate with polarity indicator

Operation of a NOR Gate

A **NOR gate** produces a LOW output when *any* of its inputs is HIGH. Only when all of its inputs are LOW is the output HIGH. For the specific case of a 2-input NOR gate, as shown in Figure 34 with the inputs labeled A and B and the output labeled X, the operation can be stated as follows:

> **For a 2-input NOR gate, output X is LOW when either input A or input B is HIGH, or when both A and B are HIGH; X is HIGH only when both A and B are LOW.**

This operation results in an output level opposite that of the OR gate. In a NOR gate, the LOW output is the active or asserted output level as indicated by the bubble on the output. Figure 35 illustrates the operation of a 2-input NOR gate for all four possible input combinations, and Table 9 is the truth table for a 2-input NOR gate.

▼ TABLE 9

Truth table for a 2-input NOR gate.

INPUTS		OUTPUT
A	B	X
0	0	1
0	1	0
1	0	0
1	1	0

1 = HIGH, 0 = LOW.

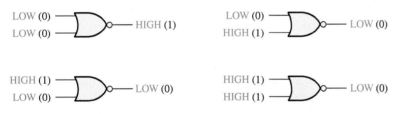

LOW (0) / LOW (0) → HIGH (1)

LOW (0) / HIGH (1) → LOW (0)

HIGH (1) / LOW (0) → LOW (0)

HIGH (1) / HIGH (1) → LOW (0)

▲ FIGURE 35

Operation of a 2-input NOR gate. Open file F03-35 to verify NOR gate operation.

Operation with Waveform Inputs

The next two examples illustrate the operation of a NOR gate with pulse waveform inputs. Again, as with the other types of gates, we will simply follow the truth table operation to determine the output waveforms in the proper time relationship to the inputs.

EXAMPLE 15

If the two waveforms shown in Figure 36 are applied to a NOR gate, what is the resulting output waveform?

▶ FIGURE 36

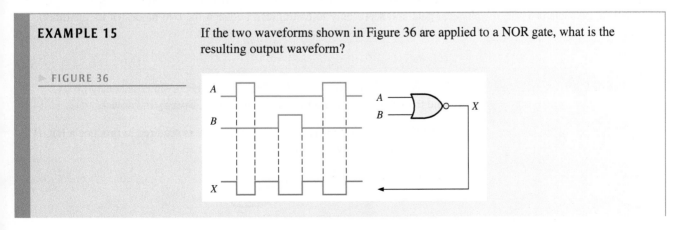

Solution Whenever any input of the NOR gate is HIGH, the output is LOW as shown by the output waveform X in the timing diagram.

Related Problem Invert input B and determine the output waveform in relation to the inputs.

EXAMPLE 16

Show the output waveform for the 3-input NOR gate in Figure 37 with the proper time relation to the inputs.

▶ FIGURE 37

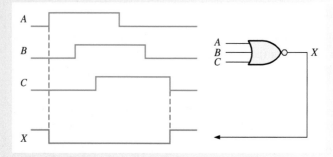

Solution The output X is LOW when any input is HIGH as shown by the output waveform X in the timing diagram.

Related Problem With the B and C inputs inverted, determine the output and show the timing diagram.

Negative-AND Equivalent Operation of the NOR Gate A NOR gate, like the NAND, has another aspect of its operation that is inherent in the way it logically functions. Table 9 shows that a HIGH is produced on the gate output only when all of the inputs are LOW. From this viewpoint, a NOR gate can be used for an AND operation that requires all LOW inputs to produce a HIGH output. This aspect of NOR operation is called **negative-AND.** The term *negative* in this context means that the inputs are defined to be in the active or asserted state when LOW.

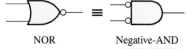

NOR   Negative-AND

▲ FIGURE 38

Standard symbols representing the two equivalent operations of a NOR gate.

For a 2-input NOR gate performing a negative-AND operation, output X is HIGH only when both inputs A and B are LOW.

When a NOR gate is used to detect all LOWs on its inputs rather than one or more HIGHs, it is performing the negative-AND operation and is represented by the standard symbol in Figure 38. Remember that the two symbols in Figure 38 represent the same physical gate and serve only to distinguish between the two modes of its operation. The following three examples illustrate this

---

EXAMPLE 17

A device is needed to indicate when two LOW levels occur simultaneously on its inputs and to produce a HIGH output as an indication. Specify the device.

Solution A 2-input NOR gate operating as a negative-AND gate is required to produce a HIGH output when both inputs are LOW, as shown in Figure 39.

▶ FIGURE 39

Related Problem   A device is needed to indicate when one or two HIGH levels occur on its inputs and to produce a LOW output as an indication. Specify the device.

EXAMPLE 18

As part of an aircraft's functional monitoring system, a circuit is required to indicate the status of the landing gears prior to landing. A green LED display turns on if all three gears are properly extended when the "gear down" switch has been activated in preparation for landing. A red LED display turns on if any of the gears fail to extend properly prior to landing. When a landing gear is extended, its sensor produces a LOW voltage. When a landing gear is retracted, its sensor produces a HIGH voltage. Implement a circuit to meet this requirement.

Solution   Power is applied to the circuit only when the "gear down" switch is activated. Use a NOR gate for each of the two requirements as shown in Figure 40. One NOR gate operates as a negative-AND to detect a LOW from each of the three landing gear sensors. When all three of the gate inputs are LOW, the three landing gears are properly extended and the resulting HIGH output from the negative-AND gate turns on the green LED display. The other NOR gate operates as a NOR to detect if one or more of the landing gears remain retracted when the "gear down" switch is activated. When one or more of the landing gears remain retracted, the resulting HIGH from the sensor is detected by the NOR gate, which produces a LOW output to turn on the red LED warning display.

▶ FIGURE 40

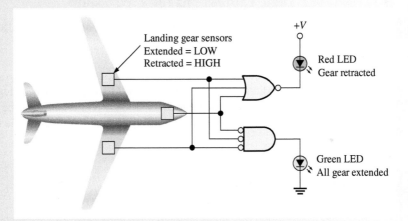

Related Problem   What type of gate should be used to detect if all three landing gears are retracted after takeoff, assuming a LOW output is required to activate an LED display?

Hands-On Tip

When driving a load such as an LED with a logic gate, consult the manufacturer's data sheet for maximum drive capabilities (output current). A regular IC logic gate may not be capable of handling the current required by certain loads such as some LEDs. Logic gates with a buffered output, such as an open-collector (OC) or open-drain (OD) output, are available in many types of IC logic gate configurations. The output current capability of typical IC logic gates is limited to the μA or relatively low mA range. For example, standard TTL can handle output currents up to 16 mA but only when the output is LOW. Most LEDs require currents in the range of about 10 mA to 50 mA.

EXAMPLE 19

For the 4-input NOR gate operating as a negative-AND in Figure 41, determine the output relative to the inputs.

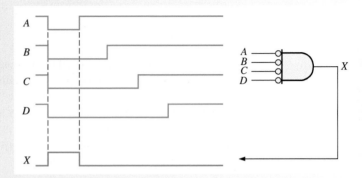

▲ FIGURE 41

Solution   Any time all of the input waveforms are LOW, the output is HIGH as shown by output waveform *X* in the timing diagram.

Related Problem   Determine the output with input *D* inverted and show the timing diagram.

▼ TABLE 10

A	*B*	$A + B = X$
0	0	$\overline{0 + 0} = \overline{0} = 1$
0	1	$\overline{0 + 1} = \overline{1} = 0$
1	0	$\overline{1 + 0} = \overline{1} = 0$
1	1	$\overline{1 + 1} = \overline{1} = 0$

Logic Expressions for a NOR Gate

The Boolean expression for the output of a 2-input NOR gate can be written as

$$X = \overline{A + B}$$

This equation says that the two input variables are first ORed and then complemented, as indicated by the bar over the OR expression. Evaluating this expression, you get the results shown in Table 10. The NOR expression can be extended to more than two input variables by including additional letters to represent the other variables.

SECTION 5
CHECKUP

1. When is the output of a NOR gate HIGH?
2. When is the output of a NOR gate LOW?
3. Describe the functional difference between a NOR gate and a negative-AND gate. Do they both have the same truth table?
4. Write the output expression for a 3-input NOR with input variables *A*, *B*, and *C*.

6   THE EXCLUSIVE-OR AND EXCLUSIVE-NOR GATES

Exclusive-OR and exclusive-NOR gates are formed by a combination of other gates already discussed. However, because of their fundamental importance in many applications, these gates are often treated as basic logic elements with their own unique symbols.

After completing this section, you should be able to

♦ Identify the exclusive-OR and exclusive-NOR gates by their distinctive shape symbols or by their rectangular outline symbols

- Describe the operations of exclusive-OR and exclusive-NOR gates
- Show the truth tables for exclusive-OR and exclusive-NOR gates
- Produce a timing diagram for an exclusive-OR or exclusive-NOR gate with any specified input waveforms
- Discuss examples of exclusive-OR and exclusive-NOR gate applications

The Exclusive-OR Gate

Standard symbols for an exclusive-OR (XOR for short) gate are shown in Figure 42. The XOR gate has only two inputs. The **exclusive-OR gate** performs modulo-2 addition. The output of an exclusive-OR gate is HIGH *only* when the two inputs are at opposite logic levels. This operation can be stated as follows with reference to inputs A and B and output X:

For an exclusive-OR gate, output X is HIGH when input A is LOW and input B is HIGH, or when input A is HIGH and input B is LOW; X is LOW when A and B are both HIGH or both LOW.

COMPUTER NOTE

Exclusive-OR gates connected to form an adder circuit allow a computer to perform addition, subtraction, multiplication, and division in its Arithmetic Logic Unit (ALU). An exclusive-OR gate combines basic AND, OR, and NOT logic.

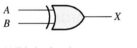
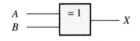

(a) Distinctive shape   (b) Rectangular outline

For an exclusive-OR gate, opposite inputs make the output HIGH.

▲ FIGURE 42

Standard logic symbols for the exclusive-OR gate.

The four possible input combinations and the resulting outputs for an XOR gate are illustrated in Figure 43. The HIGH level is the active or asserted output level and occurs only when the inputs are at opposite levels. The operation of an XOR gate is summarized in the truth table shown in Table 11.

▼ TABLE 11

Truth table for an exclusive-OR gate.

INPUTS		OUTPUT
A	B	X
0	0	0
0	1	1
1	0	1
1	1	0

▲ FIGURE 43

All possible logic levels for an exclusive-OR gate. Open file F03-43 to verify XOR gate operation.

EXAMPLE 20

A certain system contains two identical circuits operating in parallel. As long as both are operating properly, the outputs of both circuits are always the same. If one of the circuits fails, the outputs will be at opposite levels at some time. Devise a way to detect that a failure has occurred in one of the circuits.

Solution   The outputs of the circuits are connected to the inputs of an XOR gate as shown in Figure 44. A failure in either one of the circuits produces differing outputs, which

135

cause the XOR inputs to be at opposite levels. This condition produces a HIGH on the output of the XOR gate, indicating a failure in one of the circuits.

▶ FIGURE 44

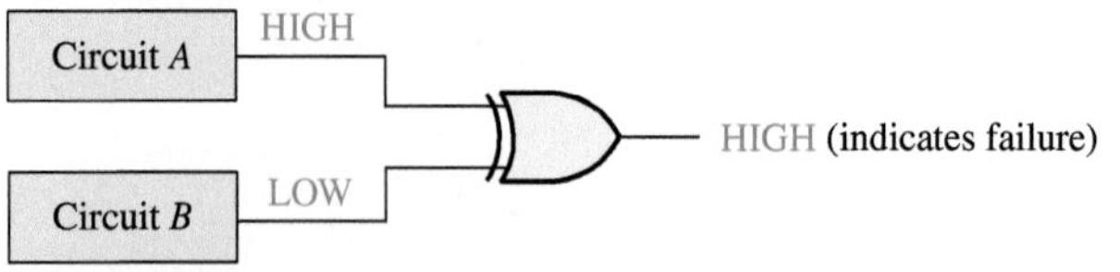

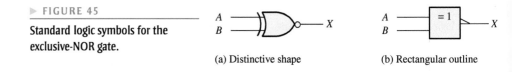

Related Problem   Will the exclusive-OR gate always detect simultaneous failures in both circuits of Figure 44? If not, under what condition?

The Exclusive-NOR Gate

Standard symbols for an **exclusive-NOR** (XNOR) **gate** are shown in Figure 45. Like the XOR gate, an XNOR has only two inputs. The bubble on the output of the XNOR symbol indicates that its output is opposite that of the XOR gate. When the two input logic levels are opposite, the output of the exclusive-NOR gate is LOW. The operation can be stated as follows (A and B are inputs, X is the output):

> **For an exclusive-NOR gate, output X is LOW when input A is LOW and input B is HIGH, or when A is HIGH and B is LOW; X is HIGH when A and B are both HIGH or both LOW.**

▶ FIGURE 45

Standard logic symbols for the exclusive-NOR gate.

(a) Distinctive shape   (b) Rectangular outline

▼ TABLE 12

Truth table for an exclusive-NOR gate.

INPUTS		OUTPUT
A	B	X
0	0	1
0	1	0
1	0	0
1	1	1

The four possible input combinations and the resulting outputs for an XNOR gate are shown in Figure 46. The operation of an XNOR gate is summarized in Table 12. Notice that the output is HIGH when the same level is on both inputs.

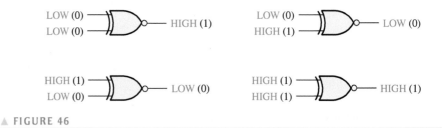

▲ FIGURE 46

All possible logic levels for an exclusive-NOR gate. Open file F03-46 to verify XNOR gate operation.

Operation with Waveform Inputs

As we have done with the other gates, let's examine the operation of XOR and XNOR gates with pulse waveform inputs. As before, we apply the truth table operation during each distinct time interval of the pulse waveform inputs, as illustrated in Figure 47 for an XOR gate. You can see that the input waveforms A and B are at opposite levels during time intervals t_2 and t_4. Therefore, the output X is HIGH during these two times. Since both inputs are at the same level, either both HIGH or both LOW, during time intervals t_1 and t_3, the output is LOW during those times as shown in the timing diagram.

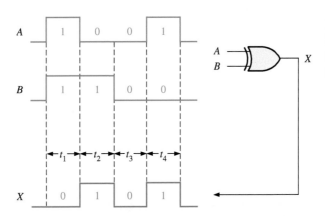

Example of exclusive-OR gate operation with pulse waveform inputs.

EXAMPLE 21

Determine the output waveforms for the XOR gate and for the XNOR gate, given the input waveforms, A and B, in Figure 48.

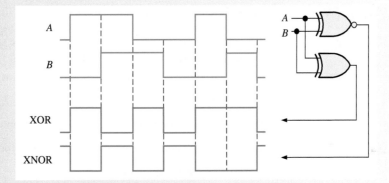

Solution The output waveforms are shown in Figure 48. Notice that the XOR output is HIGH only when both inputs are at opposite levels. Notice that the XNOR output is HIGH only when both inputs are the same.

Related Problem Determine the output waveforms if the two input waveforms, A and B, are inverted.

An Application

An exclusive-OR gate can be used as a two-bit modulo-2 adder. The basic rules for binary addition are as follows: $0 + 0 = 0$, $0 + 1 = 1$, $1 + 0 = 1$, and $1 + 1 = 10$. An examination of the truth table for an XOR gate shows that its output is the binary sum of the two input bits. In the case where the inputs are both 1s, the output is the sum 0, but you lose the carry of 1. Table 13 illustrates an XOR gate used as a modulo-2 adder. It is used in CRC systems to implement the division process.

▷ TABLE 13

An XOR gate used to add two bits.

| INPUT BITS | | OUTPUT (SUM) |
A	*B*	Σ
0	0	0
0	1	1
1	0	1
1	1	0 (without the 1 carry bit)

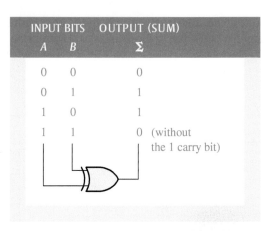

SECTION 6 CHECKUP

1. When is the output of an XOR gate HIGH?
2. When is the output of an XNOR gate HIGH?
3. How can you use an XOR gate to detect when two bits are different?

---

7 FIXED-FUNCTION LOGIC

Two major digital integrated circuit (IC) technologies that are used to implement logic gates are CMOS and bipolar (TTL). A third IC technology, BiCMOS, combines the two others. The logic operations of NOT, AND, OR, NAND, NOR, and exclusive-OR are the same regardless of the IC technology used; that is, an AND gate has the same logic function whether it is implemented with CMOS or bipolar.

After completing this section, you should be able to

* Identify the most common types of CMOS and bipolar devices
* Compare CMOS and bipolar in terms of device types and performance parameters
* Define *propagation delay time*
* Define *power dissipation*
* Define *fan-out*
* Define *speed-power product*
* Interpret basic data sheet information
* Define *unit load*

Logic Families

Three families of digital logic circuits are CMOS (complementary metal-oxide semiconductor), bipolar, and BiCMOS. They differ in the types of circuit components used internally to implement the logic function. **CMOS** is implemented with a type of field-effect transistor, **bipolar** (also known as **TTL**) logic uses bipolar junction transistors, and **BiCMOS** employs a combination of both. The logic families differ in operational parameters such as switching speed (propagation time), power consumption, and noise immunity but not in the basic logic operation. For example, a CMOS AND gate has the same logic operation as a bipolar or BiCMOS AND gate. This is true for all other logic functions.

138

CMOS Among the logic families, CMOS is the dominant one; bipolar logic appears to be on the decline, and BiCMOS is limited in the types of logic available. Within the CMOS family, there are many categories that vary in terms of supply voltage, power dissipation, switching speed, and other parameters. Table 14 lists the more common categories of CMOS logic in terms of circuit implementation and the optimized dc supply voltages for each.

Types of CMOS logic.

DESIGNATION	DESCRIPTION	V_{CC}
AC	Advanced CMOS	5.0 V
ACT	Advanced CMOS with bipolar (TTL) compatible inputs	5.0 V
AHC	Advanced high-speed CMOS	5.0 V
AHCT	Advanced high-speed CMOS with bipolar (TTL) compatible inputs	5.0 V
ALVC	Advanced low-voltage CMOS	3.3 V
AUC	Advanced ultra-low-voltage CMOS	1.8 V
AUP	Advanced ultra-low-power CMOS	3.3 V
AVC	Advanced very-low-voltage CMOS	2.5 V
CD4000	Standard CMOS	5.0 V
FCT	Fast CMOS technology	5.0 V
HC	High-speed CMOS	5.0 V
HCT	High-speed CMOS with bipolar (TTL) compatible inputs	5.0 V
LV-A	Low-voltage CMOS	3.3 V
LV-AT	Low-voltage CMOS with bipolar (TTL) compatible inputs	5.0 V
LVC	Low-voltage CMOS	3.3 V

Bipolar As with CMOS, the bipolar logic family has several categories that differ in various parameters. These categories are listed in Table 15, and all of them operate with a typical V_{CC} of 5 V.

◄ TABLE 15

Types of bipolar logic.

DESIGNATION	DESCRIPTION
ALS	Advanced low-power Schottky
AS	Advanced Schottky
F	Fast
LS	Low-power Schottky
S	Schottky
None	Standard TTL

BiCMOS Common categories in the BiCMOS logic family are shown in Table 16. All operate with a typical V_{CC} of 5 V.

◄ TABLE 16

Types of BiCMOS logic.

DESIGNATION	DESCRIPTION
ABT	Advanced BiCMOS
ALB	Advanced low-voltage BiCMOS
BCT	Standard BiCMOS
LVT	Low-voltage BiCMOS

Logic Gates

All of the basic logic operations, NOT, AND, OR, NAND, NOR, exclusive-OR (XOR), and exclusive-NOR (XNOR) are available in both CMOS and bipolar. In addition to these, buffered output gates are also available for driving loads that require high currents. The types of gate configurations typically available in IC packages are identified by the last two or three digits in the series designation. For example, 74LS04 is a low-power **Schottky** hex inverter package. Some of the common logic gate configurations and their standard identifier digits are as follows:

- Quad 2-input NAND—**00**
- Quad 2-input NOR—**02**
- Hex inverter—**04**
- Quad 2-input AND—**08**
- Triple 3-input NAND—**10**
- Triple 3-input AND—**11**

- Dual 4-input NAND—**20**
- Dual 2-input AND—**21**
- Triple 3-input NOR—**27**
- Single 8-input NAND—**30**
- Quad 2-input OR—**32**
- Quad XOR—**86**
- Quad XNOR—**266**

IC Packages All of the 74 series CMOS are pin-compatible with the same types of devices in bipolar. This means that a CMOS digital IC such as the 74HC00 (quad 2-input NAND), which contains four 2-input NAND gates in one IC package, has the identical package pin numbers for each input and output as does the corresponding bipolar device. Typical IC gate packages, the dual in-line package (DIP) for plug-in or feedthrough mounting and the small-outline integrated circuit (SOIC) package for surface mounting, are shown in Figure 49. In some cases, other types of packages are also available. The SOIC package is significantly smaller than the DIP. The pin configuration diagrams for most of the fixed-function logic devices listed above are shown in Figure 50.

Single-Gate Logic A limited selection of CMOS gates is available in single-gate packages. With one gate to a package, this series comes in tiny 5-pin packages that are intended for use in specialized applications and last-minute modifications for squeezing logic into tight spots where available space is limited.

Logic Symbols The logic symbols for fixed-function integrated circuits use the standard gate symbols and show the number of gates in the IC package and the associated pin numbers for each gate as well as the pin numbers for V_{CC} and ground. An example is shown in

Hands-On Tip

Handling Precautions for CMOS

CMOS logic is very sensitive to static charge and can be damaged by ESD (electrostatic discharge) if not handled properly as follows:

1. Store and ship in conductive foam.
2. Connect instruments to earth ground.
3. Connect wrist to earth ground through a large series resistor.
4. Do not remove devices from circuit with power on.
5. Do not apply signal voltage when power is off.

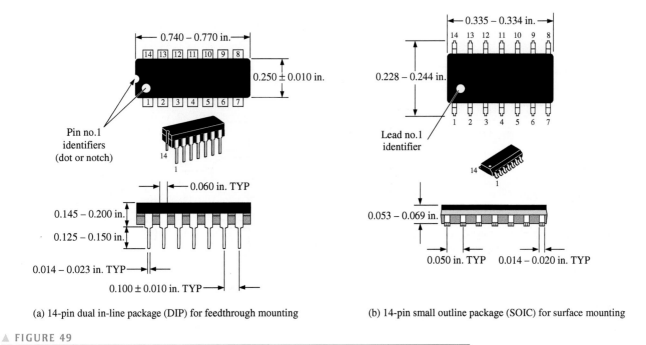

(a) 14-pin dual in-line package (DIP) for feedthrough mounting

(b) 14-pin small outline package (SOIC) for surface mounting

▲ FIGURE 49

Typical dual in-line (DIP) and small-outline (SOIC) packages showing pin numbers and basic dimensions.

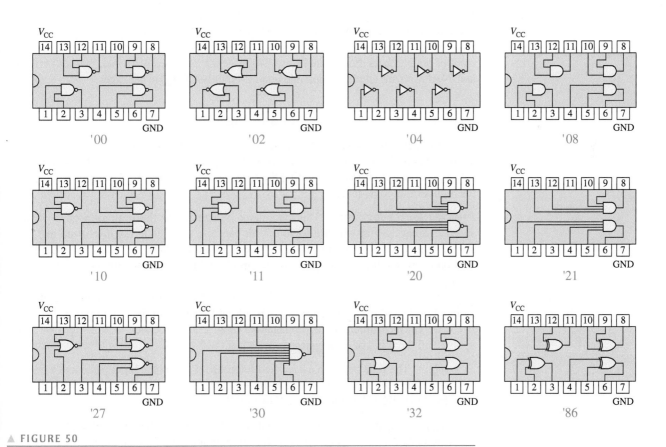

▲ FIGURE 50

Pin configuration diagrams for some common gate configurations.

141

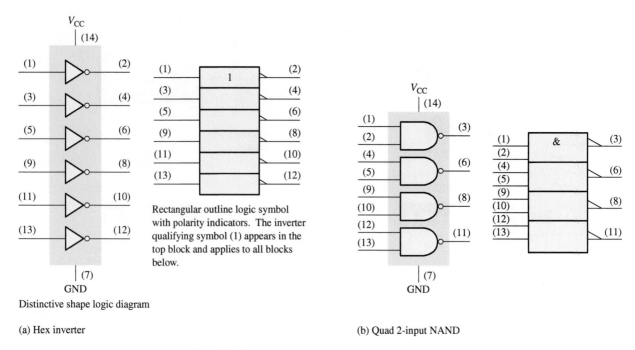

(a) Hex inverter

Distinctive shape logic diagram

Rectangular outline logic symbol with polarity indicators. The inverter qualifying symbol (1) appears in the top block and applies to all blocks below.

(b) Quad 2-input NAND

▲ FIGURE 51

Logic symbols for hex inverter (04 suffix) and quad 2-input NAND (00 suffix). The symbol applies to the same device in any CMOS or bipolar series.

Figure 51 for a hex inverter and for a quad 2-input NAND gate. Both the distinctive shape and the rectangular outline formats are shown. Regardless of the logic family, all devices with the same suffix are pin-compatible; in other words, they will have the same arrangement of pin numbers. For example, the 7400, 74S00, 74LS00, 74ALS00, 74F00, 74HC00, and 74AHC00 are all pin-compatible quad 2-input NAND gate packages.

Performance Characteristics and Parameters

High-speed logic has a short propagation delay time.

Several things define the performance of a logic circuit. These performance characteristics are the switching speed measured in terms of the propagation delay time, the power dissipation, the fan-out or drive capability, the speed-power product, the dc supply voltage, and the input/output logic levels.

Propagation Delay Time   This parameter is a result of the limitation on switching speed or frequency at which a logic circuit can operate. The terms *low speed* and *high speed,* applied to logic circuits, refer to the propagation delay time. The shorter the propagation delay, the higher the speed of the circuit and the higher the frequency at which it can operate.

Propagation delay time, t_P, of a logic gate is the time interval between the transition of an input pulse and the occurrence of the resulting transition of the output pulse. There are two different measurements of propagation delay time associated with a logic gate that apply to all the types of basic gates:

- t_{PHL}:   The time between a specified reference point on the input pulse and a corresponding reference point on the resulting output pulse, with the output changing from the HIGH level to the LOW level (HL).

- t_{PLH}:   The time between a specified reference point on the input pulse and a corresponding reference point on the resulting output pulse, with the output changing from the LOW level to the HIGH level (LH).

EXAMPLE 22

Show the propagation delay times of the inverter in Figure 52(a).

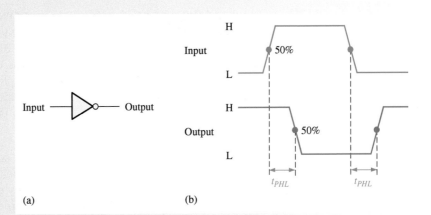

(a)   (b)

Solution   The propagation delay times, t_{PHL} and t_{PLH}, are indicated in part (b) of the figure. In this case, the delays are measured between the 50% points of the corresponding edges of the input and output pulses. The values of t_{PHL} and t_{PLH} are not necessarily equal but in many cases they are the same.

Related Problem   One type of logic gate has a specified maximum t_{PLH} and t_{PHL} of 10 ns. For another type of gate the value is 4 ns. Which gate can operate at the highest frequency?

For standard-series bipolar (TTL) gates, the typical propagation delay is 11 ns and for F-series gates it is 3.3 ns. For HCT-series CMOS, the propagation delay is 7 ns, for the AC series it is 5 ns, and for the ALVC series it is 3 ns. All specified values are dependent on certain operating conditions as stated on a data sheet.

DC Supply Voltage (V_{CC})   The typical dc supply voltage for CMOS logic is either 5 V, 3.3 V, 2.5 V, or 1.8 V, depending on the category. An advantage of CMOS is that the supply voltages can vary over a wider range than for bipolar logic. The 5 V CMOS can tolerate supply variations from 2 V to 6 V and still operate properly although propagation delay time and power dissipation are significantly affected. The 3.3 V CMOS can operate with supply voltages from 2 V to 3.6 V. The typical dc supply voltage for bipolar logic is 5.0 V with a minimum of 4.5 V and a maximum of 5.5 V.

Power Dissipation   The **power dissipation,** P_D, of a logic gate is the product of the dc supply voltage and the average supply current. Normally, the supply current when the gate output is LOW is greater than when the gate output is HIGH. The manufacturer's data sheet usually designates the supply current for the LOW output state as I_{CCL} and for the HIGH state as I_{CCH}. The average supply current is determined based on a 50% duty cycle (output LOW half the time and HIGH half the time), so the average power dissipation of a logic gate is

A lower power dissipation means less current from the dc supply.

$$P_D = V_{CC}\left(\frac{I_{CCH} + I_{CCL}}{2}\right)$$

Equation 2

CMOS gates have very low power dissipations compared to the bipolar family. However, the power dissipation of CMOS is dependent on the frequency of operation. At zero frequency the quiescent power is typically in the microwatt/gate range, and at the maximum operating frequency it can be in the low milliwatt range; therefore, power is sometimes specified at a given frequency. The HC series, for example, has a power of 2.75 μW/gate at 0 Hz (quiescent) and 600 μW/gate at 1 MHz.

Power dissipation for bipolar gates is independent of frequency. For example, the ALS series uses 1.4 mW/gate regardless of the frequency and the F series uses 6 mW/gate.

Input and Output Logic Levels V_{IL} is the LOW level input voltage for a logic gate, and V_{IH} is the HIGH level input voltage. The 5 V CMOS accepts a maximum voltage of 1.5 V as V_{IL} and a minimum voltage of 3.5 V as V_{IH}. Bipolar logic accepts a maximum voltage of 0.8 V as V_{IL} and a minimum voltage of 2 V as V_{IH}.

V_{OL} is the LOW level output voltage and V_{OH} is the HIGH level output voltage. For 5 V CMOS, the maximum V_{OL} is 0.33 V and the minimum V_{OH} is 4.4 V. For bipolar logic, the maximum V_{OL} is 0.4 V and the minimum V_{OH} is 2.4 V. All values depend on operating conditions as specified on the data sheet.

Speed-Power Product (SPP) This parameter (**speed-power product**) can be used as a measure of the performance of a logic circuit taking into account the propagation delay time and the power dissipation. It is especially useful for comparing the various logic gate series within the CMOS and bipolar families or for comparing a CMOS gate to a TTL gate.

The SPP of a logic circuit is the product of the propagation delay time and the power dissipation and is expressed in joules (J), which is the unit of energy. The formula is

Equation 3

$$SPP = t_p P_D$$

EXAMPLE 23

A certain gate has a propagation delay of 5 ns and $I_{CCH} = 1$ mA and $I_{CCL} = 2.5$ mA with a dc supply voltage of 5 V. Determine the speed-power product.

Solution

$$P_D = V_{CC}\left(\frac{I_{CCH} + I_{CCL}}{2}\right) = 5\text{ V}\left(\frac{1\text{ mA} + 2.5\text{ mA}}{2}\right) = 5\text{ V}(1.75\text{ mA}) = 8.75\text{ mW}$$

$$SPP = (5\text{ ns})(8.75\text{ mW}) = \textbf{43.75 pJ}$$

Related Problem If the propagation delay of a gate is 15 ns and its *SPP* is 150 pJ, what is its average power dissipation?

Fan-Out and Loading The **fan-out** of a logic gate is the maximum number of inputs of the same series in an IC family that can be connected to a gate's output and still maintain the output voltage levels within specified limits. Fan-out is a significant parameter only for bipolar logic because of the type of circuit technology. Since very high impedances are associated with CMOS circuits, the fan-out is very high but depends on frequency because of capacitive effects.

A higher fan-out means that a gate output can be connected to more gate inputs.

Fan-out is specified in terms of **unit loads.** A unit load for a logic gate equals one input to a like circuit. For example, a unit load for a 74LS00 NAND gate equals *one* input to another logic gate in the 74LS series (not necessarily a NAND gate). Because the current from a LOW input (I_{IL}) of a 74LS00 gate is 0.4 mA and the current that a LOW output (I_{OL}) can accept is 8.0 mA, the number of unit loads that a 74LS00 gate can drive in the LOW state is

$$\text{Unit loads} = \frac{I_{OL}}{I_{IL}} = \frac{8.0\text{ mA}}{0.4\text{ mA}} = 20$$

Figure 53 shows LS logic gates driving a number of other gates of the same circuit technology, where the number of gates depends on the particular circuit technology. For example, as you have seen, the maximum number of gate inputs (unit loads) that a 74LS series bipolar gate can drive is 20.

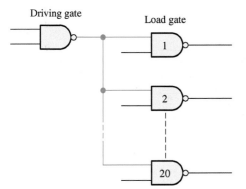

Driving gate

Load gate

◄ FIGURE 53

The LS series NAND gate output fans out to a maximum of 20 LS series gate inputs.

Data Sheets

A typical data sheet consists of an information page that shows, among other things, the logic diagram and packages, the recommended operating conditions, the electrical characteristics, and the switching characteristics. Partial data sheets for a 74LS00 and a 74HC00A are shown in Figures 54 and 55, respectively. The length of data sheets vary and some have much more information than others.

QUAD 2-INPUT NAND GATE

• ESD > 3500 Volts

SN54/74LS00

QUAD 2-INPUT NAND GATE
LOW POWER SCHOTTKY

J SUFFIX
CERAMIC
CASE 632-08

N SUFFIX
PLASTIC
CASE 646-06

D SUFFIX
SOIC
CASE 751A-02

ORDERING INFORMATION
SN54LSXXJ   Ceramic
SN74LSXXN   Plastic
SN74LSXXD   SOIC

SN54/74LS00

DC CHARACTERISTICS OVER OPERATING TEMPERATURE RANGE (unless otherwise specified)

Symbol	Parameter		Min	Typ	Max	Unit	Test Conditions
V_{IH}	Input HIGH Voltage		2.0			V	Guaranteed Input HIGH Voltage for All Inputs
V_{IL}	Input LOW Voltage	54			0.7	V	Guaranteed Input LOW Voltage for All Inputs
		74			0.8		
V_{IK}	Input Clamp Diode Voltage			−0.65	−1.5	V	V_{CC} = MIN, I_{IN} = −18 mA
V_{OH}	Ouput HIGH Voltage	54	2.5	3.5		V	V_{CC} = MIN, I_{OH} = MAX, V_{IN} = V_{IH} or V_{IL} per Truth Table
		74	2.7	3.5		V	
V_{OL}	Ouput LOW Voltage	54, 74		0.25	0.4	V	I_{OL} = 4.0 mA V_{CC} = V_{CC} MIN, V_{IN} = V_{IL}
		74		0.35	0.5	V	I_{OL} = 8.0 mA or V_{IH} per Truth Table
I_{IH}	Input HIGH Current				20	μA	V_{CC} = MAX, V_{IN} = 2.7 V
					0.1	mA	V_{CC} = MAX, V_{IN} = 7.0 V
I_{IL}	Input LOW Current				−0.4	mA	V_{CC} = MAX, I_{IN} = 0.4 V
I_{OS}	Short Circuit Current (Note 1)		−20		−100	mA	V_{CC} = MAX
I_{CC}	Power Supply Current Total, Output HIGH				1.6	mA	V_{CC} = MAX
	Total, Output LOW				4.4		

NOTE 1: Not more than one output should be shorted at a time, nor for more than 1 second.

AC CHARACTERISTICS (T_A = 25°C)

Symbol	Parameter		Min	Typ	Max	Unit	Test Conditions
t_{PLH}	Turn-Off Delay, Input to Output			9.0	15	ns	V_{CC} = 5.0 V
t_{PHL}	Turn-On Delay, Input to Output			10	15	ns	C_L = 15 pF

GUARANTEED OPERATING RANGES

Symbol	Parameter		Min	Typ	Max	Unit
V_{CC}	Supply Voltage	54	4.5	5.0	5.5	V
		74	4.75	5.0	5.25	
T_A	Operating Ambient Temperature Range	54	−55	25	125	°C
		74	0	25	70	
I_{OH}	Output Current — High	54, 74			−0.4	mA
I_{OL}	Output Current — Low	54			4.0	mA
		74			8.0	

▲ FIGURE 54

The partial data sheet for a 74LS00 quad 2-input NAND gate.

Quad 2-Input NAND Gate High-Performance Silicon–Gate CMOS

The MC54/74HC00A is identical in pinout to the LS00. The device inputs are compatible with Standard CMOS outputs; with pullup resistors, they are compatible with LSTTL outputs.

- Output Drive Capability: 10 LSTTL Loads
- Outputs Directly Interface to CMOS, NMOS and TTL
- Operating Voltage Range: 2 to 6 V
- Low Input Current: 1 μA
- High Noise Immunity Characteristic of CMOS Devices
- In Compliance With the JEDEC Standard No. 7A Requirements
- Chip Complexity: 32 FETs or 8 Equivalent Gates

LOGIC DIAGRAM

$Y = \overline{AB}$

PIN 14 = V_{CC}
PIN 7 = GND

Pinout: 14–Load Packages (Top View)

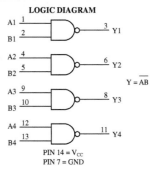

V_{CC}	B4	A4	Y4	B3	A3	Y3
14	13	12	11	10	9	8

1	2	3	4	5	6	7
A1	B1	Y1	A2	B2	Y2	GND

MC54/74HC00A

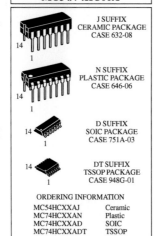

J SUFFIX
CERAMIC PACKAGE
CASE 632-08

N SUFFIX
PLASTIC PACKAGE
CASE 646-06

D SUFFIX
SOIC PACKAGE
CASE 751A-03

DT SUFFIX
TSSOP PACKAGE
CASE 948G-01

ORDERING INFORMATION

MC54HCXXAJ	Ceramic
MC74HCXXAN	Plastic
MC74HCXXAD	SOIC
MC74HCXXADT	TSSOP

FUNCTION TABLE

Inputs		Output
A	B	Y
L	L	H
L	H	H
H	L	H
H	H	L

MAXIMUM RATINGS*

Symbol	Parameter	Value	Unit
V_{CC}	DC Supply Voltage (Referenced to GND)	–0.5 to + 7.0	V
V_{in}	DC Input Voltage (Referenced to GND)	–0.5 to V_{CC} + 0.5	V
V_{out}	DC Output Voltage (Referenced to GND)	–0.5 to V_{CC} + 0.5	V
I_{in}	DC Input Current, per Pin	± 20	mA
I_{out}	DC Output Current, per Pin	± 25	mA
I_{CC}	DC Supply Current, V_{CC} and GND Pins	± 50	mA
P_D	Power Dissipation in Still Air, Plastic or Ceramic DIP†	750	mW
	SOIC Package†	500	
	TSSOP Package†	450	
T_{stg}	Storage Temperature	–65 to + 150	°C
T_L	Lead Temperature, 1 mm from Case for 10 Seconds		°C
	Plastic DIP, SOIC or TSSOP Package	260	
	Ceramic DIP	300	

* Maximum Ratings are those values beyond which damage to the device may occur. Functional operation should be restricted to the Recommended Operating Conditions.
† Derating — Plastic DIP: – 10 mW/°C from 65° to 125° C
Ceramic DIP: – 10 mW/°C from 100° to 125° C
SOIC Package: – 7 mW/°C from 65° to 125° C
TSSOP Package: – 6.1 mW/°C from 65° to 125° C

RECOMMENDED OPERATING CONDITIONS

Symbol	Parameter		in	Max	Unit
V_{CC}	DC Supply Voltage (Referenced to GND)		2.0	6.0	V
V_{in}, V_{out}	DC Input Voltage, Output Voltage (Referenced to GND)		0	V_{CC}	V
T_A	Operating Temperature, All Package Types		–55	+125	°C
t_r, t_f	Input Rise and Fall Time	V_{CC} = 2.0 V	0	1000	ns
		V_{CC} = 4.5 V	0	500	
		V_{CC} = 6.0 V	0	400	

DC CHARACTERISTICS (Voltages Referenced to GND)

MC54/74HC00A

Symbol	Parameter	Condition	V_{CC} V	Guaranteed Limit			Unit
				–55 to 25°C	≤85°C	≤125°C	
V_{IH}	Minimum High-Level Input Voltage	V_{out} = 0.1V or V_{CC} – 0.1V $|I_{out}|$ ≤ 20μA	2.0	1.50	1.50	1.50	V
			3.0	2.10	2.10	2.10	
			4.5	3.15	3.15	3.15	
			6.0	4.20	4.20	4.20	
V_{IL}	Maximum Low-Level Input Voltage	V_{out} = 0.1V or V_{CC} – 0.1V $|I_{out}|$ ≤ 20μA	2.0	0.50	0.50	0.50	V
			3.0	0.90	0.90	0.90	
			4.5	1.35	1.35	1.35	
			6.0	1.80	1.80	1.80	
V_{OH}	Minimum High-Level Output Voltage	V_{in} = V_{IH} or V_{IL} $|I_{out}|$ ≤ 20μA	2.0	1.9	1.9	1.9	V
			4.5	4.4	4.4	4.4	
			6.0	5.9	5.9	5.9	
		V_{in} = V_{IH} or V_{IL} $|I_{out}|$ ≤2.4mA	3.0	2.48	2.34	2.20	
		$|I_{out}|$ ≤4.0mA	4.5	3.98	3.84	3.70	
		$|I_{out}|$ ≤5.2mA	6.0	5.48	5.34	5.20	
V_{OL}	Maximum Low-Level Output Voltage	V_{in} = V_{IH} or V_{IL} $|I_{out}|$ ≤ 20μA	2.0	0.1	0.1	0.1	V
			4.5	0.1	0.1	0.1	
			6.0	0.1	0.1	0.1	
		V_{in} = V_{IH} or V_{IL} $|I_{out}|$ ≤2.4mA	3.0	0.26	0.33	0.40	
		$|I_{out}|$ ≤4.0mA	4.5	0.26	0.33	0.40	
		$|I_{out}|$ ≤5.2mA	6.0	0.26	0.33	0.40	
I_{in}	Maximum Input Leakage Current	V_{in} = V_{CC} or GND	6.0	±0.1	±1.0	±1.0	μA
I_{CC}	Maximum Quiescent Supply Current (per Package)	V_{in} = V_{CC} or GND I_{out} = 0μA	6.0	1.0	10	40	μA

AC CHARACTERISTICS (C_L = 50 pF, Input t_r = t_f = 6 ns)

Symbol	Parameter	V_{CC} V	Guaranteed Limit			Unit
			–55 to 25°C	≤85°C	≤125°C	
t_{PLH}, t_{PHL}	Maximum Propagation Delay, Input A or B to Output Y	2.0	75	95	110	ns
		3.0	30	40	55	
		4.5	15	19	22	
		6.0	13	16	19	
t_{TLH}, t_{THL}	Maximum Output Transition Time, Any Output	2.0	75	95	110	ns
		3.0	27	32	36	
		4.5	15	19	22	
		6.0	13	16	19	
C_{in}	Maximum Input Capacitance		10	10	10	pF

		Typical @ 25°C, V_{CC} = 5.0 V, V_{EE} = 0 V	
C_{PD}	Power Dissipation Capacitance (Per Buffer)	22	pF

▲ FIGURE 55

The partial data sheet for a 74HC00A quad 2-input NAND gate.

Hands-On Tip

Unused gate inputs for bipolar (TTL) and CMOS should be connected to the appropriate logic level (HIGH or LOW). For AND/NAND, it is recommended that unused inputs be connected to V_{CC} (through a 1.0 kΩ resistor with bipolar) and for OR/NOR, unused inputs should be connected to ground.

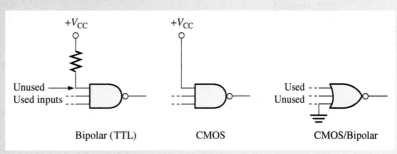

Bipolar (TTL)   CMOS   CMOS/Bipolar

SECTION 7 CHECKUP

1. List the two types of IC technologies that are the most widely used.

2. Identify the following IC logic designators:
   (a) LS   (b) ALS   (c) F   (d) HC   (e) AC   (f) HCT   (g) LV

3. Identify the following devices according to logic function:
   (a) 74LS04   (b) 74HC00   (c) 74ALS10
   (d) 7432   (e) 74ACT11   (f) 74AHC02

4. Which IC technology generally has the lowest power dissipation?

5. What does the term *hex inverter* mean? What does *quad 2-input NAND* mean?

6. A positive pulse is applied to an inverter input. The time from the leading edge of the input to the leading edge of the output is 10 ns. The time from the trailing edge of the input to the trailing edge of the output is 8 ns. What are the values of t_{PLH} and t_{PHL}?

7. A certain gate has a propagation delay time of 6 ns and a power dissipation of 3 mW. Determine the speed-power product?

8. Define I_{CCL} and I_{CCH}.

9. Define V_{IL} and V_{IH}.

10. Define V_{OL} and V_{OH}.

8   TROUBLESHOOTING

Troubleshooting is the process of recognizing, isolating, and correcting a fault or failure in a circuit or system. To be an effective troubleshooter, you must understand how the circuit or system is supposed to work and be able to recognize incorrect performance. For example, to determine whether or not a certain logic gate is faulty, you must know what the output should be for given inputs.

After completing this section, you should be able to

- ◆ Test for internally open inputs and outputs in IC gates
- ◆ Recognize the effects of a shorted IC input or output
- ◆ Test for external faults on a PC board
- ◆ Troubleshoot a simple frequency counter using an oscillosope

Internal Failures of IC Logic Gates

Opens and shorts are the most common types of internal gate failures. These can occur on the inputs or on the output of a gate inside the IC package. *Before attempting any troubleshooting, check for proper dc supply voltage and ground.*

Effects of an Internally Open Input   An internal open is the result of an open component on the chip or a break in the tiny wire connecting the IC chip to the package pin. An open input prevents a signal on that input from getting to the output of the gate, as illustrated in Figure 56(a) for the case of a 2-input NAND gate. An open TTL (bipolar) input acts effectively as a HIGH level, so pulses applied to the good input get through to the NAND gate output as shown in Figure 56(b).

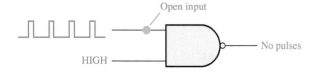

(a) Application of pulses to the open input will produce no pulses on the output.

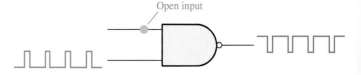

(b) Application of pulses to the good input will produce output pulses for bipolar NAND and AND gates because an open input typically acts as a HIGH. It is uncertain for CMOS.

▲ FIGURE 56

The effect of an open input on a NAND gate.

Conditions for Testing Gates   When testing a NAND gate or an AND gate, always make sure that the inputs that are not being pulsed are HIGH to enable the gate. When checking a NOR gate or an OR gate, always make sure that the inputs that are not being pulsed are LOW. When checking an XOR or XNOR gate, the level of the nonpulsed input does not matter because the pulses on the other input will force the inputs to alternate between the same level and opposite levels.

Troubleshooting an Open Input   Troubleshooting this type of failure is easily accomplished with an oscilloscope and function generator, as demonstrated in Figure 57 for the case of a 2-input NAND gate package. When measuring digital signals with a scope, always use dc coupling.

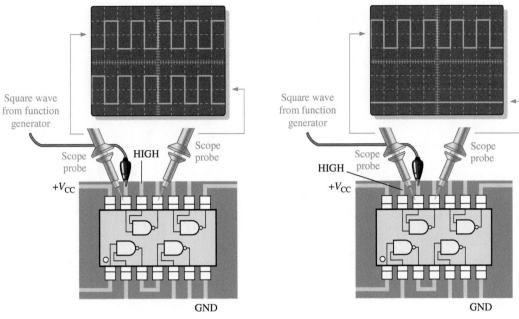

(a) Pin 13 input and pin 11 output OK   (b) Pin 12 input is open.

▲ FIGURE 57

Troubleshooting a NAND gate for an open input.

The first step in troubleshooting an IC that is suspected of being faulty is to make sure that the dc supply voltage (V_{CC}) and ground are at the appropriate pins of the IC. Next, apply continuous pulses to one of the inputs to the gate, making sure that the other input is HIGH (in the case of a NAND gate). In Figure 57(a), start by applying a pulse waveform to pin 13, which is one of the inputs to the suspected gate. If a pulse waveform is indicated on the output (pin 11 in this case), then the pin 13 input is not open. By the way, this also proves that the output is not open. Next, apply the pulse waveform to the other gate input (pin 12), making sure the other input is HIGH. There is no pulse waveform on the output at pin 11 and the output is LOW, indicating that the pin 12 input is open, as shown in Figure 57(b). The input not being pulsed must be HIGH for the case of a NAND gate or AND gate. If this were a NOR gate, the input not being pulsed would have to be LOW.

Effects of an Internally Open Output An internally open gate output prevents a signal on any of the inputs from getting to the output. Therefore, no matter what the input conditions are, the output is unaffected. The level at the output pin of the IC will depend upon what it is externally connected to. It could be either HIGH, LOW, or floating (not fixed to any reference). In any case, there will be no signal on the output pin.

Troubleshooting an Open Output Figure 58 illustrates troubleshooting an open NOR gate output. In part (a), one of the inputs of the suspected gate (pin 11 in this case) is pulsed, and the output (pin 13) has no pulse waveform. In part (b), the other input (pin 12) is pulsed and again there is no pulse waveform on the output. Under the condition that the input that is not being pulsed is at a LOW level, this test shows that the output is internally open.

Shorted Input or Output Although not as common as an open, an internal short to the dc supply voltage, ground, another input, or an output can occur. When an input or output is shorted to the supply voltage, it will be stuck in the HIGH state. If an input or output is shorted to ground, it will be stuck in the LOW state (0 V). If two inputs or an input and an output are shorted together, they will always be at the same level.

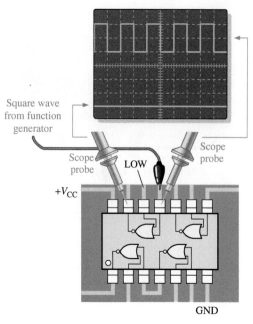

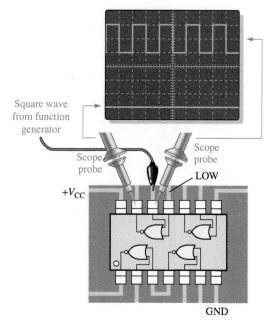

(a) Pulse input on pin 11. No pulse output.

(b) Pulse input on pin 12. No pulse output.

▲ FIGURE 58

Troubleshooting a NOR gate for an open output.

External Opens and Shorts

Many failures involving digital ICs are due to faults that are external to the IC package. These include bad solder connections, solder splashes, wire clippings, improperly etched printed circuit (PC) boards, and cracks or breaks in wires or printed circuit interconnections. These open or shorted conditions have the same effect on the logic gate as the internal faults, and troubleshooting is done in basically the same ways. A visual inspection of any circuit that is suspected of being faulty is the first thing a technician should do.

EXAMPLE 24	You are checking a 74LS10 triple 3-input NAND gate IC that is one of many ICs located on a PC board. You have checked pins 1 and 2 and they are both HIGH. Now you apply a pulse waveform to pin 13, and place your scope probe first on pin 12 and then on the connecting PC board trace, as indicated in Figure 59. Based on your observation of the scope screen, what is the most likely problem?
Solution	The waveform with the probe in position 1 shows that there is pulse activity on the gate output at pin 12, but there are no pulses on the PC board trace as indicated by the probe in position 2. The gate is working properly, but the signal is not getting from pin 12 of the IC to the PC board trace.
	Most likely there is a bad solder connection between pin 12 of the IC and the PC board, which is creating an open. You should resolder that point and check it again.
Related Problem	If there are no pulses at either probe position 1 or 2 in Figure 59, what fault(s) does this indicate?

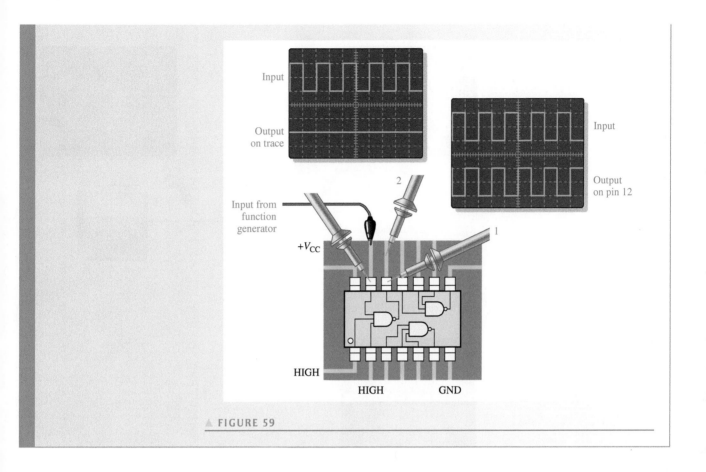

▲ FIGURE 59

In most cases, you will be troubleshooting ICs that are mounted on PC boards or proto-type assemblies and interconnected with other ICs. As you progress through this book, you will learn how different types of digital ICs are used together to perform system functions. At this point, however, we are concentrating on individual IC gates. This limitation does not prevent us from looking at the system concept at a very basic and simplified level.

To continue the emphasis on systems, Examples 25 and 26 deal with troubleshooting the frequency counter that was introduced in Section 2.

EXAMPLE 25

After trying to operate the frequency counter shown in Figure 60, you find that it con-stantly reads out all 0s on its display, regardless of the input frequency. Determine the cause of this malfunction. The enable pulse has a width of 1 ms.

Figure 60(a) gives an example of how the frequency counter should be working with a 12 kHz pulse waveform on the input to the AND gate. Part (b) shows that the display is improperly indicating 0 Hz.

Solution Three possible causes are

1. A constant active or asserted level on the counter reset input, which keeps the counter at zero.

2. No pulse signal on the input to the counter because of an internal open or short in the counter. This problem would keep the counter from advancing after being reset to zero.

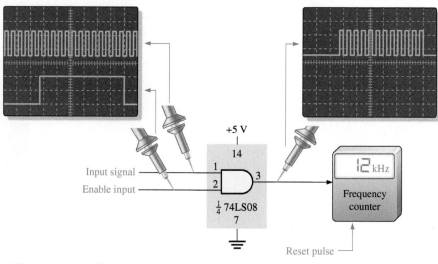

(a) The counter is working properly.

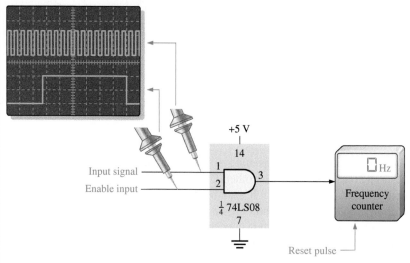

(b) The counter is not measuring a frequency.

▲ FIGURE 60

3. No pulse signal on the input to the counter because of an open AND gate output or the absence of input signals, again keeping the counter from advancing from zero.

The first step is to make sure that V_{CC} and ground are connected to all the right places; assume that they are found to be okay. Next, check for pulses on both inputs to the AND gate. The scope indicates that there are proper pulses on both of these inputs. A check of the counter reset shows a LOW level which is known to be the unasserted level and, therefore, this is not the problem. The next check on pin 3 of the 74LS08 shows that there are no pulses on the output of the AND gate, indicating that the gate output is open. Replace the 74LS08 IC and check the operation again.

Related Problem   If pin 2 of the 74LS08 AND gate is open, what indication should you see on the frequency display?

EXAMPLE 26

The frequency counter shown in Figure 61 appears to measure the frequency of input signals incorrectly. It is found that when a signal with a precisely known frequency is applied to pin 1 of the AND gate, the oscilloscope display indicates a higher frequency. Determine what is wrong. The readings on the screen indicate time per division.

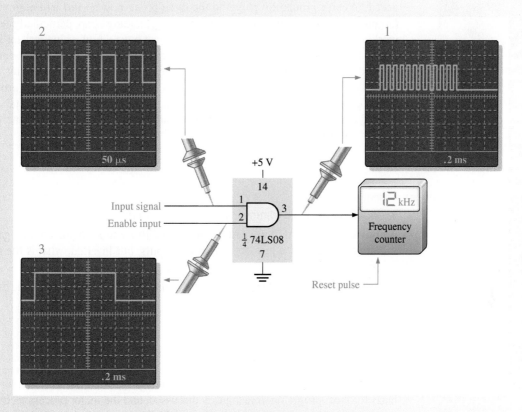

▲ FIGURE 61

Solution   Recall from Section 2 that the input pulses were allowed to pass through the AND gate for exactly 1 ms. The number of pulses counted in 1 ms is equal to the frequency in hertz. Therefore, the 1 ms interval, which is produced by the enable pulse on pin 2 of the AND gate, is very critical to an accurate frequency measurement. The enable pulses are produced internally by a precision oscillator circuit. The pulse must be exactly 1 ms in width and in this case it occurs every 3 ms to update the count. Just prior to each enable pulse, the counter is reset to zero so that it starts a new count each time.

Since the counter appears to be counting more pulses than it should to produce a frequency readout that is too high, the enable pulse is the primary suspect. Exact time-interval measurements must be made on the oscilloscope.

An input pulse waveform of exactly 10 kHz is applied to pin 1 of the AND gate and the frequency counter incorrectly shows 12 kHz. The first scope measurement, on the output of the AND gate, shows that there are 12 pulses for each enable pulse. In the second scope measurement, the input frequency is verified to be precisely 10 kHz (period = 100 μs). In the third scope measurement, the width of the enable pulse is found to be 1.2 ms rather than 1 ms.

The conclusion is that the enable pulse is out of calibration for some reason.

Related Problem   What would you suspect if the readout were indicating a frequency less than it should be?

Hands-On Tip

Proper grounding is very important when setting up to take measurements or work on a circuit. Properly grounding the oscilloscope protects you from shock and grounding yourself protects your circuits from damage. Grounding the oscilloscope means to connect it to earth ground by plugging the three-prong power cord into a grounded outlet. Grounding yourself means using a wrist-type grounding strap, particularly when you are working with CMOS logic. The wrist strap must have a high-value resistor between the strap and ground for protection against accidental contact with a voltage source.

Also, for accurate measurements, make sure that the ground in the circuit you are testing is the same as the scope ground. This can be done by connecting the ground lead on the scope probe to a known ground point in the circuit, such as the metal chassis or a ground point on the circuit board. You can also connect the circuit ground to the GND jack on the front panel of the scope.

SECTION 8 CHECKUP

1. What are the most common types of failures in ICs?
2. If two different input waveforms are applied to a 2-input bipolar NAND gate and the output waveform is just like one of the inputs, but inverted, what is the most likely problem?
3. Name two characteristics of pulse waveforms that can be measured on the oscilloscope.

9   PROGRAMMABLE LOGIC

In this section, the basic concept of the programmable AND array, which forms the basis for most programmable logic, is discussed, and the major process technologies are covered. A programmable logic device (PLD) is one that does not initially have a fixed-logic function but that can be programmed to implement just about any logic design. As you have learned, two types of PLD are the SPLD and CPLD. In addition to the PLD, the other major category of programmable logic is the FPGA. For simplicity, all of these devices will be referred to as PLDs. Also, some important concepts in programming are discussed.

After completing this section, you should be able to

- Describe the concept of a programmable AND array
- Discuss various process technologies
- Discuss downloading a design to a programmable logic device
- Discuss text entry and graphic entry as two methods for programmable logic design
- Explain in-system programming

Basic Concept of the AND Array

Most types of PLDs use some form of **AND array.** Basically, this array consists of AND gates and a matrix of interconnections with programmable links at each cross point, as shown in Figure 62(a). The purpose of the programmable links is to either make or break a connection between a row line and a column line in the interconnection matrix. For each input to an AND gate, only one programmable link is left intact in order to connect the desired variable to the gate input. Figure 62(b) illustrates an array after it has been programmed.

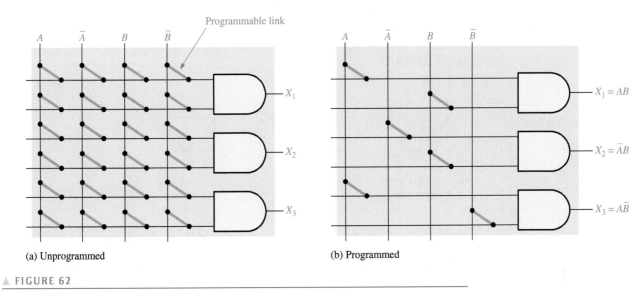

(a) Unprogrammed   (b) Programmed

▲ FIGURE 62

Basic concept of a programmable AND array.

EXAMPLE 27

Show the AND array in Figure 62(a) programmed for the following outputs:
$X_1 = A\bar{B}$, $X_2 = \bar{A}B$, and $X_3 = \bar{A}\bar{B}$

Solution   See Figure 63.

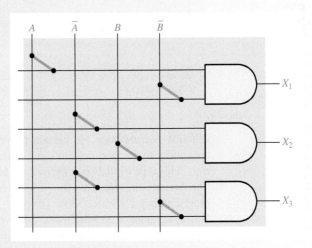

▲ FIGURE 63

Related Problem   How many rows, columns, and AND gate inputs are required for three input variables in a 3-AND gate array?

Programmable Link Process Technologies

Several different process technologies are used for programmable links in PLDs.

Fuse Technology This was the original programmable link technology. It is still used in some SPLDs. The **fuse** is a metal link that connects a row and a column in the interconnection matrix. Before programming, there is a fused connection at each intersection. To program a device, the selected fuses are opened by passing a current through them sufficient to "blow" the fuse and break the connection. The intact fuses remain and provide a connection between the rows and columns. The fuse link is illustrated in Figure 64. Programmable logic devices that use fuse technology are one-time programmable (**OTP**).

The programmable fuse link.

(a) Fuse intact before
programming

(b) Programming
current

(c) Fuse open after
programming

Antifuse Technology An **antifuse** programmable link is the opposite of a fuse link. Instead of breaking the connection, a connection is made during programming. An antifuse starts out as an open circuit whereas the fuse starts out as a short circuit. Before programming, there are no connections between the rows and columns in the interconnection matrix. An antifuse is basically two conductors separated by an insulator. To program a device with antifuse technology, a programmer tool applies a sufficient voltage across selected antifuses to break down the insulation between the two conductive materials, causing the insulator to become a low-resistance link. The antifuse link is illustrated in Figure 65. An antifuse device is also a one-time programmable (OTP) device.

The programmable antifuse link.

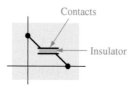

(a) Antifuse is open before
programming.

(b) Programming voltage
breaks down insulation
layer to create contact.

(c) Antifuse is effectively
shorted after programming.

EPROM Technology In certain programmable logic devices, the programmable links are similar to the memory cells in **EPROMs** (electrically programmable read-only memories). This type of PLD is programmed using a special tool known as a device programmer. The device is inserted into the programmer, which is connected to a computer running the programming software. Most EPROM-based PLDs are one-time programmable (OTP). However, those with windowed packages can be erased with UV (ultraviolet) light and reprogrammed using a standard PLD programming fixture. EPROM process technology uses a special type of MOS transistor, known as a floating-gate transistor, as the programmable link. The floating-gate device utilizes a process called Fowler-Nordheim tunneling to place electrons in the floating-gate structure.

In a programmable AND array, the floating-gate transistor acts as a switch to connect the row line to either a HIGH or a LOW, depending on the input variable. For input variables that are not used, the transistor is programmed to be permanently *off* (open).

Figure 66 shows one AND gate in a simple array. Variable *A* controls the state of the transistor in the first column, and variable *B* controls the transistor in the third column. When a transistor is *off,* like an open switch, the input line to the AND gate is at $+V$ (HIGH). When a transistor is *on,* like a closed switch, the input line is connected to ground (LOW). When variable *A* or *B* is 0 (LOW), the transistor is *on,* keeping the input line to the AND gate LOW. When *A* or *B* is 1 (HIGH), the transistor is *off,* keeping the input line to the AND gate HIGH.

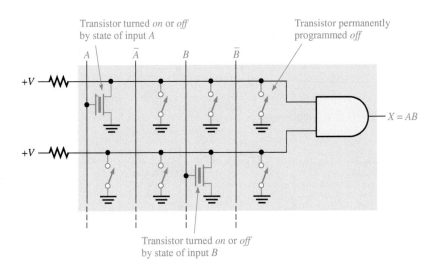

◀ FIGURE 66

A simple AND array with EPROM technology. Only one gate in the array is shown for simplicity.

EEPROM Technology   Electrically erasable programmable read-only memory technology is similar to EPROM because it also uses a type of floating-gate transistor in E^2CMOS cells. The difference is that **EEPROM** can be erased and reprogrammed electrically without the need for UV light or special fixtures. An E^2CMOS device can be programmed after being installed on a printed circuit board, and many can be reprogrammed while operating in a system. This is called **in-system programming (ISP).** Figure 66 can also be used as an example to represent an AND array with EEPROM technology.

Flash Technology   **Flash** technology is based on a single transistor link and is both nonvolatile and reprogrammable. Flash elements are a type of EEPROM but are faster and result in higher density devices than the standard EEPROM link.

SRAM Technology   Many FPGAs and some CPLDs use a process technology similar to that used in **SRAMs** (static random-access memories). The basic concept of SRAM-based programmable logic arrays is illustrated in Figure 67(a). A SRAM-type memory cell is used to turn a transistor *on* or *off* to connect or disconnect rows and columns. For example, when the memory cell contains a 1 (green), the transistor is *on* and connects the associated row and column lines, as shown in part (b). When the memory cell contains a 0 (blue), the transistor is *off* so there is no connection between the lines, as shown in part (c).

SRAM technology is different from the other process technologies discussed because it is a volatile technology. This means that a SRAM cell does not retain data when power is turned *off.* The programming data must be loaded into a memory; and when power is turned *on,* the data from the memory reprograms the SRAM-based PLD.

The fuse, antifuse, EPROM, EEPROM, and flash process technologies are nonvolatile, so they retain their programming when the power is *off.* A fuse is permanently open, an antifuse is permanently closed, and floating-gate transistors used in EPROM and EEPROM-based arrays can retain their *on* or *off* state indefinitely.

COMPUTER NOTE

Most system-level designs incorporate a variety of devices such as RAMs, ROMs, controllers, and processors that are interconnected by a large quantity of general-purpose logic devices often referred to as "glue" logic. PLDs have come to replace many of the SSI and MSI "glue" devices. The use of PLDs provides a reduction in package count.

For example, in computer memory systems, PLDs can be used for memory address decoding and to generate memory write signals as well as other functions.

▶ FIGURE 67

Basic concept of an AND array with SRAM technology.

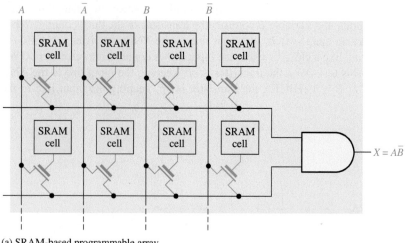

(a) SRAM-based programmable array

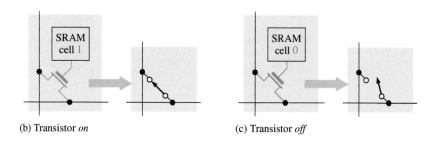

(b) Transistor *on*   (c) Transistor *off*

Device Programming

Interconnections can be made in a simple array by opening or closing the programmable links. SPLDs, CPLDs, and FPGAs are programmed in essentially the same way. The devices with OTP (one-time programmable) process technologies (fuse, antifuse, or EPROM) must be programmed with a special hardware fixture called a *programmer*. The programmer is connected to a computer by a standard interface cable, as shown in Figure 68. Development software is installed on the computer, and the device is inserted into the programmer socket. Most programmers have adapters, such as the one shown, that allow different types of packages to be plugged in.

▶ FIGURE 68

Setup for programming a PLD in a programming fixture (programmer).

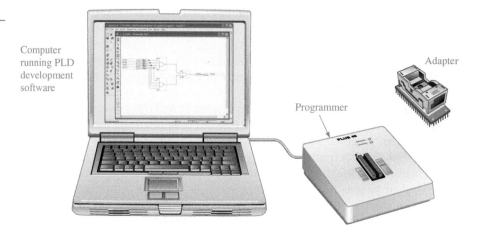

EEPROM, flash, and SRAM-based programmable logic devices are reprogrammable and can be reconfigured multiple times. Although a device programmer can be used for this type of device, it is generally programmed initially on a PLD development board, as shown in Figure 69. A logic design can be developed using this approach because any necessary changes during the design process can be readily accomplished by simply reprogramming the PLD. A PLD to which a software logic design can be downloaded is called a **target device.** In addition to the target device, development boards typically provide other circuitry and connectors for interfacing to the computer and other peripheral circuits. Also, test points and display devices for observing the operation of the programmed device are included on the development board.

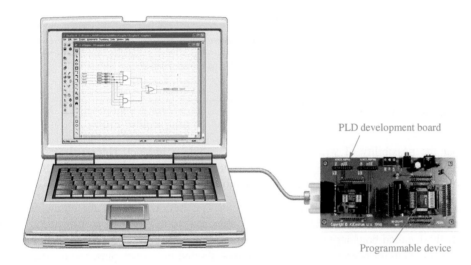

PLD development board

Programmable device

◀ FIGURE 69

Programming setup for reprogrammable logic devices.

Design Entry   Design entry is where the logic design is programmed into the development software. The two main ways to enter a design are by text entry or graphic (schematic) entry, and manufacturers of programmable logic provide software packages to support their devices that allow for both methods.

Text entry in most development software, regardless of the manufacturer, supports two or more hardware development languages (**HDLs**). For example, all software packages support both IEEE standard HDLs, VHDL, and Verilog. Some software packages also support certain proprietary languages such as AHDL.

In **graphic (schematic) entry,** logic symbols such as AND gates and OR gates are placed on the screen and interconnected to form the desired circuit. In this method you use the familiar logic symbols, but the software actually converts each symbol and interconnections to a text file for the computer to use; you do not see this process. A simple example of both a text entry screen and a graphic entry screen for an AND gate is shown in Figure 70. As a general rule, graphic entry is used for less-complex logic circuits and text entry, although it can also be used for very simple logic, is used for larger, more complex implementation.

In-System Programming (ISP)

Certain CPLDs and FPGAs can be programmed after they have been installed on a system printed circuit board (PCB). After a logic design has been developed and fully tested on a development board, it can then be programmed into a "blank" device that is already soldered onto a system board in which it will be operating. Also, if a design change is required, the device on the system board can be reconfigured to incorporate the design modifications.

In a production situation, programming a device on the system board minimizes handling and eliminates the need for keeping stocks of preprogrammed devices. It also rules

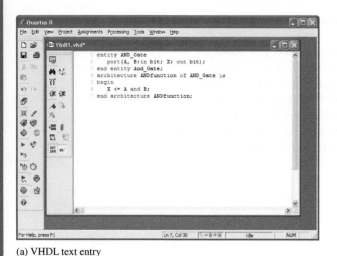

(a) VHDL text entry

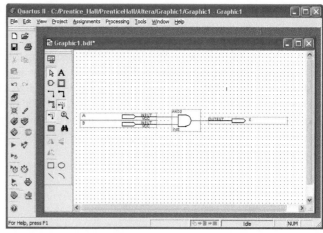

(b) Equivalent graphic (schematic) entry

▲ FIGURE 70

Examples of design entry of an AND gate.

out the possibility of wrong parts being placed in a product. Unprogrammed (blank) devices can be kept in the warehouse and programmed on-board as needed. This minimizes the capital a business needs for inventories and enhances the quality of its products.

JTAG The standard established by the Joint Test Action Group is the commonly used name for IEEE Std. 1149.1. The **JTAG** standard was developed to provide a simple method, called boundary scan, for testing programmable devices for functionality as well as testing circuit boards for bad connections—shorted pins, open pins, bad traces, and the like. More recently, JTAG has been used as a convenient way of configuring programmable devices in-system. As the demand for field-upgradable products increases, the use of JTAG as a convenient way of reprogramming CPLDs and FPGAs will continue to increase.

JTAG-compliant devices have internal dedicated hardware that interprets instructions and data provided by four dedicated signals. These signals are defined by the JTAG standard to be TDI (Test Data In), TDO (Test Data Out), TMS (Test Mode Select), and TCK (Test Clock). The dedicated JTAG hardware interprets instructions and data on the TDI and TMS signals, and drives data out on the TDO signal. The TCK signal is used to clock the process. A JTAG-compliant printed circuit board is represented in Figure 71.

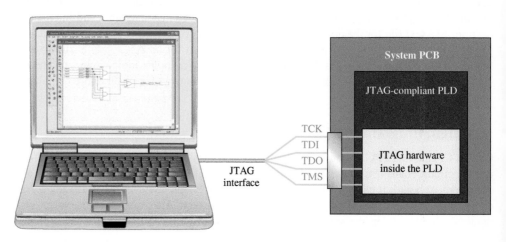

▲ FIGURE 71

Simplified illustration of in-system programming via a JTAG interface.

Embedded Processor Another approach to in-system programming is the use of an embedded microprocessor and memory. The processor is embedded within the system along with the CPLD or FPGA and other circuitry, and it is dedicated to the purpose of in-system configuration of the programmable device.

As you have learned, SRAM-based devices are volatile and lose their programmed data when the power is turned *off*. It is necessary to store the programming data in a PROM (programmable read-only memory), which is nonvolatile. When power is turned *on*, the embedded processor takes control of transferring the stored data from the PROM to the CPLD or FPGA.

Also, an embedded processor is sometimes used for reconfiguration of a programmable device while the system is running. In this case, design changes are done with software, and the new data are then loaded into a PROM without disturbing the operation of the system. The processor controls the transfer of the data to the device "on-the-fly" at an appropriate time. A simple block diagram of an embedded processor/programmable logic system is shown in Figure 72.

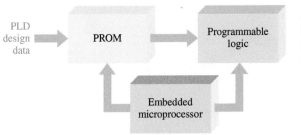

◄ FIGURE 72

Simplified block diagram of a PLD with an embedded processor and memory.

Troubleshooting problems that are keyed to the website (www.pearsoned.com/ electronics) are available in the Multisim Troubleshooting Practice section of the end-of-chapter problems.

SECTION 9 CHECKUP

1. List six process technologies used for programmable links in programmable logic.
2. What does the term *volatile* mean in relation to PLDs and which process technology is volatile?
3. What are two design entry methods for programming PLDs and FPGAs?
4. Define JTAG.

SUMMARY

- ◆ The inverter output is the complement of the input.
- ◆ The AND gate output is HIGH only when all the inputs are HIGH.
- ◆ The OR gate output is HIGH when any of the inputs is HIGH.
- ◆ The NAND gate output is LOW only when all the inputs are HIGH.
- ◆ The NAND can be viewed as a negative-OR whose output is HIGH when any input is LOW.
- ◆ The NOR gate output is LOW when any of the inputs is HIGH.
- ◆ The NOR can be viewed as a negative-AND whose output is HIGH only when all the inputs are LOW.
- ◆ The exclusive-OR gate output is HIGH when the inputs are not the same.
- ◆ The exclusive-NOR gate output is LOW when the inputs are not the same.
- ◆ Distinctive shape symbols and truth tables for various logic gates (limited to 2 inputs) are shown in Figure 73.

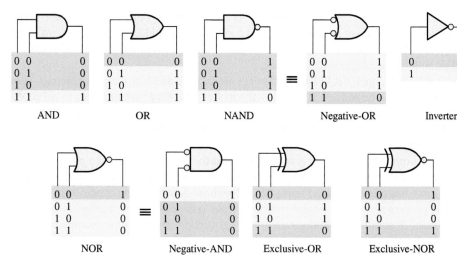

0 0	0	
0 1	0	
1 0	0	
1 1	1	

AND

0 0	0	
0 1	1	
1 0	1	
1 1	1	

OR

0 0	1	
0 1	1	
1 0	1	
1 1	0	

NAND ≡

0 0	1	
0 1	1	
1 0	1	
1 1	0	

Negative-OR

0	1
1	0

Inverter

0 0	1	
0 1	0	
1 0	0	
1 1	0	

NOR ≡

0 0	1	
0 1	0	
1 0	0	
1 1	0	

Negative-AND

0 0	0	
0 1	1	
1 0	1	
1 1	0	

Exclusive-OR

0 0	1	
0 1	0	
1 0	0	
1 1	1	

Exclusive-NOR

Note: Active states are shown in yellow.

- The average power dissipation of a logic gate is

$$P_{\text{D}} = V_{\text{CC}}\left(\frac{I_{\text{CCH}} + I_{\text{CCL}}}{2}\right)$$

- The speed-power product of a logic gate is

$$SPP = t_p P_D$$

- Most programmable logic devices (PLDs) are based on some form of AND array.
- Programmable link technologies are fuse, antifuse, EPROM, EEPROM, flash, and SRAM.
- A PLD can be programmed in a hardware fixture called a programmer or mounted on a development printed circuit board.
- PLDs have an associated software development package for programming.
- Two methods of design entry using programming software are text entry (HDL) and graphic (schematic) entry.
- ISP PLDs can be programmed after they are installed in a system, and they can be reprogrammed at any time.
- JTAG stands for Joint Test Action Group and is an interface standard (IEEE Std. 1149.1) used for programming and testing PLDs.
- An embedded processor is used to facilitate in-system programming of PLDs.
- CMOS is made with MOS field-effect transistors.
- Bipolar (TTL) is made with bipolar junction transistors.
- As a rule, CMOS has a lower power consumption than bipolar.

KEY TERMS

AND array An array of AND gates consisting of a matrix of programmable interconnections.

AND gate A logic gate that produces a HIGH output only when all of the inputs are HIGH.

Antifuse A type of PLD nonvolatile programmable link that can be left open or can be shorted once as directed by the program.

Bipolar A class of integrated logic circuits implemented with bipolar transistors; also known as TTL.

Boolean algebra The mathematics of logic circuits.

CMOS Complementary metal-oxide semiconductor; a class of integrated logic circuits that is implemented with a type of field-effect transistor.

Complement The inverse or opposite of a number. LOW is the complement of HIGH, and 0 is the complement of 1.

EEPROM A type of nonvolatile PLD reprogrammable link based on electrically erasable programmable read-only memory cells and can be turned on or off repeatedly by programming.

Enable To activate or put into an operational mode; an input on a logic circuit that enables its operation.

EPROM A type of PLD nonvolatile programmable link based on electrically programmable read-only memory cells and can be turned either on or off once with programming.

Exclusive-NOR gate A logic gate that produces a LOW only when the two inputs are at opposite levels.

Exclusive-OR (XOR) gate A logic gate that produces a HIGH output only when its two inputs are at opposite levels.

Fan-out The number of equivalent gate inputs of the same family series that a logic gate can drive.

Flash A type of PLD nonvolatile reprogrammable link technology based on a single transistor cell.

Fuse A type of PLD nonvolatile programmable link that can be left shorted or can be opened once as directed by the program.

Inverter A logic circuit that inverts or complements its input.

JTAG Joint Test Action Group; an interface standard designated IEEE Std. 1149.1.

NAND gate A logic gate that produces a LOW output only when all the inputs are HIGH.

NOR gate A logic gate in which the output is LOW when one or more of the inputs are HIGH.

OR gate A logic gate that produces a HIGH output when one or more inputs are HIGH.

Propagation delay time The time interval between the occurrence of an input transition and the occurrence of the corresponding output transition in a logic circuit.

SRAM A type of PLD volatile reprogrammable link based on static random-access memory cells and can be turned on or off repeatedly with programming.

Target device A PLD mounted on a programming fixture or development board into which a software logic design is to be downloaded.

Timing diagram A diagram of waveforms showing the proper timing relationship of all the waveforms.

Truth table A table showing the inputs and corresponding output(s) of a logic circuit.

Unit load A measure of fan-out. One gate input represents one unit load to the output of a gate within the same IC family.

TRUE/FALSE QUIZ

Answers are at the end of the chapter.

1. An inverter performs the NOR operation.
2. An AND gate can have only two inputs.
3. If any input to an OR is 1, the output is 1.
4. If all inputs to an AND gate are 1, the output is 0.
5. A NAND gate has an output that is opposite the output of an AND gate.
6. A NOR gate can be considered as an OR gate followed by an inverter.
7. The output of an exclusive-OR is 0 if the inputs are opposite.
8. Two types of fixed-function logic integrated circuits are bipolar and NMOS.
9. BCD stands for binary coded decimal.
10. Fan-out is the number of similar gates that a given gate can drive.

SELF-TEST

Answers are at the end of the chapter.

1. When the input to an inverter is HIGH (1), the output is
   (a) HIGH or 1   (b) LOW or 1   (c) HIGH or 0   (d) LOW or 0
2. An inverter performs an operation known as
   (a) complementation   (b) assertion   (c) inversion   (d) both answers (a) and (c)

3. The output of an AND gate with inputs A, B, and C is a 1 (HIGH) when

(a) $A = 1, B = 1, C = 1$ (b) $A = 1, B = 0, C = 1$ (c) $A = 0, B = 0, C = 0$

4. The output of an OR gate with inputs A, B, and C is a 1 (HIGH) when

(a) $A = 1, B = 1, C = 1$ (b) $A = 0, B = 0, C = 1$ (c) $A = 0, B = 0, C = 0$

(d) answers (a), (b), and (c)   (e) only answers (a) and (b)

5. A pulse is applied to each input of a 2-input NAND gate. One pulse goes HIGH at $t = 0$ and goes back LOW at $t = 1$ ms. The other pulse goes HIGH at $t = 0.8$ ms and goes back LOW at $t = 3$ ms. The output pulse can be described as follows:

(a) It goes LOW at $t = 0$ and back HIGH at $t = 3$ ms.

(b) It goes LOW at $t = 0.8$ ms and back HIGH at $t = 3$ ms.

(c) It goes LOW at $t = 0.8$ ms and back HIGH at $t = 1$ ms.

(d) It goes LOW at $t = 0.8$ ms and back LOW at $t = 1$ ms.

6. A pulse is applied to each input of a 2-input NOR gate. One pulse goes HIGH at $t = 0$ and goes back LOW at $t = 1$ ms. The other pulse goes HIGH at $t = 0.8$ ms and goes back LOW at $t = 3$ ms. The output pulse can be described as follows:

(a) It goes LOW at $t = 0$ and back HIGH at $t = 3$ ms.

(b) It goes LOW at $t = 0.8$ ms and back HIGH at $t = 3$ ms.

(c) It goes LOW at $t = 0.8$ ms and back HIGH at $t = 1$ ms.

(d) It goes HIGH at $t = 0.8$ ms and back LOW at $t = 1$ ms.

7. A pulse is applied to each input of an exclusive-OR gate. One pulse goes HIGH at $t = 0$ and goes back LOW at $t = 1$ ms. The other pulse goes HIGH at $t = 0.8$ ms and goes back LOW at $t = 3$ ms. The output pulse can be described as follows:

(a) It goes HIGH at $t = 0$ and back LOW at $t = 3$ ms.

(b) It goes HIGH at $t = 0$ and back LOW at $t = 0.8$ ms.

(c) It goes HIGH at $t = 1$ ms and back LOW at $t = 3$ ms.

(d) both answers (b) and (c)

8. A positive-going pulse is applied to an inverter. The time interval from the leading edge of the input to the leading edge of the output is 7 ns. This parameter is

(a) speed-power product   (b) propagation delay, t_{PHL}

(c) propagation delay, t_{PLH} (d) pulse width

9. The purpose of a programmable link in an AND array is to

(a) connect an input variable to a gate input

(b) connect a row to a column in the array matrix

(c) disconnect a row from a column in the array matrix

(d) do all of the above

10. The term OTP means

(a) open test point   (b) one-time programmable

(c) output test program   (d) output terminal positive

11. Types of PLD programmable link process technologies are

(a) antifuse   (b) flash

(c) ROM   (d) both (a) and (b)

(e) both (a) and (c)

12. A volatile programmable link technology is

(a) fuse   (b) EPROM

(c) SRAM   (d) EEPROM

13. Two ways to enter a logic design using PLD development software are

(a) text and numeric   (b) text and graphic

(c) graphic and coded   (d) compile and sort

14. JTAG stands for

  (a) Joint Test Action Group   **(b)** Java Top Array Group

  (c) Joint Test Array Group   **(d)** Joint Time Analysis Group

15. In-system programming of a PLD typically utilizes

  (a) an embedded clock generator   **(b)** an embedded processor

  (c) an embedded PROM   **(d)** both (a) and (b)

  (e) both (b) and (c)

16. To measure the period of a pulse waveform, you must use

  (a) a DMM   **(b)** a logic probe

  (c) an oscilloscope   **(d)** a logic pulser

17. Once you measure the period of a pulse waveform, the frequency is found by

  (a) using another setting   **(b)** measuring the duty cycle

  (c) finding the reciprocal of the period   **(d)** using another type of instrument

---

PROBLEMS

Answers to odd-numbered problems are at the end of the chapter.

Section 1   **The Inverter**

1. The input waveform shown in Figure 74 is applied to an inverter. Draw the timing diagram of the output waveform in proper relation to the input.

▶ FIGURE 74

V_{IN} HIGH / LOW

2. A network of cascaded inverters is shown in Figure 75. If a HIGH is applied to point A, determine the logic levels at points B through F.

▶ FIGURE 75

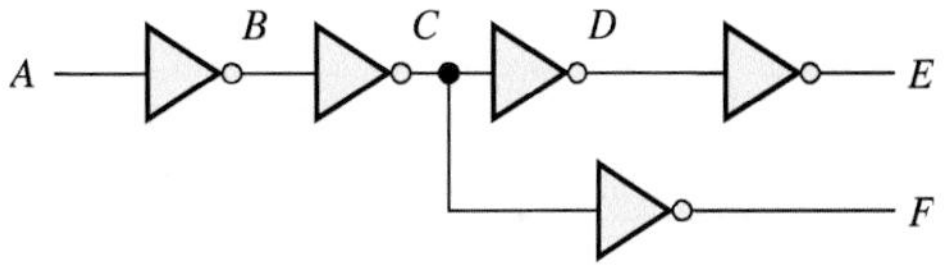

3. If the waveform in Figure 74 is applied to point A in Figure 75, determine the waveforms at points B through F.

Section 2   **The AND Gate**

4. Draw the rectangular outline symbol for a 4-input AND gate.

5. Determine the output, X, for a 2-input AND gate with the input waveforms shown in Figure 76. Show the proper relationship of output to inputs with a timing diagram.

▶ FIGURE 76

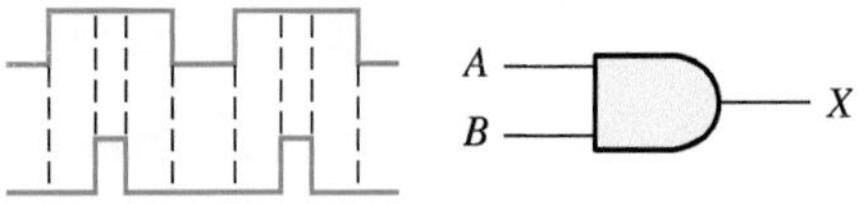

6. Repeat Problem 5 for the waveforms in Figure 77.

▶ FIGURE 77

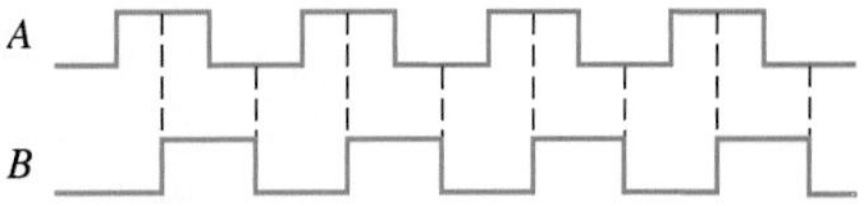

A

B

165

7. The input waveforms applied to a 3-input AND gate are as indicated in Figure 78. Show the output waveform in proper relation to the inputs with a timing diagram.

▶ FIGURE 78

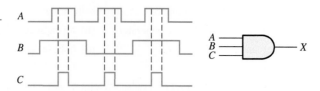

8. The input waveforms applied to a 4-input AND gate are as indicated in Figure 79. Show the output waveform in proper relation to the inputs with a timing diagram.

▶ FIGURE 79

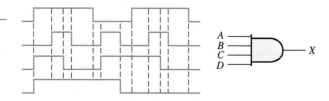

Section 3 **The OR Gate**

9. Determine the output for a 2-input OR gate when the input waveforms are as in Figure 77 and draw a timing diagram.

10. Repeat Problem 7 for a 3-input OR gate.

11. Repeat Problem 8 for a 4-input OR gate.

12. For the five input waveforms in Figure 80, determine the output if the five signals are ANDed. Determine the output if the five signals are ORed. Draw the timing diagram for each case.

▶ FIGURE 80

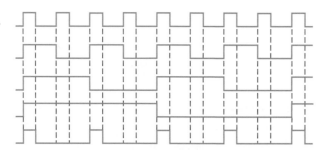

13. Draw the rectangular outline symbol for a 4-input OR gate.

14. Show the truth table for a 3-input OR gate.

Section 4 **The NAND Gate**

15. For the set of input waveforms in Figure 81, determine the output for the gate shown and draw the timing diagram.

▶ FIGURE 81

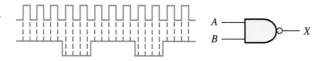

166

16. Determine the gate output for the input waveforms in Figure 82 and draw the timing diagram.

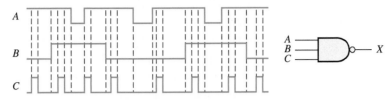

17. Determine the output waveform in Figure 83.

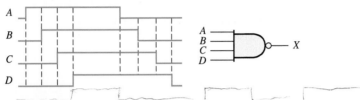

18. As you have learned, the two logic symbols shown in Figure 84 represent equivalent operations. The difference between the two is strictly from a functional viewpoint. For the NAND symbol, look for two HIGHs on the inputs to give a LOW output. For the negative-OR, look for at least one LOW on the inputs to give a HIGH on the output. Using these two functional viewpoints, show that each gate will produce the same output for the given inputs.

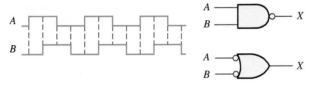

Section 5 **The NOR Gate**

19. Repeat Problem 15 for a 2-input NOR gate.

20. Determine the output waveform in Figure 85 and draw the timing diagram.

21. Repeat Problem 17 for a 4-input NOR gate.

22. The NAND and the negative-OR symbols represent equivalent operations, but they are functionally different. For the NOR symbol, look for at least one HIGH on the inputs to give a LOW on the output. For the negative-AND, look for two LOWs on the inputs to give a HIGH output. Using these two functional points of view, show that both gates in Figure 86 will produce the same output for the given inputs.

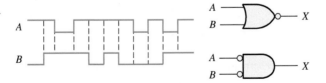

Section 6 **The Exclusive-OR and Exclusive-NOR Gates**

23. How does an exclusive-OR gate differ from an OR gate in its logical operation?

24. Repeat Problem 15 for an exclusive-OR gate.

25. Repeat Problem 15 for an exclusive-NOR gate.

26. Determine the output of an exclusive-OR gate for the inputs shown in Figure 77 and draw a timing diagram.

Section 7   **Fixed-Function Logic**

27. In the comparison of certain logic devices, it is noted that the power dissipation for one partic-ular type increases as the frequency increases. Is the device bipolar or CMOS?

28. Using the data sheets in Figures 54 and 55, determine the following:

(a) 74LS00 power dissipation at maximum supply voltage and a 50% duty cycle

(b) Minimum HIGH level output voltage for a 74LS00

(c) Maximum propagation delay for a 74LS00

(d) Maximum LOW level output voltage for a 74HC00A

(e) Maximum propagation delay for a 74HC00A

29. Determine t_{PLH} and t_{PHL} from the oscilloscope display in Figure 87. The readings indicate volts/div and sec/div for each channel.

▶ FIGURE 87

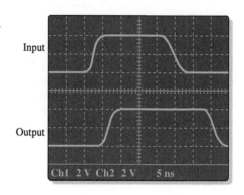

30. Gate A has $t_{PLH} = t_{PHL} = 6$ ns. Gate B has $t_{PLH} = t_{PHL} = 10$ ns. Which gate can be operated at a higher frequency?

31. If a logic gate operates on a dc supply voltage of $+5$ V and draws an average current of 4 mA, what is its power dissipation?

32. The variable I_{CCH} represents the dc supply current from V_{CC} when all outputs of an IC are HIGH. The variable I_{CCL} represents the dc supply current when all outputs are LOW. For a 74LS00 IC, determine the typical power dissipation when all four gate outputs are HIGH. (See data sheet in Figure 54.)

Section 8   **Troubleshooting**

33. Examine the conditions indicated in Figure 88, and identify the faulty gates.

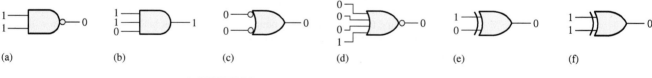

▲ FIGURE 88

34. Determine the faulty gates in Figure 89 by analyzing the timing diagrams.

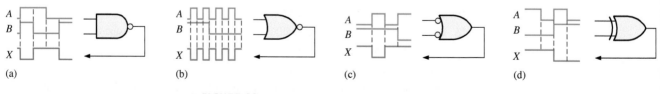

▲ FIGURE 89

35. Using an oscilloscope, you make the observations indicated in Figure 90. For each observation determine the most likely gate failure.

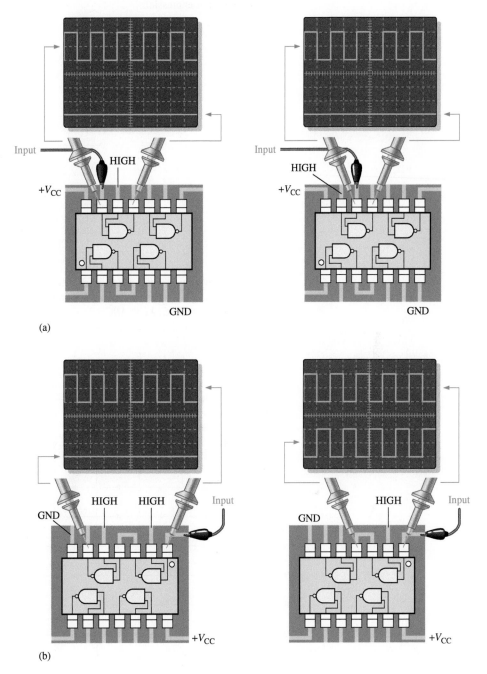

(a)

(b)

▲ FIGURE 90

36. The seat belt alarm circuit in Figure 17 has malfunctioned. You find that when the ignition switch is turned on and the seat belt is unbuckled, the alarm comes on and will not go off. What is the most likely problem? How do you troubleshoot it?

37. Every time the ignition switch is turned on in the circuit of Figure 17, the alarm comes on for thirty seconds, even when the seat belt is buckled. What is the most probable cause of this malfunction?

38. What failure(s) would you suspect if the output of a 3-input NAND gate stays HIGH no matter what the inputs are?

Section 9   **Programmable Logic**

39. In the simple programmed AND array with programmable links in Figure 91, determine the Boolean output expressions.

▶ FIGURE 91

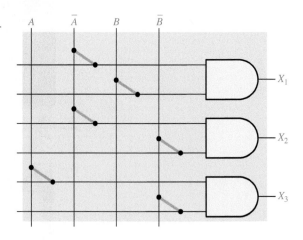

40. Determine by row and column number which fusible links must be blown in the programmable AND array of Figure 92 to implement each of the following product terms: $X_1 = \overline{A}BC, X_2 = AB\overline{C}, X_3 = \overline{A}B\overline{C}$.

▶ FIGURE 92

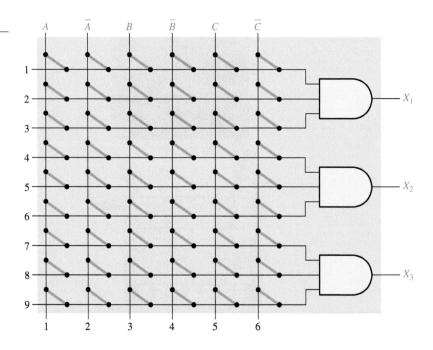

Special Design Problems

41. Sensors are used to monitor the pressure and the temperature of a chemical solution stored in a vat. The circuitry for each sensor produces a HIGH voltage when a specified maximum value is exceeded. An alarm requiring a LOW voltage input must be activated when either the pressure or the temperature is excessive. Design a circuit for this application.

42. In a certain automated manufacturing process, electrical components are automatically inserted in a PC board. Before the insertion tool is activated, the PC board must be properly positioned, and the component to be inserted must be in the chamber. Each of these prerequisite conditions is indicated by a HIGH voltage. The insertion tool requires a LOW voltage to activate it. Design a circuit to implement this process.

43. Modify the frequency counter in Figure 16 to operate with an enable pulse that is active-LOW rather than HIGH during the 1 ms interval.

44. Assume that the enable signal in Figure 16 has the waveform shown in Figure 93. Assume that waveform *B* is also available. Devise a circuit that will produce an active-HIGH reset pulse to the counter only during the time that the enable signal is LOW.

▶ FIGURE 93

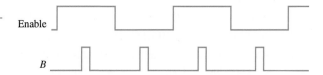

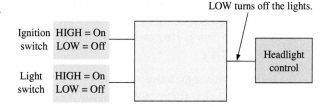

45. Design a circuit to fit in the beige block of Figure 94 that will cause the headlights of an automobile to be turned off automatically 15 s after the ignition switch is turned off, if the light switch is left on. Assume that a LOW is required to turn the lights off.

▶ FIGURE 94

46. Modify the logic circuit for the intrusion alarm in Figure 25 so that two additional rooms, each with two windows and one door, can be protected.

47. Further modify the logic circuit from Problem 46 for a change in the input sensors where Open = LOW and Closed = HIGH.

Multisim Troubleshooting Practice

48. Open file P03-48 on www.pearsoned.com/electronics, connect the Multisim logic converter to the circuit, and observe the operation of the AND gate. Based on the observed inputs and output, determine the most likely fault in the gate.

49. Open file P03-49, connect the Multisim logic converter to the circuit, and observe the operation of the NAND gate. Based on the observed inputs and output, determine the most likely fault in the gate.

50. Open file P03-50, connect the Multisim logic converter to the circuit, and observe the operation of the NOR gate. Based on the observed inputs and output, determine the most likely fault in the gate.

51. Open file P03-51, connect the Multisim logic converter to the circuit, and observe the operation of the exclusive-OR gate. Based on the observed inputs and output, determine the most likely fault in the gate.

ANSWERS

SECTION CHECKUPS

Section 1 **The Inverter**

1. When the inverter input is 1, the output is 0.

(a)

(b) A negative-going pulse is on the output (HIGH to LOW and back HIGH).

Section 2 **The AND Gate**

1. An AND gate output is HIGH only when all inputs are HIGH.

2. An AND gate output is LOW when one or more inputs are LOW.

3. Five-input AND: $X = 1$ when $ABCDE = 11111$, and $X = 0$ for all other combinations of $ABCDE$.

Section 3   The OR Gate

1. An OR gate output is HIGH when one or more inputs are HIGH.
2. An OR gate output is LOW only when all inputs are LOW.
3. Three-input OR: $X = 0$ when $ABC = 000$, and $X = 1$ for all other combinations of ABC.

Section 4   The NAND Gate

1. A NAND output is LOW only when all inputs are HIGH.
2. A NAND output is HIGH when one or more inputs are LOW.
3. NAND: active-LOW output for all HIGH inputs; negative-OR: active-HIGH output for one or more LOW inputs. They have the same truth tables.
4. $X = \overline{ABC}$

Section 5   The NOR Gate

1. A NOR output is HIGH only when all inputs are LOW.
2. A NOR output is LOW when one or more inputs are HIGH.
3. NOR: active-LOW output for one or more HIGH inputs; negative-AND: active-HIGH output for all LOW inputs. They have the same truth tables.
4. $X = \overline{A + B + C}$

Section 6   The Exclusive-OR and Exclusive-NOR Gates

1. An XOR output is HIGH when the inputs are at opposite levels.
2. An XNOR output is HIGH when the inputs are at the same levels.
3. Apply the bits to the XOR inputs; when the output is HIGH, the bits are different.

Section 7   Fixed-Function Logic

1. CMOS and bipolar (TTL)
2. (a) LS—Low-power Schottky   (b) ALS—Advanced LS
   (c) F—fast TTL   (d) HC—High-speed CMOS
   (e) AC—Advanced CMOS   (f) HCT—HC CMOS TTL compatible
   (g) LV—Low-voltage CMOS
3. (a) 74LS04—Hex inverter   (b) 74HC00—Quad 2-input NAND
   (c) 74ALS10—Triple 3-input NAND   (d) 7432—Quad 2-input OR
   (e) 74ACT11—Triple 3-input AND   (f) 74AHC02—Quad 2-input NOR
4. Lowest power—CMOS
5. Six inverters in a package; four 2-input NAND gates in a package
6. $t_{PLH} = 10$ ns; $t_{PHL} = 8$ ns
7. 18 pJ
8. I_{CCL}—dc supply current for LOW output state; I_{CCH}—dc supply current for HIGH output state
9. V_{IL}—LOW input voltage; V_{IH}—HIGH input voltage
10. V_{OL}—LOW output voltage; V_{OH}—HIGH output voltage

Section 8   Troubleshooting

1. Opens and shorts are the most common failures.
2. An open input which effectively makes input HIGH
3. Amplitude and period

Section 9   Programmable Logic

1. Fuse, antifuse, EPROM, EEPROM, flash, and SRAM
2. Volatile means that all the data are lost when power is off and the PLD must be reprogrammed; SRAM-based
3. Text entry and graphic entry
4. JTAG is Joint Test Action Group; the IEEE Std. 1149.1 for programming and test interfacing.

RELATED PROBLEMS FOR EXAMPLES

1 The timing diagram is not affected.

2 See Table 17.

▶ TABLE 17

INPUTS *ABCD*	OUTPUT *X*	INPUTS *ABCD*	OUTPUT *X*
0000	0	1000	0
0001	0	1001	0
0010	0	1010	0
0011	0	1011	0
0100	0	1100	0
0101	0	1101	0
0110	0	1110	0
0111	0	1111	1

3 See Figure 95.

▶ FIGURE 95

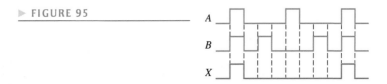

4 The output waveform is the same as input *A*.

5 See Figure 96.

6 Results are the same as example.

7 See Figure 97.

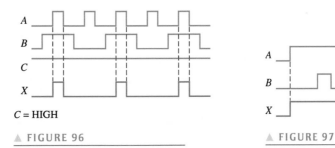

C = HIGH

▲ FIGURE 96

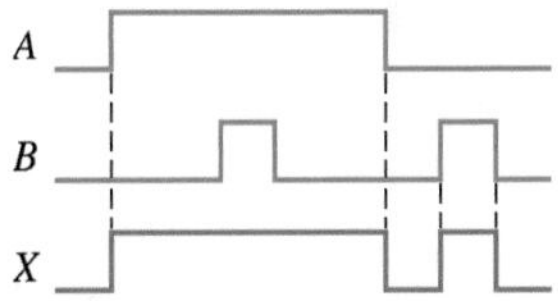

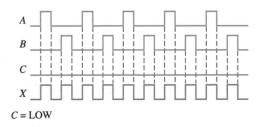

▲ FIGURE 97

8 See Figure 98.

9 See Figure 99.

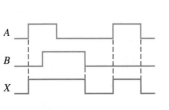

▲ FIGURE 98

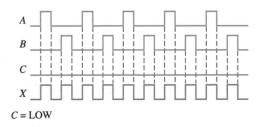

C = LOW

▲ FIGURE 99

10 See Figure 100.

11 See Figure 101.

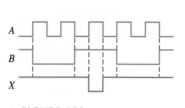

▲ FIGURE 100

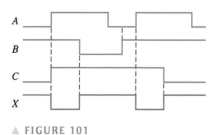

▲ FIGURE 101

12 Use a 3-input NAND gate.

13 Use a 4-input NAND gate operating as a negative-OR gate.

14 See Figure 102.

▶ FIGURE 102

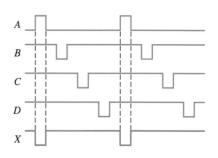

15 See Figure 103.

16 See Figure 104.

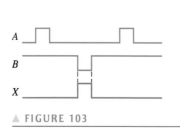

▲ FIGURE 103

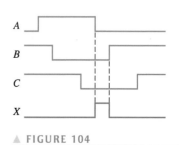

▲ FIGURE 104

17 Use a 2-input NOR gate.

18 A 3-input NAND gate.

19 The output is always LOW. The output is a straight line.

20 The exclusive-OR gate will not detect simultaneous failures if both circuits produce the same outputs.

21 The outputs are unaffected.

22 The gate with 4 ns t_{PLH} and t_{PHL} can operate at the highest frequency.

23 10 mW

24 The gate output or pin 13 input is internally open.

25 The display will show an erratic readout because the counter continues until reset.

26 The enable pulse is too short or the counter is reset too soon.

27 6 columns, 9 rows, and 3 AND gates with three inputs each.

TRUE/FALSE QUIZ

1. F **2.** F **3.** T **4.** F **5.** T

6. T **7.** F **8.** F **9.** T **10.** T

SELF-TEST

1. (d) **2.** (d) **3.** (a) **4.** (e) **5.** (c) **6.** (a) **7.** (d) **8.** (b) **9.** (d)

10. (b) **11.** (d) **12.** (c) **13.** (b) **14.** (a) **15.** (d) **16.** (c) **17.** (c)

ANSWERS TO ODD-NUMBERED PROBLEMS

1. See Figure 105.

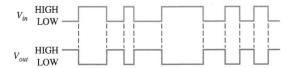

▲ FIGURE 105

3. See Figure 106.

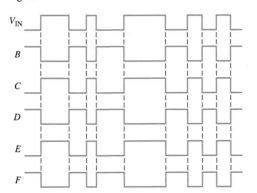

▲ FIGURE 106

5. See Figure 107.

▶ FIGURE 107

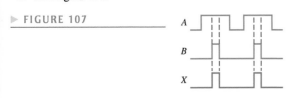

7. See Figure 108.

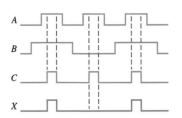

▲ FIGURE 108

9. See Figure 109.

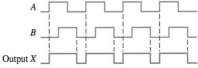

▲ FIGURE 109

11. See Figure 110.

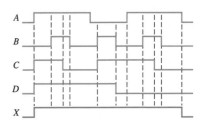

▲ FIGURE 110

13. See Figure 111.

▶ FIGURE 111

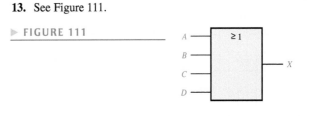

15. See Figure 112.

▶ FIGURE 112

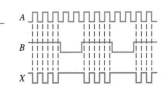

17. See Figure 113.

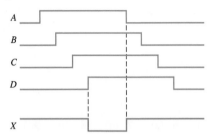

▲ FIGURE 113

19. See Figure 114.

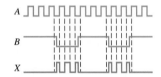

▲ FIGURE 114

21. See Figure 115.

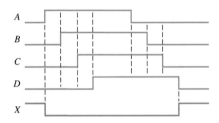

▲ FIGURE 115

23. XOR $= A\overline{B} + \overline{A}B$; OR $= A + B$

25. See Figure 116.

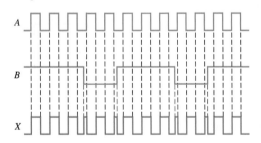

▲ FIGURE 116

27. CMOS

29. $t_{PLH} = 4.3$ ns; $t_{PHL} = 10.5$ ns

31. 20 mW

33. The gates in parts (b), (c), (e) are faulty.

35. (a) defective output (stuck LOW or open)

  (b) Pin 4 input or pin 6 output internally open.

37. The seat belt input to the AND gate is open.

39. $X_1 = \overline{A}B$, $X_2 = \overline{A}\,\overline{B}$, $X_3 = A\overline{B}$.

41. See Figure 117.

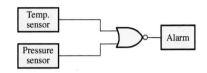

▲ FIGURE 117

43. Add an inverter to the enable input line of the AND gate.

45. See Figure 118.

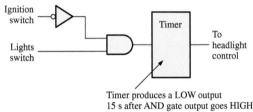

▲ FIGURE 118

47. The inputs are now active-LOW. Change the OR gates to NAND gates (negative-OR) and add two inverters.

49. Gate inputs shorted together

51. Gate output open

Boolean Algebra and Logic Simplification

From *Digital Fundamentals*, Tenth Edition, Thomas L. Floyd. Copyright © 2009 by Pearson Education, Inc. Published by Prentice Hall. All rights reserved.

BOOLEAN ALGEBRA AND LOGIC SIMPLIFICATION

CHAPTER OBJECTIVES

◆ Apply the basic laws and rules of Boolean algebra

◆ Apply DeMorgan's theorems to Boolean expressions

◆ Describe gate networks with Boolean expressions

◆ Evaluate Boolean expressions

◆ Simplify expressions by using the laws and rules of Boolean algebra

◆ Convert any Boolean expression into a sum-of-products (SOP) form

◆ Convert any Boolean expression into a product of-sums (POS) form

◆ Use a Karnaugh map to simplify Boolean expressions

◆ Use a Karnaugh map to simplify truth table functions

◆ Utilize "don't care" conditions to simplify logic functions

◆ Write a VHDL program for simple logic

◆ Apply Boolean algebra and the Karnaugh map method to a system application

KEY TERMS

◆ Variable
◆ Complement
◆ Sum term
◆ Product term
◆ Sum-of-products (SOP)
◆ Product-of-sums (POS)
◆ Karnaugh map
◆ Minimization
◆ "Don't care"
◆ VHDL

INTRODUCTION

In 1854, George Boole published a work titled *An Investigation of the Laws of Thought, on Which Are Founded the Mathematical Theories of Logic and Probabilities.* It was in this publication that a "logical algebra," known today as Boolean algebra, was formulated. Boolean algebra is a convenient and systematic way of expressing and analyzing the operation of logic circuits. Claude Shannon was the first to apply Boole's work to the analysis and design of logic circuits. In 1938, Shannon wrote a thesis at MIT titled *A Symbolic Analysis of Relay and Switching Circuits.*

This chapter covers the laws, rules, and theorems of Boolean algebra and their application to digital circuits. You will learn how to define a given circuit with a Boolean expression and then evaluate its operation. You will also learn how to simplify logic circuits using the methods of Boolean algebra and Karnaugh maps.

The hardware description language VHDL for programming logic devices is introduced.

SYSTEM APPLICATION ACTIVITY PREVIEW

The System Application Activity illustrates concepts from this chapter. The 7-segment display logic in the tablet counting and control system is a good way to illustrate the application of Boolean algebra and the Karnaugh map method to obtain the simplest possible implementation in the design of logic circuits. Therefore, in this system application activity, the focus is on the BCD to 7-segment logic that drives the two system displays. The Multisim activities are optional.

1 BOOLEAN OPERATIONS AND EXPRESSIONS

Boolean algebra is the mathematics of digital systems. A basic knowledge of Boolean algebra is indispensable to the study and analysis of logic circuits. In the last chapter, Boolean operations and expressions in terms of their relationship to NOT, AND, OR, NAND, and NOR gates were introduced.

After completing this section, you should be able to

- ◆ Define *variable*
- ◆ Define *literal*
- ◆ Identify a sum term
- ◆ Evaluate a sum term
- ◆ Identify a product term
- ◆ Evaluate a product term
- ◆ Explain Boolean addition
- ◆ Explain Boolean multiplication

Variable, complement, and *literal* are terms used in Boolean algebra. A **variable** is a symbol (usually an italic uppercase letter or word) used to represent an action, a condition, or data. Any single variable can have only a 1 or a 0 value. The **complement** is the inverse of a variable and is indicated by a bar over the variable (overbar). For example, the complement of the variable A is $\overline{A}$. If $A = 1$, then $\overline{A} = 0$. If $A = 0$, then $\overline{A} = 1$. The complement of the variable A is read as "not A" or "A bar." Sometimes a prime symbol rather than an overbar is used to denote the complement of a variable; for example, B' indicates the complement of B. In this book, only the overbar is used. A **literal** is a variable or the complement of a variable.

COMPUTER NOTE

In a microprocessor, the arithmetic logic unit (ALU) performs arithmetic and Boolean logic operations on digital data as directed by program instructions. Logical operations are equivalent to the basic gate operations that you are familiar with but deal with a minimum of 8 bits at a time. Examples of Boolean logic instructions are AND, OR, NOT, and XOR, which are called *mnemonics*. An assembly language program uses the mnemonics to specify an operation. Another program called an *assembler* translates the mnemonics into a binary code that can be understood by the microprocessor.

Boolean Addition

Boolean addition is equivalent to the OR operation and the basic rules are illustrated with their relation to the OR gate as follows:

$0 + 0 = 0$ $0 + 1 = 1$ $1 + 0 = 1$ $1 + 1 = 1$

In Boolean algebra, a **sum term** is a sum of literals. In logic circuits, a sum term is produced by an OR operation with no AND operations involved. Some examples of sum terms are $A + B$, $A + \overline{B}$, $A + B + \overline{C}$, and $\overline{A} + B + C + \overline{D}$.

A sum term is equal to 1 when one or more of the literals in the term are 1. A sum term is equal to 0 only if each of the literals is 0.

The OR operation is the Boolean form of addition.

EXAMPLE 1

Determine the values of A, B, C, and D that make the sum term $A + \overline{B} + C + \overline{D}$ equal to 0.

Solution   For the sum term to be 0, each of the literals in the term must be 0. Therefore, $A = \mathbf{0}$, $B = \mathbf{1}$ so that $\overline{B} = 0$, $C = \mathbf{0}$, and $D = \mathbf{1}$ so that $\overline{D} = 0$.

$$A + \overline{B} + C + \overline{D} = 0 + \overline{1} + 0 + \overline{1} = 0 + 0 + 0 + 0 = 0$$

Related Problem*   Determine the values of A and B that make the sum term $\overline{A} + B$ equal to 0.

*Answers are at the end of the chapter.

Boolean Multiplication

The AND operation is the Boolean form of multiplication.

Boolean multiplication is equivalent to the AND operation and the basic rules are illustrated with their relation to the AND gate as follows:

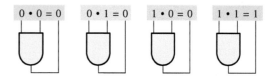

$$0 \cdot 0 = 0 \qquad 0 \cdot 1 = 0 \qquad 1 \cdot 0 = 0 \qquad 1 \cdot 1 = 1$$

In Boolean algebra, a **product term** is the product of literals. In logic circuits, a product term is produced by an AND operation with no OR operations involved. Some examples of product terms are AB, $A\overline{B}$, ABC, and $A\overline{B}C\overline{D}$.

A product term is equal to 1 only if each of the literals in the term is 1. A product term is equal to 0 when one or more of the literals are 0.

EXAMPLE 2

Determine the values of A, B, C, and D that make the product term $A\overline{B}C\overline{D}$ equal to 1.

Solution   For the product term to be 1, each of the literals in the term must be 1. Therefore, $A = \mathbf{1}$, $B = \mathbf{0}$ so that $\overline{B} = 1$, $C = \mathbf{1}$, and $D = \mathbf{0}$ so that $\overline{D} = 1$.

$$A\overline{B}C\overline{D} = 1 \cdot \overline{0} \cdot 1 \cdot \overline{0} = 1 \cdot 1 \cdot 1 \cdot 1 = 1$$

Related Problem   Determine the values of A and B that make the product term $\overline{A}\,\overline{B}$ equal to 1.

SECTION 1 CHECKUP
Answers are at the end of the chapter.

1. If $A = 0$, what does $\overline{A}$ equal?
2. Determine the values of A, B, and C that make the sum term $\overline{A} + \overline{B} + C$ equal to 0.
3. Determine the values of A, B, and C that make the product term $A\overline{B}C$ equal to 1.

2   LAWS AND RULES OF BOOLEAN ALGEBRA

As in other areas of mathematics, there are certain well-developed rules and laws that must be followed in order to properly apply Boolean algebra. The most important of these are presented in this section.

After completing this section, you should be able to

◆ Apply the commutative laws of addition and multiplication

◆ Apply the associative laws of addition and multiplication

◆ Apply the distributive law

◆ Apply twelve basic rules of Boolean algebra

Laws of Boolean Algebra

The basic laws of Boolean algebra—the **commutative laws** for addition and multiplication, the **associative laws** for addition and multiplication, and the **distributive law**—are the same as in ordinary algebra. Each of the laws is illustrated with two or three variables, but the number of variables is not limited to this.

Commutative Laws The *commutative law of addition* for two variables is written as

$$A + B = B + A$$

Equation 1

This law states that the order in which the variables are ORed makes no difference. Remember, in Boolean algebra as applied to logic circuits, addition and the OR operation are the same. Figure 1 illustrates the commutative law as applied to the OR gate and shows that it doesn't matter to which input each variable is applied. (The symbol ≡ means "equivalent to.")

◀ FIGURE 1

Application of commutative law of addition.

The *commutative law of multiplication* for two variables is

$$AB = BA$$

Equation 2

This law states that the order in which the variables are ANDed makes no difference. Figure 2 illustrates this law as applied to the AND gate.

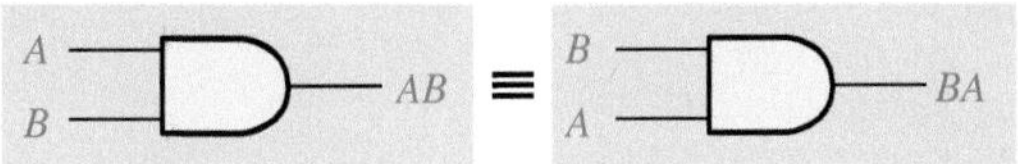

◀ FIGURE 2

Application of commutative law of multiplication.

Associative Laws The *associative law of addition* is written as follows for three variables:

$$A + (B + C) = (A + B) + C$$

Equation 3

This law states that when ORing more than two variables, the result is the same regardless of the grouping of the variables. Figure 3 illustrates this law as applied to 2-input OR gates.

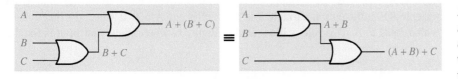

◀ FIGURE 3

Application of associative law of addition. Open file F04-03 on www.pearsoned.com/electronics to verify.

The *associative law of multiplication* is written as follows for three variables:

$$A(BC) = (AB)C$$

Equation 4

This law states that it makes no difference in what order the variables are grouped when ANDing more than two variables. Figure 4 illustrates this law as applied to 2-input AND gates.

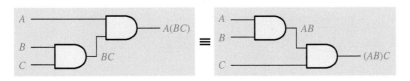

◀ FIGURE 4

Application of associative law of multiplication. Open file F04-04 to verify.

181

Distributive Law The distributive law is written for three variables as follows:

Equation 5

$$A(B + C) = AB + AC$$

This law states that ORing two or more variables and then ANDing the result with a single variable is equivalent to ANDing the single variable with each of the two or more variables and then ORing the products. The distributive law also expresses the process of *factoring* in which the common variable A is factored out of the product terms, for example, $AB + AC = A(B + C)$. Figure 5 illustrates the distributive law in terms of gate implementation.

▶ FIGURE 5

Application of distributive law. Open file F04-05 to verify.

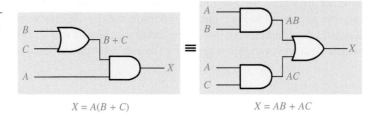

$$X = A(B + C) \qquad\qquad X = AB + AC$$

Rules of Boolean Algebra

Table 1 lists 12 basic rules that are useful in manipulating and simplifying **Boolean expressions.** Rules 1 through 9 will be viewed in terms of their application to logic gates. Rules 10 through 12 will be derived in terms of the simpler rules and the laws previously discussed.

▶ TABLE 1

Basic rules of Boolean algebra.

1. $A + 0 = A$	**7.** $A \cdot A = A$
2. $A + 1 = 1$	**8.** $A \cdot \overline{A} = 0$
3. $A \cdot 0 = 0$	**9.** $\overline{\overline{A}} = A$
4. $A \cdot 1 = A$	**10.** $A + AB = A$
5. $A + A = A$	**11.** $A + \overline{A}B = A + B$
6. $A + \overline{A} = 1$	**12.** $(A + B)(A + C) = A + BC$

A, B, or *C* can represent a single variable or a combination of variables.

Rule 1: $A + 0 = A$ A variable ORed with 0 is always equal to the variable. If the input variable A is 1, the output variable X is 1, which is equal to A. If A is 0, the output is 0, which is also equal to A. This rule is illustrated in Figure 6, where the lower input is fixed at 0.

▶ FIGURE 6

$$A = 1 \quad\boxed{}\quad X = 1 \qquad\qquad A = 0 \quad\boxed{}\quad X = 0$$
$$0 \qquad\qquad\qquad\qquad 0$$

$$X = A + 0 = A$$

Rule 2: $A + 1 = 1$ A variable ORed with 1 is always equal to 1. A 1 on an input to an OR gate produces a 1 on the output, regardless of the value of the variable on the other input. This rule is illustrated in Figure 7, where the lower input is fixed at 1.

▶ FIGURE 7

$$A = 1 \quad\boxed{}\quad X = 1 \qquad\qquad A = 0 \quad\boxed{}\quad X = 1$$
$$1 \qquad\qquad\qquad\qquad 1$$

$$X = A + 1 = 1$$

182

Rule 3: $A \cdot 0 = 0$ A variable ANDed with 0 is always equal to 0. Any time one input to an AND gate is 0, the output is 0, regardless of the value of the variable on the other input. This rule is illustrated in Figure 8, where the lower input is fixed at 0.

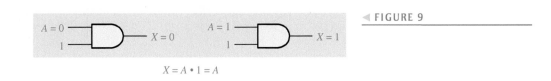

$$X = A \cdot 0 = 0$$

Rule 4: $A \cdot 1 = A$ A variable ANDed with 1 is always equal to the variable. If A is 0, the output of the AND gate is 0. If A is 1, the output of the AND gate is 1 because both inputs are now 1s. This rule is shown in Figure 9, where the lower input is fixed at 1.

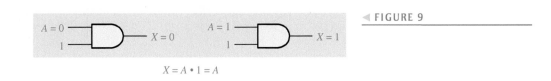

$$X = A \cdot 1 = A$$

Rule 5: $A + A = A$ A variable ORed with itself is always equal to the variable. If A is 0, then $0 + 0 = 0$; and if A is 1, then $1 + 1 = 1$. This is shown in Figure 10, where both inputs are the same variable.

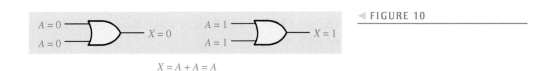

$$X = A + A = A$$

Rule 6: $A + \bar{A} = 1$ A variable ORed with its complement is always equal to 1. If A is 0, then $0 + \bar{0} = 0 + 1 = 1$. If A is 1, then $1 + \bar{1} = 1 + 0 = 1$. See Figure 11, where one input is the complement of the other.

$$X = A + \bar{A} = 1$$

Rule 7: $A \cdot A = A$ A variable ANDed with itself is always equal to the variable. If $A = 0$, then $0 \cdot 0 = 0$; and if $A = 1$, then $1 \cdot 1 = 1$. Figure 12 illustrates this rule.

$$X = A \cdot A = A$$

183

Rule 8: $A \cdot \overline{A} = 0$ A variable ANDed with its complement is always equal to 0. Either A or $\overline{A}$ will always be 0; and when a 0 is applied to the input of an AND gate, the output will be 0 also. Figure 13 illustrates this rule.

▶ FIGURE 13

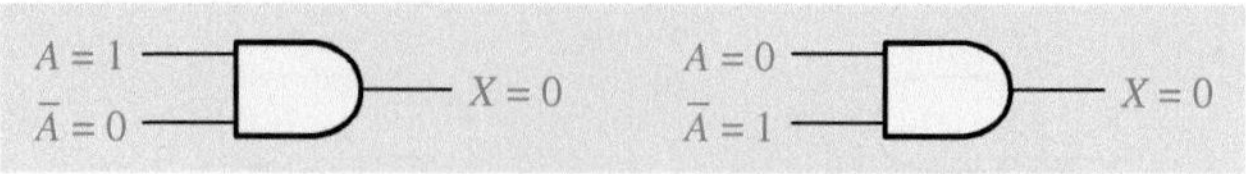

$$X = A \cdot \overline{A} = 0$$

Rule 9: $\overline{\overline{A}} = A$ The double complement of a variable is always equal to the variable. If you start with the variable A and complement (invert) it once, you get $\overline{A}$. If you then take $\overline{A}$ and complement (invert) it, you get A, which is the original variable. This rule is shown in Figure 14 using inverters.

▶ FIGURE 14

$$\overline{\overline{A}} = A$$

Rule 10: $A + AB = A$ This rule can be proved by applying the distributive law, rule 2, and rule 4 as follows:

$$A + AB = A \cdot 1 + AB = A(1 + B) \quad \text{Factoring (distributive law)}$$
$$= A \cdot 1 \qquad\qquad\qquad \text{Rule 2: } (1 + B) = 1$$
$$= A \qquad\qquad\qquad\quad \text{Rule 4: } A \cdot 1 = A$$

The proof is shown in Table 2, which shows the truth table and the resulting logic circuit simplification.

▶ TABLE 2

Rule 10: $A + AB = A$. Open file T04-02 to verify.

A	B	AB	A + AB
0	0	0	0
0	1	0	0
1	0	0	1
1	1	1	1

equal

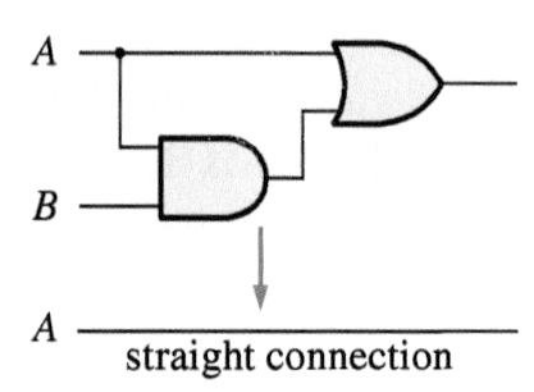

straight connection

Rule 11: $A + \overline{A}B = A + B$ This rule can be proved as follows:

$$A + \overline{A}B = (A + AB) + \overline{A}B \qquad \text{Rule 10: } A = A + AB$$
$$= (AA + AB) + \overline{A}B \qquad \text{Rule 7: } A = AA$$
$$= AA + AB + A\overline{A} + \overline{A}B \quad \text{Rule 8: adding } A\overline{A} = 0$$
$$= (A + \overline{A})(A + B) \qquad\quad \text{Factoring}$$
$$= 1 \cdot (A + B) \qquad\qquad\quad \text{Rule 6: } A + \overline{A} = 1$$
$$= A + B \qquad\qquad\qquad\quad \text{Rule 4: drop the 1}$$

The proof is shown in Table 3, which shows the truth table and the resulting logic circuit simplification.

A	B	$\overline{A}B$	$A + \overline{A}B$	$A + B$
0	0	0	0	0
0	1	1	1	1
1	0	0	1	1
1	1	0	1	1

equal

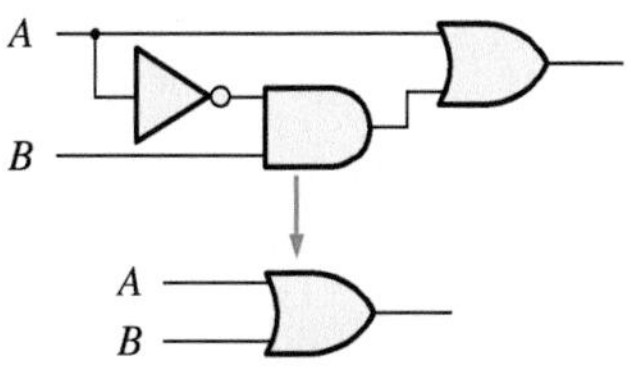

◄ TABLE 3

Rule 11: $A + \overline{A}B = A + B$. Open file T04-03 to verify.

Rule 12: $(A + B)(A + C) = A + BC$ This rule can be proved as follows:

$$(A + B)(A + C) = AA + AC + AB + BC \quad \text{Distributive law}$$
$$= A + AC + AB + BC \quad \text{Rule 7: } AA = A$$
$$= A(1 + C) + AB + BC \quad \text{Factoring (distributive law)}$$
$$= A \cdot 1 + AB + BC \quad \text{Rule 2: } 1 + C = 1$$
$$= A(1 + B) + BC \quad \text{Factoring (distributive law)}$$
$$= A \cdot 1 + BC \quad \text{Rule 2: } 1 + B = 1$$
$$= A + BC \quad \text{Rule 4: } A \cdot 1 = A$$

The proof is shown in Table 4, which shows the truth table and the resulting logic circuit simplification.

▼ TABLE 4

Rule 12: $(A + B)(A + C) = A + BC$. Open file T04-04 to verify.

A	B	C	$A + B$	$A + C$	$(A + B)(A + C)$	BC	$A + BC$
0	0	0	0	0	0	0	0
0	0	1	0	1	0	0	0
0	1	0	1	0	0	0	0
0	1	1	1	1	1	1	1
1	0	0	1	1	1	0	1
1	0	1	1	1	1	0	1
1	1	0	1	1	1	0	1
1	1	1	1	1	1	1	1

equal

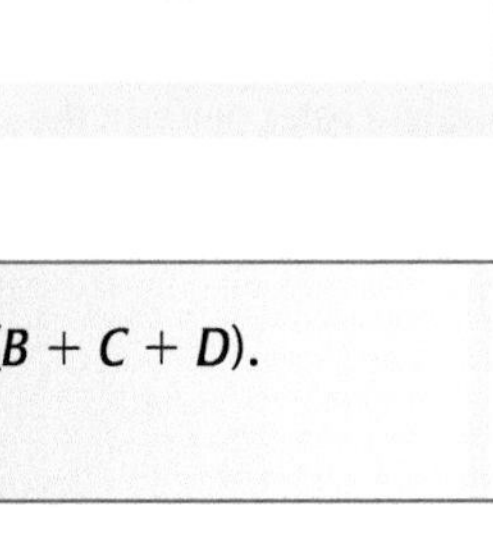

SECTION 2 CHECKUP

1. Apply the associative law of addition to the expression $A + (B + C + D)$.
2. Apply the distributive law to the expression $A(B + C + D)$.

3   DeMorgan's Theorems

DeMorgan, a mathematician who knew Boole, proposed two theorems that are an important part of Boolean algebra. In practical terms, DeMorgan's theorems provide mathematical verification of the equivalence of the NAND and negative-OR gates and the equivalence of the NOR and negative-AND gates.

After completing this section, you should be able to

◆ State DeMorgan's theorems

◆ Relate DeMorgan's theorems to the equivalency of the NAND and negative-OR gates and to the equivalency of the NOR and negative-AND gates

◆ Apply DeMorgan's theorems to the simplification of Boolean expressions

To apply DeMorgan's theorem, break the bar over the product of variables and change the sign from AND to OR.

DeMorgan's first theorem is stated as follows:

The complement of a product of variables is equal to the sum of the complements of the variables.

Stated another way,

The complement of two or more ANDed variables is equivalent to the OR of the complements of the individual variables.

The formula for expressing this theorem for two variables is

Equation 6

$$\overline{XY} = \overline{X} + \overline{Y}$$

DeMorgan's second theorem is stated as follows:

The complement of a sum of variables is equal to the product of the complements of the variables.

Stated another way,

The complement of two or more ORed variables is equivalent to the AND of the complements of the individual variables.

The formula for expressing this theorem for two variables is

Equation 7

$$\overline{X + Y} = \overline{X}\,\overline{Y}$$

Figure 15 shows the gate equivalencies and truth tables for Equations 6 and 7.

▷ FIGURE 15

Gate equivalencies and the corresponding truth tables that illustrate DeMorgan's theorems. Notice the equality of the two output columns in each table. This shows that the equivalent gates perform the same logic function.

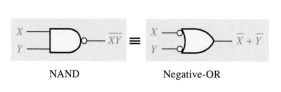

NAND   Negative-OR

INPUTS		OUTPUT	
X	Y	$\overline{XY}$	$\overline{X} + \overline{Y}$
0	0	1	1
0	1	1	1
1	0	1	1
1	1	0	0

NOR   Negative-AND

INPUTS		OUTPUT	
X	Y	$\overline{X + Y}$	$\overline{X}\,\overline{Y}$
0	0	1	1
0	1	0	0
1	0	0	0
1	1	0	0

As stated, DeMorgan's theorems also apply to expressions in which there are more than two variables. The following examples illustrate the application of DeMorgan's theorems to 3-variable and 4-variable expressions.

EXAMPLE 3

Apply DeMorgan's theorems to the expressions $\overline{XYZ}$ and $\overline{X + Y + Z}$.

Solution

$$\overline{XYZ} = \overline{X} + \overline{Y} + \overline{Z}$$
$$\overline{X + Y + Z} = \overline{X}\,\overline{Y}\,\overline{Z}$$

Related Problem   Apply DeMorgan's theorem to the expression $\overline{\overline{X} + \overline{Y} + \overline{Z}}$.

EXAMPLE 4

Apply DeMorgan's theorems to the expressions $\overline{WXYZ}$ and $\overline{W + X + Y + Z}$.

Solution

$$\overline{WXYZ} = \overline{W} + \overline{X} + \overline{Y} + \overline{Z}$$
$$\overline{W + X + Y + Z} = \overline{W}\,\overline{X}\,\overline{Y}\,\overline{Z}$$

Related Problem   Apply DeMorgan's theorem to the expression $\overline{\overline{\overline{\overline{WXYZ}}}}$.

Each variable in DeMorgan's theorems as stated in Equations 6 and 7 can also represent a combination of other variables. For example, X can be equal to the term $AB + C$, and Y can be equal to the term $A + BC$. So if you can apply DeMorgan's theorem for two variables as stated by $\overline{XY} = \overline{X} + \overline{Y}$ to the expression $\overline{(AB + C)(A + BC)}$, you get the following result:

$$\overline{(AB + C)(A + BC)} = \overline{(AB + C)} + \overline{(A + BC)}$$

Notice that in the preceding result you have two terms, $\overline{AB + C}$ and $\overline{A + BC}$, to each of which you can again apply DeMorgan's theorem $\overline{X + Y} = \overline{X}\,\overline{Y}$ individually, as follows:

$$\overline{(AB + C)} + \overline{(A + BC)} = (\overline{AB})\overline{C} + \overline{A}(\overline{BC})$$

Notice that you still have two terms in the expression to which DeMorgan's theorem can again be applied. These terms are $\overline{AB}$ and $\overline{BC}$. A final application of DeMorgan's theorem gives the following result:

$$(\overline{AB})\overline{C} + \overline{A}(\overline{BC}) = (\overline{A} + \overline{B})\overline{C} + \overline{A}(\overline{B} + \overline{C})$$

Although this result can be simplified further by the use of Boolean rules and laws, DeMorgan's theorems cannot be used any more.

Applying DeMorgan's Theorems

The following procedure illustrates the application of DeMorgan's theorems and Boolean algebra to the specific expression

$$\overline{\overline{A + B\overline{C}} + D(\overline{E + \overline{F}})}$$

Step 1: Identify the terms to which you can apply DeMorgan's theorems, and think of each term as a single variable. Let $\overline{A + B\overline{C}} = X$ and $D(\overline{E + \overline{F}}) = Y$.

Step 2: Since $\overline{X + Y} = \overline{X}\,\overline{Y}$,

$$\overline{(\overline{A + B\overline{C}}) + (D(\overline{E + \overline{F}}))} = (\overline{\overline{A + B\overline{C}}})(\overline{D(\overline{E + \overline{F}})})$$

Step 3: Use rule 9 ($\overline{\overline{A}} = A$) to cancel the double bars over the left term (this is not part of DeMorgan's theorem).

$$(\overline{\overline{A + B\overline{C}}})(\overline{D(\overline{E + \overline{F}})}) = (A + B\overline{C})(\overline{D(\overline{E + \overline{F}})})$$

Step 4: Applying DeMorgan's theorem to the second term,

$$(A + B\overline{C})(\overline{D(\overline{\overline{E + \overline{F}}})}) = (A + B\overline{C})(\overline{D} + (\overline{\overline{E + \overline{F}}}))$$

Step 5: Use rule 9 ($\overline{\overline{A}} = A$) to cancel the double bars over the $E + \overline{F}$ part of the term.

$$(A + B\overline{C})(\overline{D} + \overline{\overline{E + \overline{F}}}) = (A + B\overline{C})(\overline{D} + E + \overline{F})$$

The following three examples will further illustrate how to use DeMorgan's theorems.

EXAMPLE 5

Apply DeMorgan's theorems to each of the following expressions:

(a) $\overline{(A + B + C)D}$

(b) $\overline{ABC + DEF}$

(c) $\overline{A\overline{B} + \overline{C}D + EF}$

Solution (a) Let $A + B + C = X$ and $D = Y$. The expression $\overline{(A + B + C)D}$ is of the form $\overline{XY} = \overline{X} + \overline{Y}$ and can be rewritten as

$$\overline{(A + B + C)D} = \overline{A + B + C} + \overline{D}$$

Next, apply DeMorgan's theorem to the term $\overline{A + B + C}$.

$$\overline{A + B + C} + \overline{D} = \overline{A}\,\overline{B}\,\overline{C} + \overline{D}$$

(b) Let $ABC = X$ and $DEF = Y$. The expression $\overline{ABC + DEF}$ is of the form $\overline{X + Y} = \overline{X}\overline{Y}$ and can be rewritten as

$$\overline{ABC + DEF} = (\overline{ABC})(\overline{DEF})$$

Next, apply DeMorgan's theorem to each of the terms $\overline{ABC}$ and $\overline{DEF}$.

$$(\overline{ABC})(\overline{DEF}) = (\overline{A} + \overline{B} + \overline{C})(\overline{D} + \overline{E} + \overline{F})$$

(c) Let $A\overline{B} = X$, $\overline{C}D = Y$, and $EF = Z$. The expression $\overline{A\overline{B} + \overline{C}D + EF}$ is of the form $\overline{X + Y + Z} = \overline{X}\overline{Y}\overline{Z}$ and can be rewritten as

$$\overline{A\overline{B} + \overline{C}D + EF} = (\overline{A\overline{B}})(\overline{\overline{C}D})(\overline{EF})$$

Next, apply DeMorgan's theorem to each of the terms $\overline{A\overline{B}}$, $\overline{\overline{C}D}$, and $\overline{EF}$.

$$(\overline{A\overline{B}})(\overline{\overline{C}D})(\overline{EF}) = (\overline{A} + B)(C + \overline{D})(\overline{E} + \overline{F})$$

Related Problem Apply DeMorgan's theorems to the expression $\overline{ABC + D + E}$.

EXAMPLE 6

Apply DeMorgan's theorems to each expression:

(a) $\overline{(\overline{A + B}) + \overline{C}}$

(b) $\overline{(\overline{A} + B) + CD}$

(c) $\overline{(A + B)\overline{C}D + E + \overline{F}}$

Solution (a) $\overline{(\overline{A + B}) + \overline{C}} = (\overline{\overline{A + B}})\overline{\overline{C}} = (A + B)C$

(b) $\overline{(\overline{A} + B) + CD} = (\overline{\overline{A} + B})\overline{CD} = (\overline{\overline{A}}\overline{B})(\overline{C} + \overline{D}) = A\overline{B}(\overline{C} + \overline{D})$

(c) $\overline{(A + B)\overline{C}D + E + \overline{F}} = ((\overline{A + B)\overline{C}D})(\overline{E + \overline{F}}) = (\overline{A}\overline{B} + C + D)\overline{E}F$

Related Problem Apply DeMorgan's theorems to the expression $\overline{AB(C + \overline{D}) + E}$.

EXAMPLE 7

The Boolean expression for an exclusive-OR gate is $A\overline{B} + \overline{A}B$. With this as a starting point, use DeMorgan's theorems and any other rules or laws that are applicable to develop an expression for the exclusive-NOR gate.

Solution

Start by complementing the exclusive-OR expression and then applying DeMorgan's theorems as follows:

$$\overline{A\overline{B} + \overline{A}B} = (\overline{A\overline{B}})(\overline{\overline{A}B}) = (\overline{A} + \overline{\overline{B}})(\overline{\overline{A}} + \overline{B}) = (\overline{A} + B)(A + \overline{B})$$

Next, apply the distributive law and rule 8 ($A \cdot \overline{A} = 0$).

$$(\overline{A} + B)(A + \overline{B}) = \overline{A}A + \overline{A}\,\overline{B} + AB + B\overline{B} = \overline{A}\,\overline{B} + AB$$

The final expression for the XNOR is $\overline{A}\,\overline{B} + AB$. Note that this expression equals 1 any time both variables are 0s or both variables are 1s.

Related Problem

Starting with the expression for a 4-input NAND gate, use DeMorgan's theorems to develop an expression for a 4-input negative-OR gate.

SECTION 3 CHECKUP

1. Apply DeMorgan's theorems to the following expressions:

(a) $\overline{\overline{ABC} + (\overline{D + E})}$ (b) $\overline{(\overline{A + B})C}$ (c) $\overline{\overline{A} + B + C + \overline{\overline{DE}}}$

---

4 BOOLEAN ANALYSIS OF LOGIC CIRCUITS

Boolean algebra provides a concise way to express the operation of a logic circuit formed by a combination of logic gates so that the output can be determined for various combinations of input values.

After completing this section, you should be able to

* Determine the Boolean expression for a combination of gates

* Evaluate the logic operation of a circuit from the Boolean expression

* Construct a truth table

Boolean Expression for a Logic Circuit

To derive the Boolean expression for a given combinational logic circuit, begin at the left-most inputs and work toward the final output, writing the expression for each gate. For the example circuit in Figure 16, the Boolean expression is determined in the following three steps:

A combinational logic circuit can be described by a Boolean equation.

1. The expression for the left-most AND gate with inputs C and D is CD.

2. The output of the left-most AND gate is one of the inputs to the OR gate and B is the other input. Therefore, the expression for the OR gate is $B + CD$.

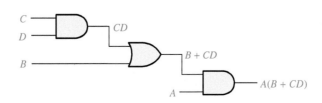

◀ **FIGURE 16**

A combinational logic circuit showing the development of the Boolean expression for the output.

3. The output of the OR gate is one of the inputs to the right-most AND gate and A is the other input. Therefore, the expression for this AND gate is $A(B + CD)$, which is the final output expression for the entire circuit.

Constructing a Truth Table for a Logic Circuit

A combinational logic circuit can be described by a truth table.

Once the Boolean expression for a given logic circuit has been determined, a truth table that shows the output for all possible values of the input variables can be developed. The procedure requires that you evaluate the Boolean expression for all possible combinations of values for the input variables. In the case of the circuit in Figure 16, there are four input variables $(A, B, C,$ and $D)$ and therefore sixteen $(2^4 = 16)$ combinations of values are possible.

Evaluating the Expression   To evaluate the expression $A(B + CD)$, first find the values of the variables that make the expression equal to 1, using the rules for Boolean addition and multiplication. In this case, the expression equals 1 only if $A = 1$ and $B + CD = 1$ because

$$A(B + CD) = 1 \cdot 1 = 1$$

Now determine when the $B + CD$ term equals 1. The term $B + CD = 1$ if either $B = 1$ or $CD = 1$ or if both B and CD equal 1 because

$$B + CD = 1 + 0 = 1$$
$$B + CD = 0 + 1 = 1$$
$$B + CD = 1 + 1 = 1$$

The term $CD = 1$ only if $C = 1$ and $D = 1$.

To summarize, the expression $A(B + CD) = 1$ when $A = 1$ and $B = 1$ regardless of the values of C and D or when $A = 1$ and $C = 1$ and $D = 1$ regardless of the value of B. The expression $A(B + CD) = 0$ for all other value combinations of the variables.

Putting the Results in Truth Table Format   The first step is to list the sixteen input variable combinations of 1s and 0s in a binary sequence as shown in Table 5. Next, place a 1 in the output column for each combination of input variables that was determined in the evaluation. Finally, place a 0 in the output column for all other combinations of input variables. These results are shown in the truth table in Table 5.

▶ TABLE 5

Truth table for the logic circuit in Figure 16.

INPUTS				OUTPUT
A	B	C	D	$A(B + CD)$
0	0	0	0	0
0	0	0	1	0
0	0	1	0	0
0	0	1	1	0
0	1	0	0	0
0	1	0	1	0
0	1	1	0	0
0	1	1	1	0
1	0	0	0	0
1	0	0	1	0
1	0	1	0	0
1	0	1	1	1
1	1	0	0	1
1	1	0	1	1
1	1	1	0	1
1	1	1	1	1

EXAMPLE 8

Use Multisim to generate the truth table for the logic circuit in Figure 16.

Solution

Construct the circuit in Multisim and connect the Multisim Logic Converter to the inputs and output, as shown in Figure 17. Click on the ⟶ conversion bar, and the truth table appears in the display as shown.

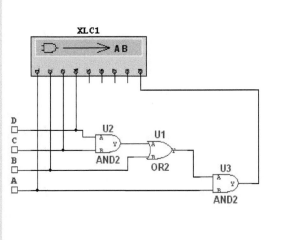

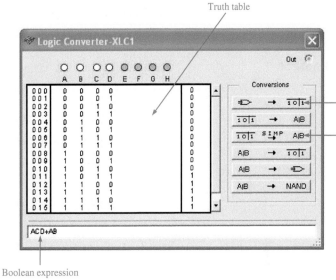

Truth table

Boolean expression

▲ FIGURE 17

You can also generate the simplified Boolean expression from the truth table by clicking on [101 SIMP A|B].

Related Problem

Open Multisim to create the setup and do the conversions shown in this example.

<table>
<tr><td>SECTION 4
CHECKUP</td><td>1. Replace the AND gates with OR gates and the OR gate with an AND gate in Figure 16 and determine the Boolean expression for the output.

2. Construct a truth table for the circuit in Question 1.</td></tr>
</table>

5 SIMPLIFICATION USING BOOLEAN ALGEBRA

Many times in the application of Boolean algebra, you have to reduce a particular expression to its simplest form or change its form to a more convenient one to implement the expression most efficiently. The approach taken in this section is to use the basic laws, rules, and theorems of Boolean algebra to manipulate and simplify an expression. This method depends on a thorough knowledge of Boolean algebra and considerable practice in its application, not to mention a little ingenuity and cleverness.

After completing this section, you should be able to

♦ Apply the laws, rules, and theorems of Boolean algebra to simplify general expressions

A simplified Boolean expression uses the fewest gates possible to implement a given expression. Examples 9 through 12 illustrate Boolean simplification.

EXAMPLE 9

Using Boolean algebra techniques, simplify this expression:

$$AB + A(B + C) + B(B + C)$$

Solution The following is not necessarily the only approach.

Step 1: Apply the distributive law to the second and third terms in the expression, as follows:

$$AB + AB + AC + BB + BC$$

Step 2: Apply rule 7 ($BB = B$) to the fourth term.

$$AB + AB + AC + B + BC$$

Step 3: Apply rule 5 ($AB + AB = AB$) to the first two terms.

$$AB + AC + B + BC$$

Step 4: Apply rule 10 ($B + BC = B$) to the last two terms.

$$AB + AC + B$$

Step 5: Apply rule 10 ($AB + B = B$) to the first and third terms.

$$B + AC$$

At this point the expression is simplified as much as possible. Once you gain experience in applying Boolean algebra, you can often combine many individual steps.

Related Problem Simplify the Boolean expression $A\overline{B} + A(\overline{B + C}) + B(\overline{B + C})$.

Simplification means fewer gates for the same function.

Figure 18 shows that the simplification process in Example 9 has significantly reduced the number of logic gates required to implement the expression. Part (a) shows that five gates are required to implement the expression in its original form; however, only two gates are needed for the simplified expression, shown in part (b). It is important to realize that these two gate circuits are equivalent. That is, for any combination of levels on the A, B, and C inputs, you get the same output from either circuit.

▶ FIGURE 18

Gate circuits for Example 9. Open file F04-18 to verify equivalency.

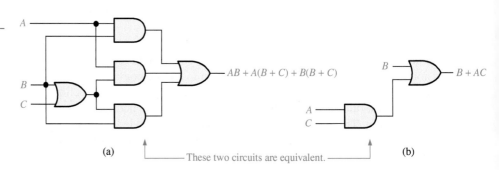

(a) ——— These two circuits are equivalent. ——— (b)

EXAMPLE 10

Simplify the following Boolean expression:

$$[A\overline{B}(C + BD) + \overline{A}\,\overline{B}]C$$

Note that brackets and parentheses mean the same thing: the term inside is multiplied (ANDed) with the term outside.

Solution

Step 1: Apply the distributive law to the terms within the brackets.

$$(A\overline{B}C + A\overline{B}BD + \overline{A}\,\overline{B})C$$

Step 2: Apply rule 8 ($\overline{B}B = 0$) to the second term within the parentheses.

$$(A\overline{B}C + A \cdot 0 \cdot D + \overline{A}\,\overline{B})C$$

Step 3: Apply rule 3 ($A \cdot 0 \cdot D = 0$) to the second term within the parentheses.

$$(A\overline{B}C + 0 + \overline{A}\,\overline{B})C$$

Step 4: Apply rule 1 (drop the 0) within the parentheses.

$$(A\overline{B}C + \overline{A}\,\overline{B})C$$

Step 5: Apply the distributive law.

$$A\overline{B}CC + \overline{A}\,\overline{B}C$$

Step 6: Apply rule 7 ($CC = C$) to the first term.

$$A\overline{B}C + \overline{A}\,\overline{B}C$$

Step 7: Factor out $\overline{B}C$.

$$\overline{B}C(A + \overline{A})$$

Step 8: Apply rule 6 ($A + \overline{A} = 1$).

$$\overline{B}C \cdot 1$$

Step 9: Apply rule 4 (drop the 1).

$$\overline{B}C$$

Related Problem Simplify the Boolean expression $[AB(C + \overline{B}D) + \overline{A}B]CD$.

EXAMPLE 11

Simplify the following Boolean expression:

$$\overline{A}BC + A\overline{B}\,\overline{C} + \overline{A}\,\overline{B}\,\overline{C} + A\overline{B}C + ABC$$

Solution

Step 1: Factor BC out of the first and last terms.

$$BC(\overline{A} + A) + A\overline{B}\,\overline{C} + \overline{A}\,\overline{B}\,\overline{C} + A\overline{B}C$$

Step 2: Apply rule 6 ($\overline{A} + A = 1$) to the term in parentheses, and factor $A\overline{B}$ from the second and last terms.

$$BC \cdot 1 + A\overline{B}(\overline{C} + C) + \overline{A}\,\overline{B}\,\overline{C}$$

Step 3: Apply rule 4 (drop the 1) to the first term and rule 6 ($\overline{C} + C = 1$) to the term in parentheses.

$$BC + A\overline{B} \cdot 1 + \overline{A}\,\overline{B}\,\overline{C}$$

Step 4: Apply rule 4 (drop the 1) to the second term.

$$BC + A\overline{B} + \overline{A}\overline{B}C$$

Step 5: Factor $\overline{B}$ from the second and third terms.

$$BC + \overline{B}(A + \overline{A}C)$$

Step 6: Apply rule 11 $(A + \overline{A}C = A + \overline{C})$ to the term in parentheses.

$$BC + \overline{B}(A + \overline{C})$$

Step 7: Use the distributive and commutative laws to get the following expression:

$$BC + A\overline{B} + \overline{B}\overline{C}$$

Related Problem Simplify the Boolean expression $AB\overline{C} + \overline{A}BC + \overline{A}BC + \overline{A}\overline{B}\overline{C}$.

EXAMPLE 12

Simplify the following Boolean expression:

$$\overline{AB + AC} + \overline{A}\overline{B}C$$

Solution **Step 1:** Apply DeMorgan's theorem to the first term.

$$(\overline{AB})(\overline{AC}) + \overline{A}\overline{B}C$$

Step 2: Apply DeMorgan's theorem to each term in parentheses.

$$(\overline{A} + \overline{B})(\overline{A} + \overline{C}) + \overline{A}\overline{B}C$$

Step 3: Apply the distributive law to the two terms in parentheses.

$$\overline{A}\overline{A} + \overline{A}\overline{C} + \overline{A}\overline{B} + \overline{B}\overline{C} + \overline{A}\overline{B}C$$

Step 4: Apply rule 7 $(\overline{A}\overline{A} = \overline{A})$ to the first term, and apply rule 10 $[\overline{A}\overline{B} + \overline{A}\overline{B}C = \overline{A}\overline{B}(1 + C) = \overline{A}\overline{B}]$ to the third and last terms.

$$\overline{A} + \overline{A}\overline{C} + \overline{A}\overline{B} + \overline{B}\overline{C}$$

Step 5: Apply rule 10 $[\overline{A} + \overline{A}\overline{C} = \overline{A}(1 + \overline{C}) = \overline{A}]$ to the first and second terms.

$$\overline{A} + \overline{A}\overline{B} + \overline{B}\overline{C}$$

Step 6: Apply rule 10 $[\overline{A} + \overline{A}\overline{B} = \overline{A}(1 + \overline{B}) = \overline{A}]$ to the first and second terms.

$$\overline{A} + \overline{B}\overline{C}$$

Related Problem Simplify the Boolean expression $\overline{AB + \overline{A}C} + \overline{A}\overline{B}C$.

EXAMPLE 13

Use Multisim to perform the logic simplification shown in Figure 18.

Solution **Step 1:** Connect the Multisim Logic Converter to the circuit as shown in Figure 19.
Step 2: Generate the truth table by clicking on ![button].
Step 3: Generate the simplified Boolean expression by clicking on ![button].
Step 4: Generate the simplified logic circuit by clicking on ![button].

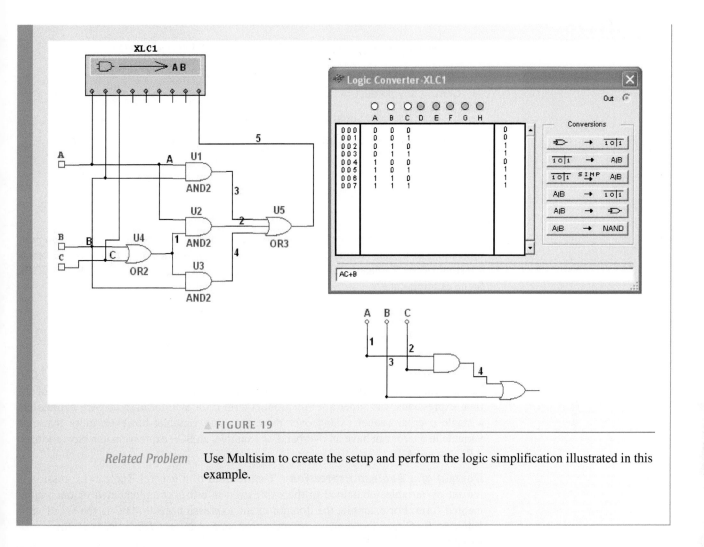

▲ FIGURE 19

Related Problem Use Multisim to create the setup and perform the logic simplification illustrated in this example.

**SECTION 5
CHECKUP**

1. Simplify the following Boolean expressions if possible:
   (a) $A + AB + A\overline{B}C$ (b) $(\overline{A} + B)C + ABC$ (c) $A\overline{B}C(BD + CDE) + A\overline{C}$

2. Implement each expression in Question 1 as originally stated with the appropriate logic gates. Then implement the simplified expression, and compare the number of gates.

---

6 STANDARD FORMS OF BOOLEAN EXPRESSIONS

All Boolean expressions, regardless of their form, can be converted into either of two standard forms: the sum-of-products form or the product-of-sums form. Standardization makes the evaluation, simplification, and implementation of Boolean expressions much more systematic and easier.

After completing this section, you should be able to

- Identify a sum-of-products expression
- Determine the domain of a Boolean expression
- Convert any sum-of-products expression to a standard form

- ◆ Evaluate a standard sum-of-products expression in terms of binary values
- ◆ Identify a product-of-sums expression
- ◆ Convert any product-of-sums expression to a standard form
- ◆ Evaluate a standard product-of-sums expression in terms of binary values
- ◆ Convert from one standard form to the other

The Sum-of-Products (SOP) Form

An SOP expression can be implemented with one OR gate and two or more AND gates.

A product term was defined in Section 1 as a term consisting of the product (Boolean multiplication) of literals (variables or their complements). When two or more product terms are summed by Boolean addition, the resulting expression is a **sum-of-products** (SOP). Some examples are

$$AB + ABC$$
$$ABC + CDE + \overline{B}C\overline{D}$$
$$\overline{A}B + \overline{A}B\overline{C} + AC$$

Also, an SOP expression can contain a single-variable term, as in $A + \overline{A}\,\overline{B}C + BC\overline{D}$. Refer to the simplification examples in the last section, and you will see that each of the final expressions was either a single product term or in SOP form. In an SOP expression, a single overbar cannot extend over more than one variable; however, more than one variable in a term can have an overbar. For example, an SOP expression can have the term $\overline{A}\,\overline{B}C$ but not $\overline{ABC}$.

Domain of a Boolean Expression The **domain** of a general Boolean expression is the set of variables contained in the expression in either complemented or uncomplemented form. For example, the domain of the expression $\overline{A}B + A\overline{B}C$ is the set of variables A, B, C and the domain of the expression $AB\overline{C} + C\overline{D}E + \overline{B}C\overline{D}$ is the set of variables A, B, C, D, E.

AND/OR Implementation of an SOP Expression Implementing an SOP expression simply requires ORing the outputs of two or more AND gates. A product term is produced by an AND operation, and the sum (addition) of two or more product terms is produced by an OR operation. Therefore, an SOP expression can be implemented by AND-OR logic in which the outputs of a number (equal to the number of product terms in the expression) of AND gates connect to the inputs of an OR gate, as shown in Figure 20 for the expression $AB + BCD + AC$. The output X of the OR gate equals the SOP expression.

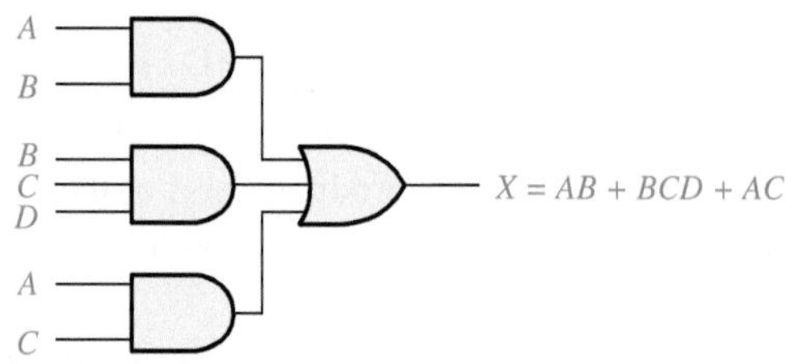

▶ FIGURE 20

Implementation of the SOP expression $AB + BCD + AC$.

$$X = AB + BCD + AC$$

NAND/NAND Implementation of an SOP Expression NAND gates can be used to implement an SOP expression. By using only NAND gates, an AND/OR function can be accomplished, as illustrated in Figure 21. The first level of NAND gates feed into a NAND gate that acts as a negative-OR gate. The NAND and negative-OR inversions cancel and the result is effectively an AND/OR circuit.

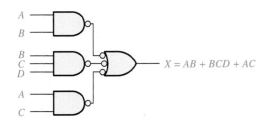

► **FIGURE 21**

This NAND/NAND implementation is equivalent to the AND/OR in Figure 20.

$X = AB + BCD + AC$

Conversion of a General Expression to SOP Form

Any logic expression can be changed into SOP form by applying Boolean algebra techniques. For example, the expression $A(B + CD)$ can be converted to SOP form by applying the distributive law:

$$A(B + CD) = AB + ACD$$

EXAMPLE 14

Convert each of the following Boolean expressions to SOP form:

(a) $AB + B(CD + EF)$ **(b)** $(A + B)(B + C + D)$ **(c)** $\overline{(\overline{A + B}) + C}$

Solution   **(a)** $AB + B(CD + EF) = AB + BCD + BEF$

(b) $(A + B)(B + C + D) = AB + AC + AD + BB + BC + BD$

(c) $\overline{(\overline{A + B}) + C} = (\overline{\overline{A + B}})\overline{C} = (A + B)\overline{C} = A\overline{C} + B\overline{C}$

Related Problem   Convert $\overline{A}B\overline{C} + (A + \overline{B})(B + \overline{C} + A\overline{B})$ to SOP form.

The Standard SOP Form

So far, you have seen SOP expressions in which some of the product terms do not contain all of the variables in the domain of the expression. For example, the expression $\overline{A}B\overline{C} + A\overline{B}D + \overline{A}BCD$ has a domain made up of the variables A, B, C, and D. However, notice that the complete set of variables in the domain is not represented in the first two terms of the expression; that is, D or $\overline{D}$ is missing from the first term and C or $\overline{C}$ is missing from the second term.

A *standard SOP expression* is one in which *all* the variables in the domain appear in each product term in the expression. For example, $\overline{A}B\overline{C}D + \overline{A}\,\overline{B}C\overline{D} + ABC\overline{D}$ is a standard SOP expression. Standard SOP expressions are important in constructing truth tables, covered in Section 7, and in the Karnaugh map simplification method, which is covered in Section 8. Any nonstandard SOP expression (referred to simply as SOP) can be converted to the standard form using Boolean algebra.

Converting Product Terms to Standard SOP   Each product term in an SOP expression that does not contain all the variables in the domain can be expanded to standard form to include all variables in the domain and their complements. As stated in the following steps, a nonstandard SOP expression is converted into standard form using Boolean algebra rule 6 ($A + \overline{A} = 1$) from Table 1: A variable added to its complement equals 1.

Step 1: Multiply each nonstandard product term by a term made up of the sum of a missing variable and its complement. This results in two product terms. As you know, you can multiply anything by 1 without changing its value.

Step 2: Repeat Step 1 until all resulting product terms contain all variables in the domain in either complemented or uncomplemented form. In converting a product term to standard form, the number of product terms is doubled for each missing variable, as Example 15 shows.

EXAMPLE 15

Convert the following Boolean expression into standard SOP form:

$$A\overline{B}C + \overline{A}\,\overline{B} + AB\overline{C}D$$

Solution

The domain of this SOP expression is A, B, C, D. Take one term at a time. The first term, $A\overline{B}C$, is missing variable D or $\overline{D}$, so multiply the first term by $D + \overline{D}$ as follows:

$$A\overline{B}C = A\overline{B}C(D + \overline{D}) = A\overline{B}CD + A\overline{B}C\overline{D}$$

In this case, two standard product terms are the result.

The second term, $\overline{A}\,\overline{B}$, is missing variables C or $\overline{C}$ and D or $\overline{D}$, so first multiply the second term by $C + \overline{C}$ as follows:

$$\overline{A}\,\overline{B} = \overline{A}\,\overline{B}(C + \overline{C}) = \overline{A}\,\overline{B}C + \overline{A}\,\overline{B}\,\overline{C}$$

The two resulting terms are missing variable D or $\overline{D}$, so multiply both terms by $D + \overline{D}$ as follows:

$$\overline{A}\,\overline{B} = \overline{A}\,\overline{B}C + \overline{A}\,\overline{B}\,\overline{C} = \overline{A}\,\overline{B}C(D + \overline{D}) + \overline{A}\,\overline{B}\,\overline{C}(D + \overline{D})$$
$$= \overline{A}\,\overline{B}CD + \overline{A}\,\overline{B}C\overline{D} + \overline{A}\,\overline{B}\,\overline{C}D + \overline{A}\,\overline{B}\,\overline{C}\,\overline{D}$$

In this case, four standard product terms are the result.

The third term, $AB\overline{C}D$, is already in standard form. The complete standard SOP form of the original expression is as follows:

$$A\overline{B}C + \overline{A}\,\overline{B} + AB\overline{C}D = A\overline{B}CD + A\overline{B}C\overline{D} + \overline{A}\,\overline{B}CD + \overline{A}\,\overline{B}C\overline{D} + \overline{A}\,\overline{B}\,\overline{C}D + \overline{A}\,\overline{B}\,\overline{C}\,\overline{D} + AB\overline{C}D$$

Related Problem

Convert the expression $W\overline{X}Y + \overline{X}Y\overline{Z} + WX\overline{Y}$ to standard SOP form.

Binary Representation of a Standard Product Term   A standard product term is equal to 1 for only one combination of variable values. For example, the product term $A\overline{B}C\overline{D}$ is equal to 1 when $A = 1$, $B = 0$, $C = 1$, $D = 0$, as shown below, and is 0 for all other combinations of values for the variables.

$$A\overline{B}C\overline{D} = 1 \cdot \overline{0} \cdot 1 \cdot \overline{0} = 1 \cdot 1 \cdot 1 \cdot 1 = 1$$

In this case, the product term has a binary value of 1010 (decimal ten).

Remember, a product term is implemented with an AND gate whose output is 1 only if each of its inputs is 1. Inverters are used to produce the complements of the variables as required.

An SOP expression is equal to 1 only if one or more of the product terms in the expression is equal to 1.

EXAMPLE 16

Determine the binary values for which the following standard SOP expression is equal to 1:

$$ABCD + A\overline{B}\,\overline{C}D + \overline{A}\,\overline{B}\,\overline{C}\,\overline{D}$$

Solution

The term $ABCD$ is equal to 1 when $A = 1$, $B = 1$, $C = 1$, and $D = 1$.

$$ABCD = 1 \cdot 1 \cdot 1 \cdot 1 = 1$$

The term $A\overline{B}\,\overline{C}D$ is equal to 1 when $A = 1$, $B = 0$, $C = 0$, and $D = 1$.

$$A\overline{B}\,\overline{C}D = 1 \cdot \overline{0} \cdot \overline{0} \cdot 1 = 1 \cdot 1 \cdot 1 \cdot 1 = 1$$

The term $\overline{A}\,\overline{B}\,C\,\overline{D}$ is equal to 1 when $A = 0$, $B = 0$, $C = 0$, and $D = 0$.

$$\overline{A}\,\overline{B}\,C\,\overline{D} = \overline{0} \cdot \overline{0} \cdot \overline{0} \cdot \overline{0} = 1 \cdot 1 \cdot 1 \cdot 1 = 1$$

The SOP expression equals 1 when any or all of the three product terms is 1.

Related Problem   Determine the binary values for which the following SOP expression is equal to 1:

$$\overline{X}YZ + X\overline{Y}Z + XY\overline{Z} + \overline{X}Y\overline{Z} + XYZ$$

Is this a standard SOP expression?

The Product-of-Sums (POS) Form

A sum term was defined in Section 1 as a term consisting of the sum (Boolean addition) of literals (variables or their complements). When two or more sum terms are multiplied, the resulting expression is a **product-of-sums (POS)**. Some examples are

$$(\overline{A} + B)(A + \overline{B} + C)$$
$$(\overline{A} + \overline{B} + \overline{C})(C + \overline{D} + E)(\overline{B} + C + D)$$
$$(A + B)(A + \overline{B} + C)(\overline{A} + C)$$

A POS expression can contain a single-variable term, as in $\overline{A}(A + \overline{B} + C)(\overline{B} + \overline{C} + D)$. In a POS expression, a single overbar cannot extend over more than one variable; however, more than one variable in a term can have an overbar. For example, a POS expression can have the term $\overline{A} + \overline{B} + \overline{C}$ but not $\overline{A + B + C}$.

Implementation of a POS Expression   Implementing a POS expression simply requires ANDing the outputs of two or more OR gates. A sum term is produced by an OR operation, and the product of two or more sum terms is produced by an AND operation. Therefore, a POS expression can be implemented by logic in which the outputs of a number (equal to the number of sum terms in the expression) of OR gates connect to the inputs of an AND gate, as Figure 22 shows for the expression $(A + B)(B + C + D)(A + C)$. The output X of the AND gate equals the POS expression.

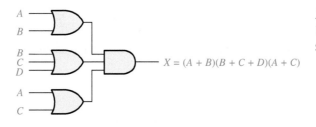

$X = (A + B)(B + C + D)(A + C)$

◀ FIGURE 22

Implementation of the POS expression $(A + B)(B + C + D)(A + C)$.

The Standard POS Form

So far, you have seen POS expressions in which some of the sum terms do not contain all of the variables in the domain of the expression. For example, the expression

$$(A + \overline{B} + C)(A + B + \overline{D})(A + \overline{B} + \overline{C} + D)$$

has a domain made up of the variables A, B, C, and D. Notice that the complete set of variables in the domain is not represented in the first two terms of the expression; that is, D or $\overline{D}$ is missing from the first term and C or $\overline{C}$ is missing from the second term.

A *standard POS expression* is one in which *all* the variables in the domain appear in each sum term in the expression. For example,

$$(\overline{A} + \overline{B} + \overline{C} + \overline{D})(A + \overline{B} + C + D)(A + B + \overline{C} + D)$$

is a standard POS expression. Any nonstandard POS expression (referred to simply as POS) can be converted to the standard form using Boolean algebra.

Converting a Sum Term to Standard POS Each sum term in a POS expression that does not contain all the variables in the domain can be expanded to standard form to include all variables in the domain and their complements. As stated in the following steps, a nonstandard POS expression is converted into standard form using Boolean algebra rule 8 $(A \cdot \overline{A} = 0)$ from Table 1: A variable multiplied by its complement equals 0.

Step 1: Add to each nonstandard product term a term made up of the product of the missing variable and its complement. This results in two sum terms. As you know, you can add 0 to anything without changing its value.

Step 2: Apply rule 12 from Table 1: $A + BC = (A + B)(A + C)$

Step 3: Repeat Step 1 until all resulting sum terms contain all variables in the domain in either complemented or uncomplemented form.

EXAMPLE 17

Convert the following Boolean expression into standard POS form:

$$(A + \overline{B} + C)(\overline{B} + C + \overline{D})(A + \overline{B} + \overline{C} + D)$$

Solution The domain of this POS expression is A, B, C, D. Take one term at a time. The first term, $A + \overline{B} + C$, is missing variable D or $\overline{D}$, so add $D\overline{D}$ and apply rule 12 as follows:

$$A + \overline{B} + C = A + \overline{B} + C + D\overline{D} = (A + \overline{B} + C + D)(A + \overline{B} + C + \overline{D})$$

The second term, $\overline{B} + C + \overline{D}$, is missing variable A or $\overline{A}$, so add $A\overline{A}$ and apply rule 12 as follows:

$$\overline{B} + C + \overline{D} = \overline{B} + C + \overline{D} + A\overline{A} = (A + \overline{B} + C + \overline{D})(\overline{A} + \overline{B} + C + \overline{D})$$

The third term, $A + \overline{B} + \overline{C} + D$, is already in standard form. The standard POS form of the original expression is as follows:

$$(A + \overline{B} + C)(\overline{B} + C + \overline{D})(A + \overline{B} + \overline{C} + D) =$$
$$(A + \overline{B} + C + D)(A + \overline{B} + C + \overline{D})(A + \overline{B} + C + \overline{D})(\overline{A} + \overline{B} + C + \overline{D})(A + \overline{B} + \overline{C} + D)$$

Related Problem Convert the expression $(A + \overline{B})(B + C)$ to standard POS form.

Binary Representation of a Standard Sum Term A standard sum term is equal to 0 for only one combination of variable values. For example, the sum term $A + \overline{B} + C + \overline{D}$ is 0 when $A = 0, B = 1, C = 0$, and $D = 1$, as shown below, and is 1 for all other combinations of values for the variables.

$$A + \overline{B} + C + \overline{D} = 0 + \overline{1} + 0 + \overline{1} = 0 + 0 + 0 + 0 = 0$$

In this case, the sum term has a binary value of 0101 (decimal 5). Remember, a sum term is implemented with an OR gate whose output is 0 only if each of its inputs is 0. Inverters are used to produce the complements of the variables as required.

A POS expression is equal to 0 only if one or more of the sum terms in the expression is equal to 0.

EXAMPLE 18

Determine the binary values of the variables for which the following standard POS expression is equal to 0:

$$(A + B + C + D)(A + \overline{B} + \overline{C} + D)(\overline{A} + \overline{B} + \overline{C} + \overline{D})$$

Solution The term $A + B + C + D$ is equal to 0 when $A = 0$, $B = 0$, $C = 0$, and $D = 0$.

$$A + B + C + D = 0 + 0 + 0 + 0 = 0$$

The term $A + \overline{B} + \overline{C} + D$ is equal to 0 when $A = 0$, $B = 1$, $C = 1$, and $D = 0$.

$$A + \overline{B} + \overline{C} + D = 0 + \overline{1} + \overline{1} + 0 = 0 + 0 + 0 + 0 = 0$$

The term $\overline{A} + \overline{B} + \overline{C} + \overline{D}$ is equal to 0 when $A = 1$, $B = 1$, $C = 1$, and $D = 1$.

$$\overline{A} + \overline{B} + \overline{C} + \overline{D} = \overline{1} + \overline{1} + \overline{1} + \overline{1} = 0 + 0 + 0 + 0 = 0$$

The POS expression equals 0 when any of the three sum terms equals 0.

Related Problem Determine the binary values for which the following POS expression is equal to 0:

$$(X + \overline{Y} + Z)(\overline{X} + Y + Z)(X + Y + \overline{Z})(\overline{X} + \overline{Y} + \overline{Z})(X + \overline{Y} + \overline{Z})$$

Is this a standard POS expression?

Converting Standard SOP to Standard POS

The binary values of the product terms in a given standard SOP expression are not present in the equivalent standard POS expression. Also, the binary values that are not represented in the SOP expression are present in the equivalent POS expression. Therefore, to convert from standard SOP to standard POS, the following steps are taken:

Step 1: Evaluate each product term in the SOP expression. That is, determine the binary numbers that represent the product terms.

Step 2: Determine all of the binary numbers not included in the evaluation in Step 1.

Step 3: Write the equivalent sum term for each binary number from Step 2 and express in POS form.

Using a similar procedure, you can go from POS to SOP.

EXAMPLE 19

Convert the following SOP expression to an equivalent POS expression:

$$\overline{A}\,\overline{B}\,\overline{C} + \overline{A}\,B\overline{C} + \overline{A}BC + A\overline{B}C + ABC$$

Solution The evaluation is as follows:

$$000 + 010 + 011 + 101 + 111$$

Since there are three variables in the domain of this expression, there are a total of eight (2^3) possible combinations. The SOP expression contains five of these combinations, so the POS must contain the other three which are 001, 100, and 110. Remember, these are the binary values that make the sum term 0. The equivalent POS expression is

$$(A + B + \overline{C})(\overline{A} + B + C)(\overline{A} + \overline{B} + C)$$

Related Problem Verify that the SOP and POS expressions in this example are equivalent by substituting binary values into each.

1. Identify each of the following expressions as SOP, standard SOP, POS, or standard POS:

(a) $AB + \overline{A}BD + \overline{A}C\overline{D}$ (b) $(A + \overline{B} + C)(A + B + \overline{C})$

(c) $\overline{A}BC + AB\overline{C}$ (d) $(A + \overline{C})(A + B)$

2. Convert each SOP expression in Question 1 to standard form.

3. Convert each POS expression in Question 1 to standard form.

7   BOOLEAN EXPRESSIONS AND TRUTH TABLES

All standard Boolean expressions can be easily converted into truth table format using binary values for each term in the expression. The truth table is a common way of presenting, in a concise format, the logical operation of a circuit. Also, standard SOP or POS expressions can be determined from a truth table. You will find truth tables in data sheets and other literature related to the operation of digital circuits.

After completing this section, you should be able to

- Convert a standard SOP expression into truth table format
- Convert a standard POS expression into truth table format
- Derive a standard expression from a truth table
- Properly interpret truth table data

Converting SOP Expressions to Truth Table Format

Recall from Section 6 that an SOP expression is equal to 1 only if at least one of the product terms is equal to 1. A truth table is simply a list of the possible combinations of input variable values and the corresponding output values (1 or 0). For an expression with a domain of two variables, there are four different combinations of those variables ($2^2 = 4$). For an expression with a domain of three variables, there are eight different combinations of those variables ($2^3 = 8$). For an expression with a domain of four variables, there are sixteen different combinations of those variables ($2^4 = 16$), and so on.

The first step in constructing a truth table is to list all possible combinations of binary values of the variables in the expression. Next, convert the SOP expression to standard form if it is not already. Finally, place a 1 in the output column (X) for each binary value that makes the standard SOP expression a 1 and place a 0 for all the remaining binary values. This procedure is illustrated in Example 20.

EXAMPLE 20

Develop a truth table for the standard SOP expression $\overline{A}\,\overline{B}C + A\overline{B}\,\overline{C} + ABC$.

Solution   There are three variables in the domain, so there are eight possible combinations of binary values of the variables as listed in the left three columns of Table 6. The binary values that make the product terms in the expressions equal to 1 are $\overline{A}\,\overline{B}C$: 001; $A\overline{B}\,\overline{C}$: 100; and ABC: 111. For each of these binary values, place a 1 in the output column as shown in the table. For each of the remaining binary combinations, place a 0 in the output column.

TABLE 6

INPUTS			OUTPUT	PRODUCT TERM
A	B	C	X	
0	0	0	0	
0	0	1	1	$\overline{A}\,\overline{B}C$
0	1	0	0	
0	1	1	0	
1	0	0	1	$A\overline{B}\,\overline{C}$
1	0	1	0	
1	1	0	0	
1	1	1	1	ABC

Related Problem Create a truth table for the standard SOP expression $\overline{A}B\overline{C} + A\overline{B}C$.

Converting POS Expressions to Truth Table Format

Recall that a POS expression is equal to 0 only if at least one of the sum terms is equal to 0. To construct a truth table from a POS expression, list all the possible combinations of binary values of the variables just as was done for the SOP expression. Next, convert the POS expression to standard form if it is not already. Finally, place a 0 in the output column (*X*) for each binary value that makes the expression a 0 and place a 1 for all the remaining binary values. This procedure is illustrated in Example 21.

EXAMPLE 21

Determine the truth table for the following standard POS expression:

$$(A + B + C)(A + \overline{B} + C)(A + \overline{B} + \overline{C})(\overline{A} + B + \overline{C})(\overline{A} + \overline{B} + C)$$

Solution There are three variables in the domain and the eight possible binary values are listed in the left three columns of Table 7. The binary values that make the sum terms in the expression equal to 0 are $A + B + C$: 000; $A + \overline{B} + C$: 010; $A + \overline{B} + \overline{C}$: 011; $\overline{A} + B + \overline{C}$: 101; and $\overline{A} + \overline{B} + C$: 110. For each of these binary values, place a 0 in the output column as shown in the table. For each of the remaining binary combinations, place a 1 in the output column.

TABLE 7

INPUTS			OUTPUT	SUM TERM
A	B	C	X	
0	0	0	0	$(A + B + C)$
0	0	1	1	
0	1	0	0	$(A + \overline{B} + C)$
0	1	1	0	$(A + \overline{B} + \overline{C})$
1	0	0	1	
1	0	1	0	$(\overline{A} + B + \overline{C})$
1	1	0	0	$(\overline{A} + \overline{B} + C)$
1	1	1	1	

Notice that the truth table in this example is the same as the one in Example 20. This means that the SOP expression in the previous example and the POS expression in this example are equivalent.

Related Problem Develop a truth table for the following standard POS expression:

$$(A + \overline{B} + C)(A + B + \overline{C})(\overline{A} + \overline{B} + \overline{C})$$

Determining Standard Expressions from a Truth Table

To determine the standard SOP expression represented by a truth table, list the binary values of the input variables for which the output is 1. Convert each binary value to the corresponding product term by replacing each 1 with the corresponding variable and each 0 with the corresponding variable complement. For example, the binary value 1010 is converted to a product term as follows:

$$1010 \longrightarrow A\overline{B}C\overline{D}$$

If you substitute, you can see that the product term is 1:

$$A\overline{B}C\overline{D} = 1 \cdot \overline{0} \cdot 1 \cdot \overline{0} = 1 \cdot 1 \cdot 1 \cdot 1 = 1$$

To determine the standard POS expression represented by a truth table, list the binary values for which the output is 0. Convert each binary value to the corresponding sum term by replacing each 1 with the corresponding variable complement and each 0 with the corresponding variable. For example, the binary value 1001 is converted to a sum term as follows:

$$1001 \longrightarrow \overline{A} + B + C + \overline{D}$$

If you substitute, you can see that the sum term is 0:

$$\overline{A} + B + C + \overline{D} = \overline{1} + 0 + 0 + \overline{1} = 0 + 0 + 0 + 0 = 0$$

EXAMPLE 22

From the truth table in Table 8, determine the standard SOP expression and the equivalent standard POS expression.

▼ TABLE 8

INPUTS			OUTPUT
A	B	C	X
0	0	0	0
0	0	1	0
0	1	0	0
0	1	1	1
1	0	0	1
1	0	1	0
1	1	0	1
1	1	1	1

Solution   There are four 1s in the output column and the corresponding binary values are 011, 100, 110, and 111. Convert these binary values to product terms as follows:

$$011 \longrightarrow \overline{A}BC$$
$$100 \longrightarrow A\overline{B}\,\overline{C}$$
$$110 \longrightarrow AB\overline{C}$$
$$111 \longrightarrow ABC$$

The resulting standard SOP expression for the output X is

$$X = \overline{A}BC + A\overline{B}\,\overline{C} + AB\overline{C} + ABC$$

For the POS expression, the output is 0 for binary values 000, 001, 010, and 101. Convert these binary values to sum terms as follows:

$$000 \longrightarrow A + B + C$$
$$001 \longrightarrow A + B + \overline{C}$$
$$010 \longrightarrow A + \overline{B} + C$$
$$101 \longrightarrow \overline{A} + B + \overline{C}$$

The resulting standard POS expression for the output X is

$$X = (A + B + C)(A + B + \overline{C})(A + \overline{B} + C)(\overline{A} + B + \overline{C})$$

Related Problem   By substitution of binary values, show that the SOP and the POS expressions derived in this example are equivalent; that is, for any binary value each SOP and POS term should either both be 1 or both be 0, depending on the binary value.

**SECTION 7
CHECKUP**

1. If a certain Boolean expression has a domain of five variables, how many binary values will be in its truth table?
2. In a certain truth table, the output is a 1 for the binary value 0110. Convert this binary value to the corresponding product term using variables W, X, Y, and Z.
3. In a certain truth table, the output is a 0 for the binary value 1100. Convert this binary value to the corresponding sum term using variables W, X, Y, and Z.

---

8   THE KARNAUGH MAP

A Karnaugh map provides a systematic method for simplifying Boolean expressions and, if properly used, will produce the simplest SOP or POS expression possible, known as the minimum expression. As you have seen, the effectiveness of algebraic simplification depends on your familiarity with all the laws, rules, and theorems of Boolean algebra and on your ability to apply them. The Karnaugh map, on the other hand, provides a "cookbook" method for simplification. Other simplification techniques include the Quine-McClusky method and the Espresso algorithm.

After completing this section, you should be able to

- Construct a Karnaugh map for three or four variables
- Determine the binary value of each cell in a Karnaugh map
- Determine the standard product term represented by each cell in a Karnaugh map
- Explain cell adjacency and identify adjacent cells

The purpose of a Karnaugh map is to simplify a Boolean expression.

A **Karnaugh map** is similar to a truth table because it presents all of the possible values of input variables and the resulting output for each value. Instead of being organized into columns and rows like a truth table, the Karnaugh map is an array of **cells** in which each cell represents a binary value of the input variables. The cells are arranged in a way so that simplification of a given expression is simply a matter of properly grouping the cells. Karnaugh maps can be used for expressions with two, three, four, and five variables, but we will discuss only 3-variable and 4-variable situations to illustrate the principles. Section 10 deals with five variables using a 32-cell Karnaugh map.

The number of cells in a Karnaugh map, as well as the number of rows in a truth table, is equal to the total number of possible input variable combinations. For three variables, the number of cells is $2^3 = 8$. For four variables, the number of cells is $2^4 = 16$.

The 3-Variable Karnaugh Map

The 3-variable Karnaugh map is an array of eight cells, as shown in Figure 23(a). In this case, A, B, and C are used for the variables although other letters could be used. Binary values of A and B are along the left side (notice the sequence) and the values of C are across the top. The value of a given cell is the binary values of A and B at the left in the same row combined with the value of C at the top in the same column. For example, the cell in the upper left corner has a binary value of 000 and the cell in the lower right corner has a binary value of 101. Figure 23(b) shows the standard product terms that are represented by each cell in the Karnaugh map.

▶ FIGURE 23

A 3-variable Karnaugh map showing product terms.

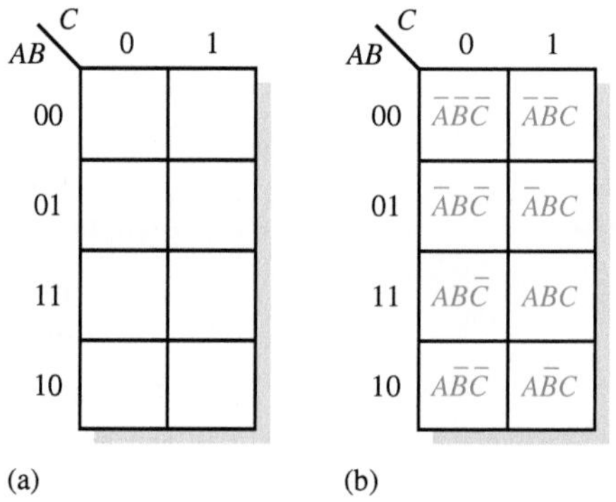

(a)   (b)

The 4-Variable Karnaugh Map

The 4-variable Karnaugh map is an array of sixteen cells, as shown in Figure 24(a). Binary values of A and B are along the left side and the values of C and D are across the top. The value of a given cell is the binary values of A and B at the left in the same row combined with the binary values of C and D at the top in the same column. For example, the cell in the upper right corner has a binary value of 0010 and the cell in the lower right corner has a binary value of 1010. Figure 24(b) shows the standard product terms that are represented by each cell in the 4-variable Karnaugh map.

Cell Adjacency

Cells that differ by only one variable are adjacent.

Cells with values that differ by more than one variable are not adjacent.

The cells in a Karnaugh map are arranged so that there is only a single-variable change between adjacent cells. **Adjacency** is defined by a single-variable change. In the 3-variable map the 010 cell is adjacent to the 000 cell, the 011 cell, and the 110 cell. The 010 cell is not adjacent to the 001 cell, the 111 cell, the 100 cell, or the 101 cell.

Physically, each cell is adjacent to the cells that are immediately next to it on any of its four sides. A cell is not adjacent to the cells that diagonally touch any of its corners. Also,

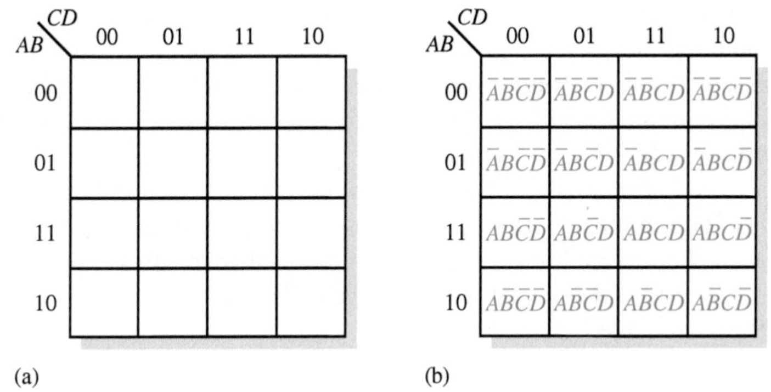

CD\AB	00	01	11	10
00				
01				
11				
10				

(a)

CD\AB	00	01	11	10
00	$\overline{A}\overline{B}\overline{C}\overline{D}$	$\overline{A}\overline{B}\overline{C}D$	$\overline{A}\overline{B}CD$	$\overline{A}\overline{B}C\overline{D}$
01	$\overline{A}B\overline{C}\overline{D}$	$\overline{A}B\overline{C}D$	$\overline{A}BCD$	$\overline{A}BC\overline{D}$
11	$AB\overline{C}\overline{D}$	$AB\overline{C}D$	$ABCD$	$ABC\overline{D}$
10	$A\overline{B}\overline{C}\overline{D}$	$A\overline{B}\overline{C}D$	$A\overline{B}CD$	$A\overline{B}C\overline{D}$

(b)

◀ FIGURE 24

A 4-variable Karnaugh map.

the cells in the top row are adjacent to the corresponding cells in the bottom row and the cells in the outer left column are adjacent to the corresponding cells in the outer right column. This is called "wrap-around" adjacency because you can think of the map as wrapping around from top to bottom to form a cylinder or from left to right to form a cylinder. Figure 25 illustrates the cell adjacencies with a 4-variable map, although the same rules for adjacency apply to Karnaugh maps with any number of cells.

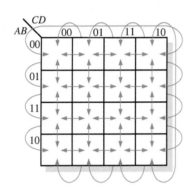

◀ FIGURE 25

Adjacent cells on a Karnaugh map are those that differ by only one variable. Arrows point between adjacent cells.

The Quine-McClusky Method

Minimizing Boolean functions using Karnaugh maps is not applicable for more than five variables and practical only for up to four variables. Also, this method does not lend itself to be automated in the form of a computer program.

The Quine-McClusky method is more practical for logic simplification of functions with more than four or five variables. It also has the advantage of being easily implemented with a computer or programmable calculator.

The Quine-McClusky method is functionally similar to Karnaugh mapping, but the tabular form makes it more efficient for use in computer algorithms, and it also gives a way to check that the minimal form of a Boolean function has been reached. This method is sometimes referred to as the *tabulation method*.

Espresso Algorithm

Although the Quine-McCluskey method is well suited to be implemented in a computer program and can handle more variables than the Karnaugh map method, the result is still far from efficient in terms of processing time and memory usage. Adding a variable to the function will roughly double both of these parameters because the truth table length increases exponentially with the number of variables. Functions with a large number of variables have to be minimized with other methods such as the Espresso logic minimizer, which has become the de facto world standard.

Compared to the other methods, Espresso is essentially more efficient in terms of reducing memory usage and computation time by several orders of magnitude. There is essentially no restrictions to the number of variables, output functions, and product terms of a combinational logic function. In general, tens of variables with tens of output functions can be handled by Espresso.

The Espresso algorithm has been incorporated as a standard logic function minimization step in most logic synthesis tools for programmable logic devices. For implementing a function in multilevel logic, the minimization result is optimized by factorization and mapped onto the available basic logic cells in the target device, such as an FPGA (Field-Programmable Gate Array).

SECTION 8 CHECKUP

1. In a 3-variable Karnaugh map, what is the binary value for the cell in each of the following locations:
   - (a) upper left corner
   - (b) lower right corner
   - (c) lower left corner
   - (d) upper right corner
2. What is the standard product term for each cell in Question 1 for variables X, Y, and Z?
3. Repeat Question 1 for a 4-variable map.
4. Repeat Question 2 for a 4-variable map using variables W, X, Y, and Z.

---

9 KARNAUGH MAP SOP MINIMIZATION

As stated in the last section, the Karnaugh map is used for simplifying Boolean expressions to their minimum form. A minimized SOP expression contains the fewest possible terms with the fewest possible variables per term. Generally, a minimum SOP expression can be implemented with fewer logic gates than a standard expression.

After completing this section, you should be able to

- ◆ Map a standard SOP expression on a Karnaugh map
- ◆ Combine the 1s on the map into maximum groups
- ◆ Determine the minimum product term for each group on the map
- ◆ Combine the minimum product terms to form a minimum SOP expression
- ◆ Convert a truth table into a Karnaugh map for simplification of the represented expression
- ◆ Use "don't care" conditions on a Karnaugh map

Mapping a Standard SOP Expression

For an SOP expression in standard form, a 1 is placed on the Karnaugh map for each product term in the expression. Each 1 is placed in a cell corresponding to the value of a product term. For example, for the product term $A\overline{B}C$, a 1 goes in the 101 cell on a 3-variable map.

When an SOP expression is completely mapped, there will be a number of 1s on the Karnaugh map equal to the number of product terms in the standard SOP expression. The cells that do not have a 1 are the cells for which the expression is 0. Usually, when working with SOP expressions, the 0s are left off the map. The following steps and the illustration in Figure 26 show the mapping process.

Step 1: Determine the binary value of each product term in the standard SOP expression. After some practice, you can usually do the evaluation of terms mentally.

Step 2: As each product term is evaluated, place a 1 on the Karnaugh map in the cell having the same value as the product term.

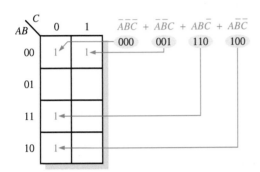

◄ FIGURE 26

Example of mapping a standard SOP expression.

EXAMPLE 23

Map the following standard SOP expression on a Karnaugh map:

$$\overline{A}\,\overline{B}C + \overline{A}B\overline{C} + AB\overline{C} + ABC$$

Solution   Evaluate the expression as shown below. Place a 1 on the 3-variable Karnaugh map in Figure 27 for each standard product term in the expression.

$$\overline{A}\,\overline{B}C + \overline{A}B\overline{C} + AB\overline{C} + ABC$$
$$\quad 001 \qquad 010 \qquad 110 \qquad 111$$

▶ FIGURE 27

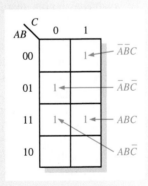

Related Problem   Map the standard SOP expression $\overline{A}BC + A\overline{B}C + A\overline{B}\,\overline{C}$ on a Karnaugh map.

EXAMPLE 24

Map the following standard SOP expression on a Karnaugh map:

$$\overline{A}\,\overline{B}CD + \overline{A}B\overline{C}\,\overline{D} + AB\overline{C}D + ABCD + AB\overline{C}\,\overline{D} + \overline{A}\,\overline{B}\,\overline{C}D + A\overline{B}C\overline{D}$$

Solution   Evaluate the expression as shown below. Place a 1 on the 4-variable Karnaugh map in Figure 28 for each standard product term in the expression.

$$\overline{A}\,\overline{B}CD + \overline{A}B\overline{C}\,\overline{D} + AB\overline{C}D + ABCD + AB\overline{C}\,\overline{D} + \overline{A}\,\overline{B}\,\overline{C}D + A\overline{B}C\overline{D}$$
$$\quad 0011 \qquad 0100 \qquad 1101 \qquad 1111 \qquad 1100 \qquad 0001 \qquad 1010$$

209

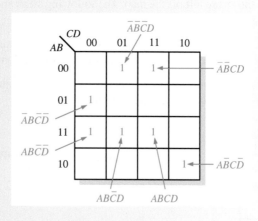

▲ FIGURE 28

Related Problem   Map the following standard SOP expression on a Karnaugh map:

$$\overline{A}BC\overline{D} + ABC\overline{D} + AB\overline{C}\,\overline{D} + ABCD$$

Mapping a Nonstandard SOP Expression

A Boolean expression must first be in standard form before you use a Karnaugh map. If an expression is not in standard form, then it must be converted to standard form by the procedure covered in Section 6 or by numerical expansion. Since an expression should be evaluated before mapping anyway, numerical expansion is probably the most efficient approach.

Numerical Expansion of a Nonstandard Product Term   Recall that a nonstandard product term has one or more missing variables. For example, assume that one of the product terms in a certain 3-variable SOP expression is $A\overline{B}$. This term can be expanded numerically to standard form as follows. First, write the binary value of the two variables and attach a 0 for the missing variable $\overline{C}$: 100. Next, write the binary value of the two variables and attach a 1 for the missing variable C: 101. The two resulting binary numbers are the values of the standard SOP terms $A\overline{B}\,\overline{C}$ and $A\overline{B}C$.

As another example, assume that one of the product terms in a 3-variable expression is B (remember that a single variable counts as a product term in an SOP expression). This term can be expanded numerically to standard form as follows. Write the binary value of the variable; then attach all possible values for the missing variables A and C as follows:

$$B$$
$$010$$
$$011$$
$$110$$
$$111$$

The four resulting binary numbers are the values of the standard SOP terms $\overline{A}B\overline{C}$, $\overline{A}BC$, $AB\overline{C}$, and ABC.

EXAMPLE 25

Map the following SOP expression on a Karnaugh map: $\overline{A} + A\overline{B} + AB\overline{C}$.

Solution

The SOP expression is obviously not in standard form because each product term does not have three variables. The first term is missing two variables, the second term is missing one variable, and the third term is standard. First expand the terms numerically as follows:

$$\overline{A} \quad + A\overline{B} \quad + AB\overline{C}$$

000	100	110
001	101	
010		
011		

Map each of the resulting binary values by placing a 1 in the appropriate cell of the 3-variable Karnaugh map in Figure 29.

▶ FIGURE 29

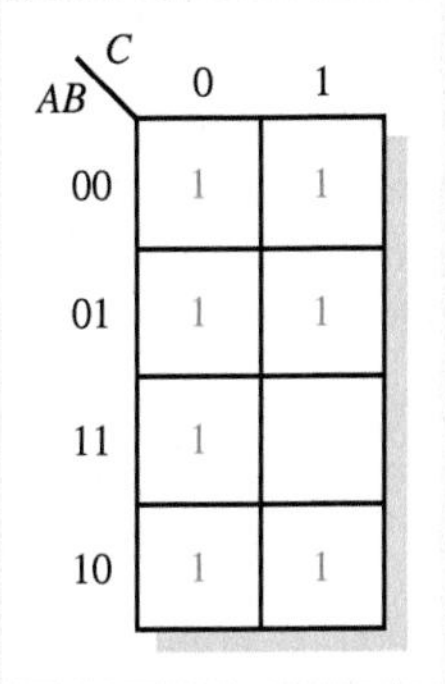

Related Problem Map the SOP expression $BC + \overline{A}\,\overline{C}$ on a Karnaugh map.

EXAMPLE 26

Map the following SOP expression on a Karnaugh map:

$$\overline{B}\,\overline{C} + A\overline{B} + AB\overline{C} + \overline{A}B\overline{C}D + \overline{A}\,\overline{B}C\overline{D} + A\overline{B}CD$$

Solution

The SOP expression is obviously not in standard form because each product term does not have four variables. The first and second terms are both missing two variables, the third term is missing one variable, and the rest of the terms are standard. First expand the terms by including all combinations of the missing variables numerically as follows:

$$\overline{B}\,\overline{C} \;+\; A\overline{B} \quad + \;AB\overline{C} + \overline{A}B\overline{C}D + \overline{A}\,\overline{B}C\overline{D} + A\overline{B}CD$$

0000	1000	1100	1010	0001	1011
0001	1001	1101			
1000	1010				
1001	1011				

Map each of the resulting binary values by placing a 1 in the appropriate cell of the 4-variable Karnaugh map in Figure 30. Notice that some of the values in the expanded expression are redundant.

211

FIGURE 30

AB \ CD	00	01	11	10
00	1	1		
01				
11	1	1		
10	1	1	1	1

Related Problem Map the expression $A + \overline{C}D + AC\overline{D} + \overline{A}BC\overline{D}$ on a Karnaugh map.

Karnaugh Map Simplification of SOP Expressions

The process that results in an expression containing the fewest possible terms with the fewest possible variables is called **minimization.** After an SOP expression has been mapped, a minimum SOP expression is obtained by grouping the 1s and determining the minimum SOP expression from the map.

Grouping the 1s You can group 1s on the Karnaugh map according to the following rules by enclosing those adjacent cells containing 1s. The goal is to maximize the size of the groups and to minimize the number of groups.

1. A group must contain either 1, 2, 4, 8, or 16 cells, which are all powers of two. In the case of a 3-variable map, $2^3 = 8$ cells is the maximum group.
2. Each cell in a group must be adjacent to one or more cells in that same group, but all cells in the group do not have to be adjacent to each other.
3. Always include the largest possible number of 1s in a group in accordance with rule 1.
4. Each 1 on the map must be included in at least one group. The 1s already in a group can be included in another group as long as the overlapping groups include non-common 1s.

EXAMPLE 27 Group the 1s in each of the Karnaugh maps in Figure 31.

(a)

AB \ C	0	1
00	1	
01		1
11	1	1
10		

(b)

AB \ C	0	1
00	1	1
01	1	
11		1
10	1	1

(c)

AB \ CD	00	01	11	10
00	1	1		
01	1	1	1	1
11				
10		1	1	

(d)

AB \ CD	00	01	11	10
00	1			1
01	1	1		1
11	1	1		1
10	1		1	1

FIGURE 31

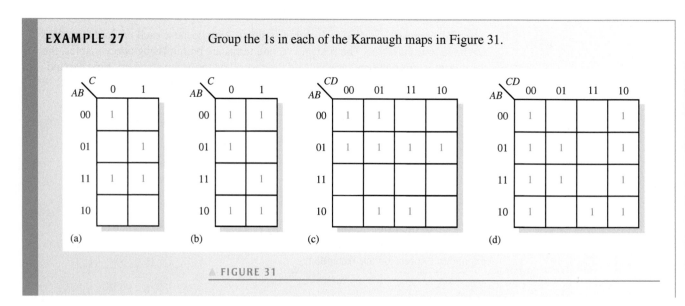

Solution The groupings are shown in Figure 32. In some cases, there may be more than one way to group the 1s to form maximum groupings.

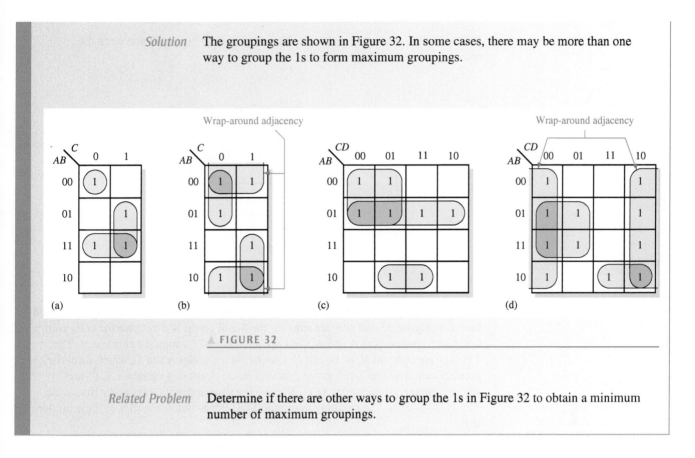

▲ FIGURE 32

Related Problem Determine if there are other ways to group the 1s in Figure 32 to obtain a minimum number of maximum groupings.

Determining the Minimum SOP Expression from the Map When all the 1s representing the standard product terms in an expression are properly mapped and grouped, the process of determining the resulting minimum SOP expression begins. The following rules are applied to find the minimum product terms and the minimum SOP expression:

1. Group the cells that have 1s. Each group of cells containing 1s creates one product term composed of all variables that occur in only one form (either uncomplemented or complemented) within the group. Variables that occur both uncomplemented and complemented within the group are eliminated. These are called *contradictory variables*.

2. Determine the minimum product term for each group.
   a. For a 3-variable map:
      (1) A 1-cell group yields a 3-variable product term
      (2) A 2-cell group yields a 2-variable product term
      (3) A 4-cell group yields a 1-variable term
      (4) An 8-cell group yields a value of 1 for the expression
   b. For a 4-variable map:
      (1) A 1-cell group yields a 4-variable product term
      (2) A 2-cell group yields a 3-variable product term
      (3) A 4-cell group yields a 2-variable product term
      (4) An 8-cell group yields a 1-variable term
      (5) A 16-cell group yields a value of 1 for the expression

3. When all the minimum product terms are derived from the Karnaugh map, they are summed to form the minimum SOP expression.

EXAMPLE 28

Determine the product terms for the Karnaugh map in Figure 33 and write the resulting minimum SOP expression.

▶ FIGURE 33

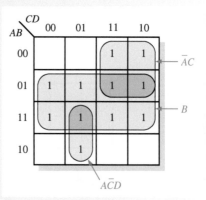

Solution Eliminate variables that are in a grouping in both complemented and uncomplemented forms. In Figure 33, the product term for the 8-cell group is B because the cells within that group contain both A and $\overline{A}$, C and $\overline{C}$, and D and $\overline{D}$, which are eliminated. The 4-cell group contains B, $\overline{B}$, D, and $\overline{D}$, leaving the variables $\overline{A}$ and C, which form the product term $\overline{A}C$. The 2-cell group contains B and $\overline{B}$, leaving variables A, $\overline{C}$, and D which form the product term $A\overline{C}D$. Notice how overlapping is used to maximize the size of the groups. The resulting minimum SOP expression is the sum of these product terms:

$$B + \overline{A}C + A\overline{C}D$$

Related Problem For the Karnaugh map in Figure 33, add a 1 in the lower right cell (1010) and determine the resulting SOP expression.

EXAMPLE 29

Determine the product terms for each of the Karnaugh maps in Figure 34 and write the resulting minimum SOP expression.

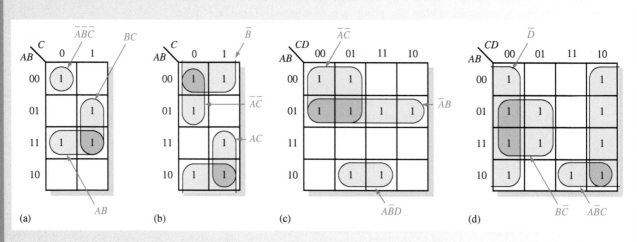

▲ FIGURE 34

Solution   The resulting minimum product term for each group is shown in Figure 34. The minimum SOP expressions for each of the Karnaugh maps in the figure are

(a) $AB + BC + \overline{A}\,\overline{B}\,\overline{C}$

(b) $\overline{B} + \overline{A}\,\overline{C} + AC$

(c) $\overline{A}B + \overline{A}\,\overline{C} + A\overline{B}D$

(d) $\overline{D} + A\overline{B}C + B\overline{C}$

Related Problem   For the Karnaugh map in Figure 34(d), add a 1 in the 0111 cell and determine the resulting SOP expression.

EXAMPLE 30

Use a Karnaugh map to minimize the following standard SOP expression:

$$A\overline{B}C + \overline{A}BC + \overline{A}\,\overline{B}C + \overline{A}\,\overline{B}\,\overline{C} + A\overline{B}\,\overline{C}$$

Solution   The binary values of the expression are

$$101 + 011 + 001 + 000 + 100$$

Map the standard SOP expression and group the cells as shown in Figure 35.

▶ FIGURE 35

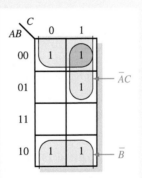

Notice the "wrap around" 4-cell group that includes the top row and the bottom row of 1s. The remaining 1 is absorbed in an overlapping group of two cells. The group of four 1s produces a single variable term, $\overline{B}$. This is determined by observing that within the group, $\overline{B}$ is the only variable that does not change from cell to cell. The group of two 1s produces a 2-variable term $\overline{A}C$. This is determined by observing that within the group, $\overline{A}$ and C do not change from one cell to the next. The product term for each group is shown. The resulting minimum SOP expression is

$$\overline{B} + \overline{A}C$$

Keep in mind that this minimum expression is equivalent to the original standard expression.

Related Problem   Use a Karnaugh map to simplify the following standard SOP expression:

$$X\overline{Y}Z + XY\overline{Z} + \overline{X}YZ + \overline{X}Y\overline{Z} + X\overline{Y}\,\overline{Z} + XYZ$$

EXAMPLE 31

Use a Karnaugh map to minimize the following SOP expression:

$$\overline{B}\,\overline{C}\,\overline{D} + \overline{A}\,\overline{B}C\overline{D} + AB\overline{C}\overline{D} + \overline{A}\,\overline{B}CD + A\overline{B}CD + \overline{A}\,\overline{B}C\overline{D} + \overline{A}BC\overline{D} + ABC\overline{D} + A\overline{B}C\overline{D}$$

Solution   The first term $\overline{B}\,\overline{C}\,\overline{D}$ must be expanded into $A\overline{B}\,\overline{C}\,\overline{D}$ and $\overline{A}\,\overline{B}\,\overline{C}\,\overline{D}$ to get the standard SOP expression, which is then mapped; the cells are grouped as shown in Figure 36.

▶ FIGURE 36

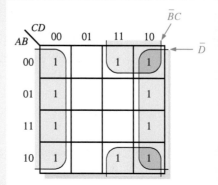

Notice that both groups exhibit "wrap around" adjacency. The group of eight is formed because the cells in the outer columns are adjacent. The group of four is formed to pick up the remaining two 1s because the top and bottom cells are adjacent. The product term for each group is shown. The resulting minimum SOP expression is

$$\overline{D} + \overline{B}C$$

Keep in mind that this minimum expression is equivalent to the original standard expression.

Related Problem   Use a Karnaugh map to simplify the following SOP expression:

$$\overline{W}\,\overline{X}\,\overline{Y}\,\overline{Z} + \overline{W}\overline{X}YZ + W\overline{X}\,\overline{Y}Z + \overline{W}YZ + W\overline{X}\,\overline{Y}\,\overline{Z}$$

Mapping Directly from a Truth Table

You have seen how to map a Boolean expression; now you will learn how to go directly from a truth table to a Karnaugh map. Recall that a truth table gives the output of a Boolean expression for all possible input variable combinations. An example of a Boolean expression and its truth table representation is shown in Figure 37. Notice in the truth table that the output X is 1 for four different input variable combinations. The 1s in the output column

▶ FIGURE 37

Example of mapping directly from a truth table to a Karnaugh map.

$$X = \overline{A}\,\overline{B}\,\overline{C} + A\overline{B}\,\overline{C} + AB\overline{C} + ABC$$

INPUTS			OUTPUT
A	B	C	X
0	0	0	1
0	0	1	0
0	1	0	0
0	1	1	0
1	0	0	1
1	0	1	0
1	1	0	1
1	1	1	1

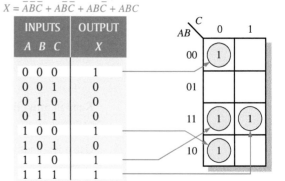

of the truth table are mapped directly onto a Karnaugh map into the cells corresponding to the values of the associated input variable combinations, as shown in Figure 37. In the figure you can see that the Boolean expression, the truth table, and the Karnaugh map are simply different ways to represent a logic function.

"Don't Care" Conditions

Sometimes a situation arises in which some input variable combinations are not allowed. For example, recall that in the BCD code, there are six invalid combinations: 1010, 1011, 1100, 1101, 1110, and 1111. Since these unallowed states will never occur in an application involving the BCD code, they can be treated as **"don't care"** terms with respect to their effect on the output. That is, for these "don't care" terms either a 1 or a 0 may be assigned to the output; it really does not matter since they will never occur.

The "don't care" terms can be used to advantage on the Karnaugh map. Figure 38 shows that for each "don't care" term, an X is placed in the cell. When grouping the 1s, the Xs can be treated as 1s to make a larger grouping or as 0s if they cannot be used to advantage. The larger a group, the simpler the resulting term will be.

◀ FIGURE 38

Example of the use of "don't care" conditions to simplify an expression.

INPUTS	OUTPUT
A B C D	Y
0 0 0 0	0
0 0 0 1	0
0 0 1 0	0
0 0 1 1	0
0 1 0 0	0
0 1 0 1	0
0 1 1 0	0
0 1 1 1	1
1 0 0 0	1
1 0 0 1	1
1 0 1 0	X
1 0 1 1	X
1 1 0 0	X
1 1 0 1	X
1 1 1 0	X
1 1 1 1	X

Don't cares

(a) Truth table

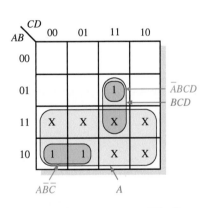

(b) Without "don't cares" $Y = A\overline{B}\,\overline{C} + \overline{A}BCD$
With "don't cares" $Y = A + BCD$

The truth table in Figure 38(a) describes a logic function that has a 1 output only when the BCD code for 7, 8, or 9 is present on the inputs. If the "don't cares" are used as 1s, the resulting expression for the function is $A + BCD$, as indicated in part (b). If the "don't cares" are not used as 1s, the resulting expression is $A\overline{B}\,\overline{C} + \overline{A}BCD$; so you can see the advantage of using "don't care" terms to get the simplest expression.

EXAMPLE 32

In a 7-segment display, each of the seven segments is activated for various digits. For example, segment a is activated for the digits 0, 2, 3, 5, 6, 7, 8, and 9, as illustrated in Figure 39. Since each digit can be represented by a BCD code, derive an SOP expression for segment a using the variables $ABCD$ and then minimize the expression using a Karnaugh map.

▶ FIGURE 39

7-segment display.

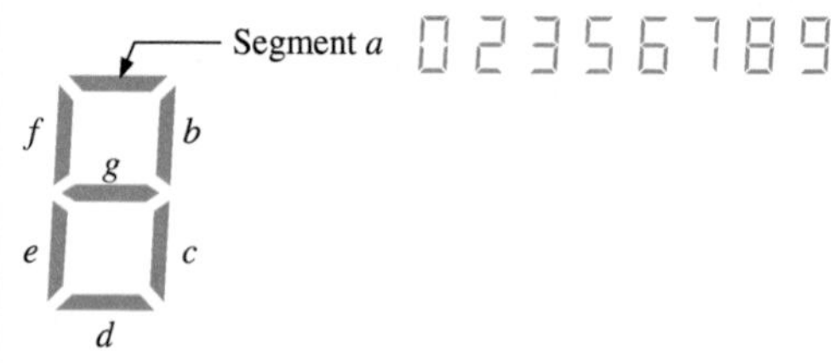

Segment *a* ◻ ◻ ◻ ◻ ◻ ◻ ◻ ◻

0 2 3 5 6 7 8 9

Solution   The expression for segment *a* is

$$a = \overline{A}\,\overline{B}\,\overline{C}\,\overline{D} + \overline{A}\,\overline{B}\,C\overline{D} + \overline{A}\,BC\overline{D} + \overline{A}\,BC\overline{D} + \overline{A}\,BCD + \overline{A}\,BCD + A\overline{B}\,\overline{C}\,\overline{D} + A\overline{B}\,\overline{C}\,\overline{D}$$

Each term in the expression represents one of the digits in which segment *a* is used. The Karnaugh map minimization is shown in Figure 40. X's (don't cares) are entered for those states that do not occur in the BCD code.

▶ FIGURE 40

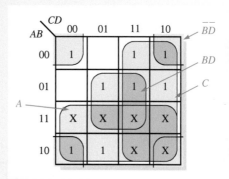

From the Karnaugh map, the minimized expression for segment *a* is

$$a = A + C + BD + \overline{B}\,\overline{D}$$

Related Problem   Draw the logic diagram for the segment-*a* logic.

SECTION 9
CHECKUP

1. Lay out Karnaugh maps for three and four variables.

2. Group the 1s and write the simplified SOP expression for the Karnaugh map in Figure 27.

3. Write the original standard SOP expressions for each of the Karnaugh maps in Figure 34.

10 FIVE-VARIABLE KARNAUGH MAPS

Boolean functions with five variables can be simplified using a 32-cell Karnaugh map. Actually, two 4-variable maps (16 cells each) are used to construct a 5-variable map. You already know the cell adjacencies within each of the 4-variable maps and how to form groups of cells containing 1s to simplify an SOP expression. All you need to learn for five variables is the cell adjacencies between the two 4-variable maps and how to group those adjacent 1s.

After completing this section, you should be able to

- Determine cell adjacencies in a 5-variable map
- Form maximum cell groupings in a 5-variable map
- Minimize 5-variable Boolean expressions using the Karnaugh map

A Karnaugh map for five variables (*ABCDE*) can be constructed using two 4-variable maps with which you are already familiar. Each map contains 16 cells with all combinations of variables *B*, *C*, *D*, and *E*. One map is for *A* = 0 and the other is for *A* = 1, as shown in Figure 41.

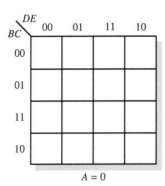

◀ FIGURE 41

A 5-variable Karnaugh map.

Cell Adjacencies

You already know how to determine adjacent cells within the 4-variable map. The best way to visualize cell adjacencies between the two 16-cell maps is to imagine that the *A* = 0 map is placed on top of the *A* = 1 map. Each cell in the *A* = 0 map is adjacent to the cell directly below it in the *A* = 1 map.

To illustrate, an example with four groups is shown in Figure 42 with the maps in a 3-dimensional arrangement. The 1s in the yellow cells form an 8-bit group (four in the *A* = 0

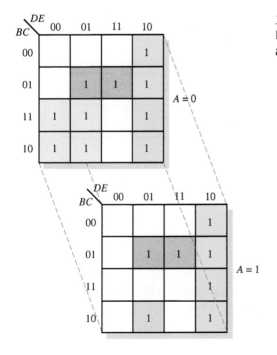

◀ FIGURE 42

Illustration of groupings of 1s in adjacent cells of a 5-variable map.

map combined with four in the $A = 1$ map). The 1s in the orange cells form a 4-bit group. The 1s in the light red cells form a 4-bit group only in the $A = 0$ map. The 1 in the gray cell in the $A = 1$ map is grouped with the 1 in the lower right light red cell in the $A = 0$ map to form a 2-bit group.

Determining the Boolean Expression   The original SOP Boolean expression that is plotted on the Karnaugh map in Figure 42 contains seventeen 5-variable terms because there are seventeen 1s on the map. As you know, only the variables that do not change from uncomplemented to complemented or vice versa within a group remain in the expression for that group. The simplified expression taken from the map is developed as follows:

* The term for the yellow group is $D\overline{E}$.

* The term for the orange group is $\overline{B}CE$.

* The term for the light red group is $\overline{A}\overline{B}\overline{D}$.

* The term for the gray cell grouped with the light red cell is $B\overline{C}\,\overline{D}E$.

Combining these terms into the simplified SOP expression yields

$$X = D\overline{E} + \overline{B}CE + \overline{A}\overline{B}\overline{D} + B\overline{C}\,\overline{D}E$$

EXAMPLE 33

Use a Karnaugh map to minimize the following standard SOP 5-variable expression:

$$X = \overline{A}\,\overline{B}\,\overline{C}\,\overline{D}\,\overline{E} + \overline{A}\,\overline{B}\,C\,\overline{D}\,\overline{E} + \overline{A}\,B\,C\,\overline{D}\,\overline{E} + \overline{A}\,B\,\overline{C}\,\overline{D}\,\overline{E} + \overline{A}\,B\,C\,\overline{D}\,E + \overline{A}\,B\,C\,D\overline{E}$$
$$+ \overline{A}\,B\,C\,D\,E + A\,\overline{B}\,\overline{C}\,\overline{D}\,\overline{E} + A\,\overline{B}\,\overline{C}\,\overline{D}\,E + A\,B\,C\,\overline{D}\,E + A\,B\,C\,D\,E + A\,\overline{B}\,C\,D\,E$$

Solution   Map the SOP expression. Figure 43 shows the groupings and their corresponding terms. Combining the terms yields the following minimized SOP expression:

$$X + \overline{A}\,\overline{D}\,\overline{E} + \overline{B}\,\overline{C}\,\overline{D} + BCE + ACDE$$

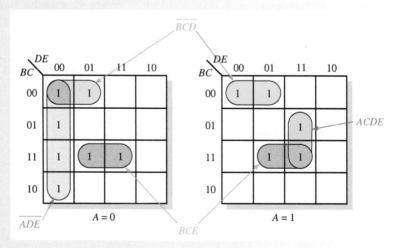

▲ FIGURE 43

Related Problem   Minimize the following expression:

$$Y = \overline{A}\,\overline{B}\,\overline{C}\,\overline{D}\,\overline{E} + \overline{A}\,\overline{B}\,\overline{C}\,D\,\overline{E} + \overline{A}\,\overline{B}\,C\,\overline{D}\,\overline{E} + \overline{A}\,B\,\overline{C}\,\overline{D}\,\overline{E} + \overline{A}\,B\,\overline{C}\,\overline{D}\,E + \overline{A}\,B\,\overline{C}\,D\,\overline{E} + \overline{A}\,B\,C\,\overline{D}\,\overline{E} + \overline{A}\,B\,C\,D\,\overline{E}$$
$$+ \overline{A}\,B\,\overline{C}\,D\,\overline{E} + \overline{A}\,B\,C\,D\,\overline{E} + \overline{A}\,B\,C\,D\,\overline{E} + \overline{A}\,B\,C\,D\,\overline{E} + A\,\overline{B}\,C\,D\,\overline{E} + A\,\overline{B}\,C\,D\,\overline{E} + A\,B\,C\,D\,\overline{E} + A\,B\,\overline{C}\,D\,\overline{E}$$

SECTION 10 CHECKUP

1. Why does a 5-variable Karnaugh map require 32 cells?
2. What is the expression represented by a 5-variable Karnaugh map in which each cell contains a 1?

11 DESCRIBING LOGIC WITH AN HDL

Hardware description languages (HDLs) are tools for logic design entry, called text entry, that are used to implement logic designs in programmable logic devices. This section provides a brief introduction to VHDL and is not meant to teach the complete structure and syntax of the language. For more detailed information and instruction, refer to the footnote. Although VHDL provides multiple ways to describe a logic circuit, only the simplest and most direct programming examples of text entry are discussed here.

After completing this section, you should be able to

- State the essential elements of VHDL
- Write a simple VHDL program

The V in VHDL[*] stands for VHSIC (*Very High Speed Integrated Circuit*) and the HDL, of course, stands for hardware description language. As mentioned, VHDL is a standard language adopted by the IEEE (Institute of Electrical and Electronics Engineers) and is designated IEEE Std. 1076-1993. VHDL is a complex and comprehensive language and using it to its full potential involves a lot of effort and experience.

VHDL provides three basic approaches to describing a digital circuit using software: *behavioral, data flow,* and *structural.* We will restrict this discussion to the data flow approach in which you write Boolean-type statements to describe a logic circuit. Keep in mind that VHDL, as well as the other HDLs, is a tool for implementing digital designs and is, therefore, a means to an end and not an end in itself.

It is relatively easy to write programs to describe simple logic circuits in VHDL. The logical operators are the following VHDL keywords: **and, or, not, nand, nor, xor,** and **xnor.** The two essential elements in any VHDL program are the entity and the architecture, and they must be used together. The **entity** describes a given logic function in terms of its external inputs and outputs, called ports. The **architecture** describes the internal operation of the logic function.

In its simplest form, the entity element consists of three statements: The first statement assigns a name to a logic function; the second statement, called the *port* statement which is indented, specifies the inputs and outputs; and the third statement is the *end* statement. Although you would probably not write a VHDL program for a single gate, it is instructive to start with a simple example such as an AND gate. The VHDL entity declaration for a 2-input AND gate is

entity AND_Gate2 **is**

　port (A, B: **in** bit; X: **out** bit);

end entity AND_Gate2;

Colons and semicolons must be used appropriately in all VHDL programs.

The blue boldface terms are VHDL keywords; the other terms are identifiers that you assign; and the parentheses, colons, and semicolons are required VHDL syntax. As you can see, A and

---

[*]See Floyd, Thomas. 2003. *Digital Fundamentals with VHDL.* Prentice Hall; Pellerin, David and Taylor, Douglas. 1997. *VHDL Made Easy!* Prentice Hall; Bhasker, Jayaram. 1999. *A VHDL Primer,* 3 ed. Prentice Hall.

B are specified as input bits and X is specified as an output bit. The port identifiers A, B, and X as well as the entity name AND_Gate2 are user-defined and can be renamed. As in all HDLs, the placement of colons and semicolons is crucial and must be strictly adhered to.

The VHDL architecture element of the program for the 2-input AND gate described by the entity is

architecture LogicFunction **of** AND_Gate2 **is**

begin

   X ⇐ A **and** B;

end architecture LogicFunction;

Again, the VHDL keywords are blue boldface, and the semicolons and the assignment operator ⇐ are required syntax. The first statement of the architecture element must reference the entity name.

The entity and the architecture are combined into a single VHDL program to describe an AND gate, as illustrated in Figure 44.

▶ FIGURE 44

A VHDL program for a 2-input AND gate.

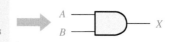

```
entity AND_Gate2 is
  port (A, B: in bit; X: out bit);
end entity AND_Gate2;

architecture LogicFunction of AND_Gate2 is
begin
  X <= A and B;
end architecture LogicFunction;
```

Writing Boolean Expressions in VHDL   As you saw, the expression for a 2-input AND gate, $X = AB$, is written in VHDL as X ⇐ A **and** B;. Any Boolean expression can be written using VHDL keywords **not, and, or, nand, nor, xor,** and **xnor.** For example, the Boolean expression $X = A + B + C$ is written in VHDL as X ⇐ A **or** B **or** C;. The Boolean expression $X = A\overline{B} + \overline{C}D$ can be written as the VHDL statement X ⇐ (A **and not** B) **or** (**not** C **and** D);. As another example, the VHDL statement for a 2-input NAND gate can be written as X ⇐ **not**(A **and** B); or it can be written as X ⇐ A **nand** B;.

EXAMPLE 34

Write a VHDL program to describe the logic circuit in Figure 45.

▶ FIGURE 45

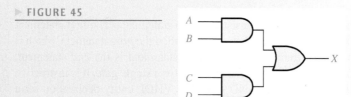

Solution   This AND/OR logic circuit is described in Boolean algebra as

$$X = AB + CD$$

The VHDL program follows. The entity name is AND_OR.

entity AND_OR **is**

   port (A, B, C, D: **in** bit; X: **out** bit);

end entity AND_OR;

architecture LogicFunction of AND_OR is

begin

   X <= (A and B) or (C and D);

end architecture LogicFunction;

Related Problem   Write the VHDL statement to describe the logic circuit if a NOR gate replaces the OR gate in Figure 45.

SECTION 11 CHECKUP

1. What is an HDL?
2. Name the two essential design elements in a VHDL program.
3. What does the entity do?
4. What does the architecture do?

System Application Activity

Seven-Segment Display Logic

Seven-segment displays are used in many types of products that you see every day. These displays are also used in the tablet-bottling system. The displays in the bottling system are driven by logic circuits that decode a binary coded decimal (BCD) number and activate the appropriate digits on the display. BCD-to-7-segment decoder/drivers are readily available as single IC packages for activating the ten decimal digits.

In addition to the numbers from 0 to 9, the 7-segment display can show certain letters. For the tablet-bottling system, a requirement has been added to display the letters A, b, C, d, and E on a separate common-anode 7-segment display that uses a hexadecimal keypad for both the numerical inputs and the letters. These letters will be used to identify the type of vitamin tablet that is being bottled at any given time. In this application activity, the decoding logic for displaying the five letters is developed for use in the system.

The 7-Segment Display

Two types of 7-segment displays are the LED and the LCD. Each of the seven segments in an LED display uses a light-emitting diode to produce a colored light when there is current through it and can be seen in the dark. An LCD or liquid-crystal display operates by polarizing light so that when a segment is not activated by a voltage, it reflects incident light and appears invisible against its background; however, when a segment is activated, it does not reflect light and appears black. LCD displays cannot be seen in the dark.

The seven segments in both LED and LCD displays are arranged as shown in Figure 46 and labeled *a*, *b*, *c*, *d*, *e*, *f*, and *g* as indicated in part (a). Selected segments are activated to create each of the ten decimal digits as well as certain letters of

FIGURE 46

Seven-segment display.

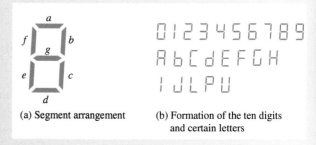

(a) Segment arrangement

(b) Formation of the ten digits and certain letters

the alphabet, as shown in part (b). The letter b is shown as lowercase because a capital B would be the same as the digit 8. Similarly, for d, a capital letter would appear as a 0.

1. List the segments used to form the digit 2.
2. List the segments used to form the digit 5.
3. List the segments used to form the letter A.
4. List the segments used to form the letter E.
5. Is there any one segment that is common to all digits?
6. Is there any one segment that is common to all letters?

Display Logic

The segments in a 7-segment display can be used in the formation of various letters as shown in Figure 46(b). Each segment must be activated by its own decoding circuit that detects the code for any of the letters in which that segment is used. Because a common-anode display is used, the segments are turned *on* with a LOW (0) logic level and turned *off* with a HIGH (1) logic level. The active segments are shown for each of the letters required for the tablet-bottling system in Table 9. Even though the active level is LOW (lighting the LED), the logic expressions are developed exactly the same way as discussed in this chapter, by mapping the desired output (1, 0, or X) for every possible input, grouping the 1s on the map, and reading the SOP expression from the map. In effect, the reduced logic expression is the logic for keeping a given segment OFF. At first, this may sound confusing, but it is simple in practice and it avoids an output current capability issue with bipolar (TTL) logic.

TABLE 9

Active segments for each of the five letters used in the system display.

LETTER	SEGMENTS ACTIVATED
A	a, b, c, e, f, g
b	c, d, e, f, g
C	a, d, e, f
d	b, c, d, e, g
E	a, d, e, f, g

A block diagram of a 7-segment logic and display for generating the five letters is shown in Figure 47(a), and the truth table is shown in part (b). The logic has four hexadecimal inputs and seven outputs, one for each segment. Because the letter F is not used as an input, we will show it on the truth table with all outputs set to 1 (OFF).

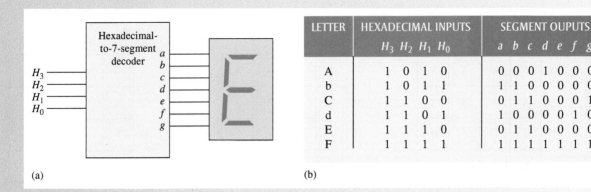

LETTER	HEXADECIMAL INPUTS				SEGMENT OUPUTS						
	H_3	H_2	H_1	H_0	a	b	c	d	e	f	g
A	1	0	1	0	0	0	0	1	0	0	0
b	1	0	1	1	1	1	0	0	0	0	0
C	1	1	0	0	0	1	1	0	0	0	1
d	1	1	0	1	1	0	0	0	0	1	0
E	1	1	1	0	0	1	1	0	0	0	0
F	1	1	1	1	1	1	1	1	1	1	1

(a) (b)

FIGURE 47

Hexadecimal-to-7-segment decoder for letters *A* through *E*, used in the system.

Karnaugh Maps and the Invalid BCD Code Detector

To develop the simplified logic for each segment, the truth table information in Figure 47 is mapped onto Karnaugh maps. Recall that the BCD numbers will not be shown on the letter display. For this reason, an entry that represents a BCD number will be entered as an "X" (don't care) on the K-maps. This makes the logic much simpler but would put some strange outputs on the display unless steps are taken to eliminate that possibility. Because all of the letters are *invalid* BCD characters, the display is activated only when an invalid BCD code is entered into the keypad, thus allowing only letters to be displayed. The logic for the invalid BCD code detector is developed in the lab experiment.

Expressions for the Segment Logic

Using the table in 47(b), a standard SOP expression can be written for each segment and then minimized using a K-map. The desired outputs from the truth table are entered in the appropriate cells representing the hex inputs. To obtain the minimum SOP expressions for the display logic, the 1s and Xs are grouped.

Segment a Segment *a* is used for the letters A, C, and E. For the letter A, the hexadecimal code is 1010 or, in terms of variables, $H_3\overline{H_2}H_1\overline{H_0}$. For the letter C, the hexadecimal code is 1100 or $H_3H_2\overline{H_1}\overline{H_0}$. For the letter E, the code is 1110 or $H_3H_2H_1\overline{H_0}$. The complete standard SOP expression for segment *a* is

$$a = H_3\overline{H_2}H_1\overline{H_0} + H_3H_2\overline{H_1}\overline{H_0} + H_3H_2H_1\overline{H_0}$$

Because a LOW is the active output state for each segment logic circuit, a 0 is entered on the Karnaugh map in each cell that represents the code for the letters in which the segment is *on*. The simplification of the expression for segment *a* is shown in Figure 48(a) after grouping the 1s and 0s.

Segment b Segment *b* is used for the letters A and d. The complete standard SOP expression for segment *b* is

$$b = H_3\overline{H_2}H_1\overline{H_0} + H_3H_2\overline{H_1}H_0$$

The simplification of the expression for segment *b* is shown in Figure 48(b).

Segment c Segment *c* is used for the letters A, b, and d. The complete standard SOP expression for segment *c* is

$$c = H_3\overline{H_2}H_1\overline{H_0} + H_3\overline{H_2}H_1H_0 + H_3H_2\overline{H_1}H_0$$

225

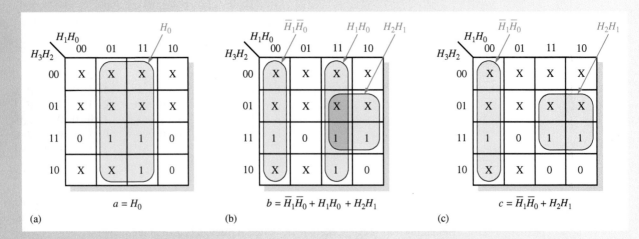

(a) $a = H_0$

(b) $b = \overline{H}_1\overline{H}_0 + H_1 H_0 + H_2 H_1$

(c) $c = \overline{H}_1\overline{H}_0 + H_2 H_1$

FIGURE 48

Minimization of the expressions for segments *a*, *b*, and *c*.

The simplification of the expression for segment c is shown in Figure 48(c).

7. Develop the minimum expression for segment d.
8. Develop the minimum expression for segment e.
9. Develop the minimum expression for segment f.
10. Develop the minimum expression for segment g.

The Logic Circuits

From the minimum expressions, the logic circuits for each segment can be implemented. For segment a, connect the H_0 input directly to the a segment on the display (no gates are required). The segment b and segment c logic are shown in Figure 49 using AND or OR gates. Notice that two of the terms ($H_2 H_1$ and $\overline{H}_1\overline{H}_0$) appear in the expressions for both b and c logic so two of the AND gates can be used in both, as indicated.

11. Show the logic for segment d.
12. Show the logic for segment e.
13. Show the logic for segment f.
14. Show the logic for segment g.

FIGURE 49

Segment-*b* and segment-*c* logic circuits.

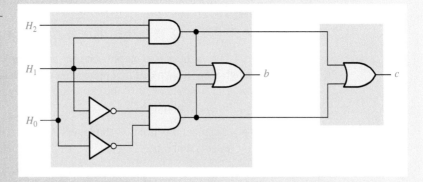

Simulation

The decoder simulation using Multisim is shown in Figure 50 with the letter E selected. Subcircuits are used for the segment logic to be developed as activities or in the lab.

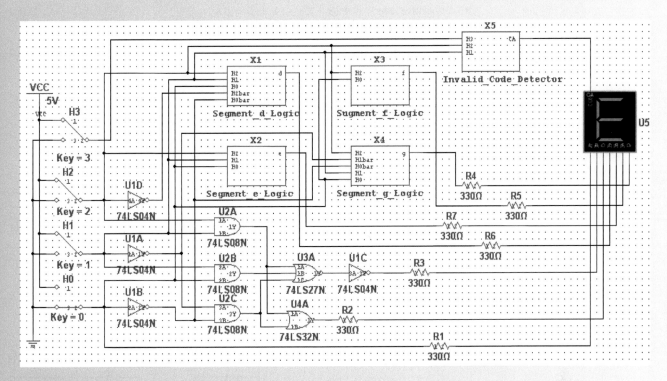

▲ FIGURE 50

Multisim circuit screen for decoder and display.

Open file SAA04 on www.pearsoned.com/electronics. Run the simulation of the decoder and display using your Multisim software and observe the operation for the specified letters.

Putting Your Knowledge to Work

How would you modify the decoder for a common-cathode 7-segment display.

SUMMARY

♦ Gate symbols and Boolean expressions for the outputs of an inverter and 2-input gates are shown in Figure 51.

▶ FIGURE 51

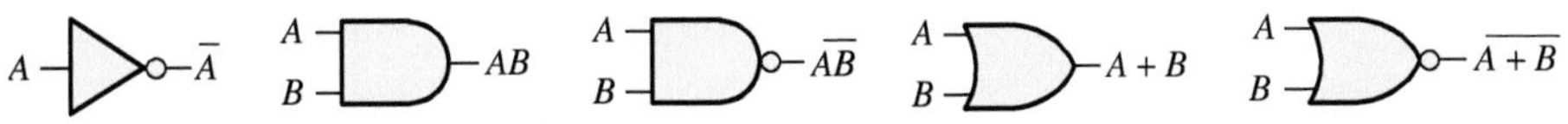

$A \rightarrow \overline{A}$ $\begin{matrix} A \\ B \end{matrix} \rightarrow AB$ $\begin{matrix} A \\ B \end{matrix} \rightarrow \overline{AB}$ $\begin{matrix} A \\ B \end{matrix} \rightarrow A + B$ $\begin{matrix} A \\ B \end{matrix} \rightarrow \overline{A + B}$

♦ Commutative laws: $A + B = B + A$
$$AB = BA$$

◆ Associative laws: $A + (B + C) = (A + B) + C$

$$A(BC) = (AB)C$$

◆ Distributive law: $A(B + C) = AB + AC$

◆ Boolean rules:

1. $A + 0 = A$		**7.** $A \cdot A = A$	
2. $A + 1 = 1$		**8.** $A \cdot \overline{A} = 0$	
3. $A \cdot 0 = 0$		**9.** $\overline{\overline{A}} = A$	
4. $A \cdot 1 = A$		**10.** $A + AB = A$	
5. $A + A = A$		**11.** $A + \overline{A}B = A + B$	
6. $A + \overline{A} = 1$		**12.** $(A + B)(A + C) = A + BC$	

◆ DeMorgan's theorems:

1. The complement of a product is equal to the sum of the complements of the terms in the product.

$$\overline{XY} = \overline{X} + \overline{Y}$$

2. The complement of a sum is equal to the product of the complements of the terms in the sum.

$$\overline{X + Y} = \overline{X}\,\overline{Y}$$

◆ Karnaugh maps for 3 and 4 variables are shown in Figure 52. A 5-variable map is formed from two 4-variable maps.

▶ FIGURE 52

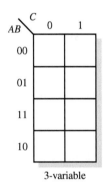

3-variable

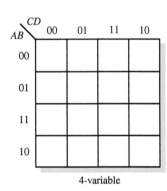

4-variable

◆ The basic design element in VHDL is an entity/architecture pair.

KEY TERMS

Complement   The inverse or opposite of a number. In Boolean algebra, the inverse function, expressed with a bar over a variable. The complement of a 1 is 0, and vice versa.

"Don't care"   A combination of input literals that cannot occur and can be used as a 1 or a 0 on a Karnaugh map for simplification.

Karnaugh map   An arrangement of cells representing the combinations of literals in a Boolean expression and used for a systematic simplification of the expression.

Minimization   The process that results in an SOP or POS Boolean expression that contains the fewest possible literals per term.

Product-of-sums (POS)   A form of Boolean expression that is basically the ANDing of ORed terms.

Product term   The Boolean product of two or more literals equivalent to an AND operation.

Sum-of-products (SOP)   A form of Boolean expression that is basically the ORing of ANDed terms.

Sum term   The Boolean sum of two or more literals equivalent to an OR operation.

Variable   A symbol used to represent an action, a condition, or data that can have a value of 1 or 0, usually designated by an italic letter or word.

VHDL   A standard hardware description language. IEEE Std. 1076-1993.

TRUE/FALSE QUIZ

Answers are at the end of the chapter.

1. *Variable, complement,* and *literal* are all terms used in Boolean algebra.
2. Addition in Boolean algebra is equivalent to the OR function.
3. Multiplication in Boolean algebra is equivalent to the NAND function.
4. The commutative law, associative law, and distributive law are all laws in Boolean algebra.
5. The complement of a 1 is 0.
6. When a Boolean variable is multiplied by its complement, the result is the variable.
7. "The complement of a product of variables is equal to the sum of the complements of each variable" is a statement of DeMorgan's theorem.
8. SOP means series of products.
9. Karnaugh maps can be used to simplify Boolean expressions.
10. A 4-variable Karnaugh map has eight cells.

SELF-TEST

Answers are at the end of the chapter.

1. The complement of a variable is always
   - (a) 0
   - (b) 1
   - (c) equal to the variable
   - (d) the inverse of the variable
2. The Boolean expression $A + \bar{B} + C$ is
   - (a) a sum term
   - (b) a literal term
   - (c) a product term
   - (d) a complemented term
3. The Boolean expression $\overline{AB}\,\overline{CD}$ is
   - (a) a sum term
   - (b) a product term
   - (c) a literal term
   - (d) always 1
4. The domain of the expression $A\bar{B}CD + A\bar{B} + \bar{C}D + B$ is
   - (a) A and D
   - (b) B only
   - (c) $A, B, C,$ and D
   - (d) none of these
5. According to the commutative law of addition,
   - (a) $AB = BA$
   - (b) $A = A + A$
   - (c) $A + (B + C) = (A + B) + C$
   - (d) $A + B = B + A$
6. According to the associative law of multiplication,
   - (a) $B = BB$
   - (b) $A(BC) = (AB)C$
   - (c) $A + B = B + A$
   - (d) $B + B(B + 0)$
7. According to the distributive law,
   - (a) $A(B + C) = AB + AC$
   - (b) $A(BC) = ABC$
   - (c) $A(A + 1) = A$
   - (d) $A + AB = A$
8. Which one of the following is *not* a valid rule of Boolean algebra?
   - (a) $A + 1 = 1$
   - (b) $A = \bar{A}$
   - (c) $AA = A$
   - (d) $A + 0 = A$
9. Which of the following rules states that if one input of an AND gate is always 1, the output is equal to the other input?
   - (a) $A + 1 = 1$
   - (b) $A + A = A$
   - (c) $A \cdot A = A$
   - (d) $A \cdot 1 = A$
10. According to DeMorgan's theorems, the following equality(s) is (are) correct:
    - (a) $\overline{AB} = \bar{A} + \bar{B}$
    - (b) $\overline{XYZ} = \bar{X} + \bar{Y} + \bar{Z}$
    - (c) $\overline{A + B + C} = \overline{AB}\,\overline{C}$
    - (d) all of these

11. The Boolean expression $X = AB + CD$ represents

    (**a**) two ORs ANDed together   (**b**) a 4-input AND gate

    (**c**) two ANDs ORed together   (**d**) an exclusive-OR

12. An example of a sum-of-products expression is

    (**a**) $A + B(C + D)$ (**b**) $\overline{A}B + A\overline{C} + A\overline{B}C$

    (**c**) $(\overline{A} + B + C)(A + \overline{B} + C)$ (**d**) both answers (a) and (b)

13. An example of a product-of-sums expression is

    (**a**) $A(B + C) + A\overline{C}$ (**b**) $(A + B)(\overline{A} + B + \overline{C})$

    (**c**) $\overline{A} + \overline{B} + BC$ (**d**) both answers (a) and (b)

14. An example of a standard SOP expression is

    (**a**) $\overline{A}B + A\overline{B}C + AB\overline{D}$ (**b**) $A\overline{B}C + A\overline{C}D$

    (**c**) $A\overline{B} + \overline{A}B + AB$ (**d**) $A\overline{B}CD + \overline{A}B + \overline{A}$

15. A 3-variable Karnaugh map has

    (**a**) eight cells   (**b**) three cells

    (**c**) sixteen cells   (**d**) four cells

16. In a 4-variable Karnaugh map, a 2-variable product term is produced by

    (**a**) a 2-cell group of 1s   (**b**) an 8-cell group of 1s

    (**c**) a 4-cell group of 1s   (**d**) a 4-cell group of 0s

17. A 5-variable Karnaugh map has

    (**a**) sixteen cells   (**b**) thirty-two cells   (**c**) sixty-four cells

18. The Quine-McClusky method can be used to

    (**a**) replace the Karnaugh map method   (**b**) simplify expressions with 5 or more variables

    (**c**) both (a) and (b)   (**d**) none of the above

19. VHDL is a type of

    (**a**) programmable logic   (**b**) hardware description language

    (**c**) programmable array   (**d**) logical mathematics

20. In VHDL, a port is

    (**a**) a type of entity   (**b**) a type of architecture

    (**c**) an input or output   (**d**) a type of variable

PROBLEMS

Answers to odd-numbered problems are at the end of the chapter.

Section 1   **Boolean Operations and Expressions**

1. Using Boolean notation, write an expression that is a 1 whenever one or more of its variables $(A, B, C,$ and $D)$ are 1s.

2. Write an expression that is a 1 only if all of its variables $(A, B, C, D,$ and $E)$ are 1s.

3. Write an expression that is a 1 when one or more of its variables $(A, B,$ and $C)$ are 0s.

4. Evaluate the following operations:

    (**a**) $0 + 0 + 1$ (**b**) $1 + 1 + 1$ (**c**) $1 \cdot 0 \cdot 0$

    (**d**) $1 \cdot 1 \cdot 1$ (**e**) $1 \cdot 0 \cdot 1$ (**f**) $1 \cdot 1 + 0 \cdot 1 \cdot 1$

5. Find the values of the variables that make each product term 1 and each sum term 0.

    (**a**) AB (**b**) $A\overline{B}C$ (**c**) $A + B$ (**d**) $\overline{A} + B + \overline{C}$

    (**e**) $\overline{A} + \overline{B} + C$ (**f**) $\overline{A} + B$ (**g**) $A\overline{B}\,\overline{C}$

6. Find the value of X for all possible values of the variables.

    (**a**) $X = (A + B)C + B$ (**b**) $X = (\overline{A + B})C$ (**c**) $X = A\overline{B}C + AB$

    (**d**) $X = (A + B)(\overline{A} + B)$ (**e**) $X = (A + BC)(\overline{B} + \overline{C})$

Section 2 **Laws and Rules of Boolean Algebra**

7. Identify the law of Boolean algebra upon which each of the following equalities is based:

(a) $A\overline{B} + CD + A\overline{C}D + B = B + A\overline{B} + A\overline{C}D + CD$

(b) $AB\overline{C}D + \overline{A}BC = D\overline{C}BA + \overline{C}B\overline{A}$

(c) $AB(CD + \overline{E}F + GH) = ABCD + AB\overline{E}F + ABGH$

8. Identify the Boolean rule(s) on which each of the following equalities is based:

(a) $\overline{\overline{AB + CD}} + \overline{EF} = AB + CD + \overline{EF}$ (b) $A\overline{A}B + AB\overline{C} + AB\overline{B} = AB\overline{C}$

(c) $A(\overline{B}C + BC) + AC = A(BC) + AC$ (d) $AB(C + \overline{C}) + AC = AB + AC$

(e) $A\overline{B} + A\overline{B}C = A\overline{B}$ (f) $ABC + \overline{AB} + \overline{AB}CD = ABC + \overline{AB} + D$

Section 3 **DeMorgan's Theorems**

9. Apply DeMorgan's theorems to each expression:

(a) $\overline{A + \overline{B}}$ (b) $\overline{\overline{A}B}$ (c) $\overline{A + B + C}$ (d) $\overline{ABC}$

(e) $\overline{A(B + C)}$ (f) $\overline{AB + CD}$ (g) $\overline{A\overline{B} + \overline{C}D}$ (h) $\overline{(A + \overline{B})(\overline{C} + D)}$

10. Apply DeMorgan's theorems to each expression:

(a) $\overline{A\overline{B}(C + \overline{D})}$ (b) $\overline{AB(CD + EF)}$

(c) $\overline{(\overline{A} + \overline{B} + C + \overline{D}) + ABC\overline{D}}$ (d) $\overline{(\overline{A} + B + C + D)(\overline{A\overline{B}\overline{C}D})}$

(e) $\overline{A\overline{B}(CD + \overline{E}F)(\overline{AB} + \overline{CD})}$

11. Apply DeMorgan's theorems to the following:

(a) $\overline{\overline{(ABC)(EFG)} + \overline{(HIJ)(KLM)}}$ (b) $\overline{(A + \overline{BC} + CD) + \overline{BC}}$

(c) $\overline{\overline{(\overline{A} + B)(\overline{C} + D)(\overline{E} + F)(\overline{G} + H)}}$

Section 4 **Boolean Analysis of Logic Circuits**

12. Write the Boolean expression for each of the logic gates in Figure 53.

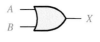

(a)   (b)   (c)   (d)

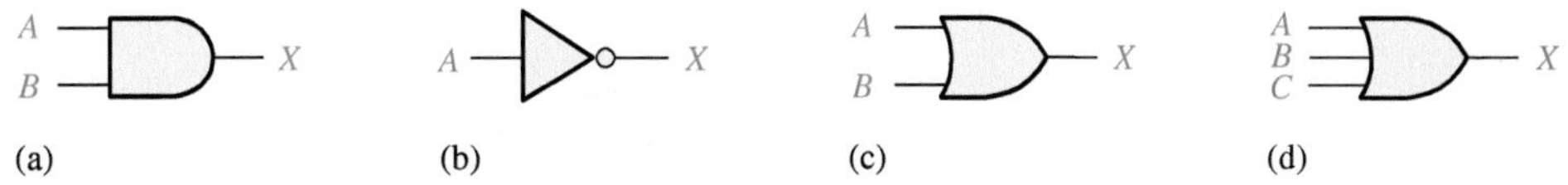

13. Write the Boolean expression for each of the logic circuits in Figure 54.

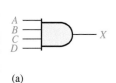

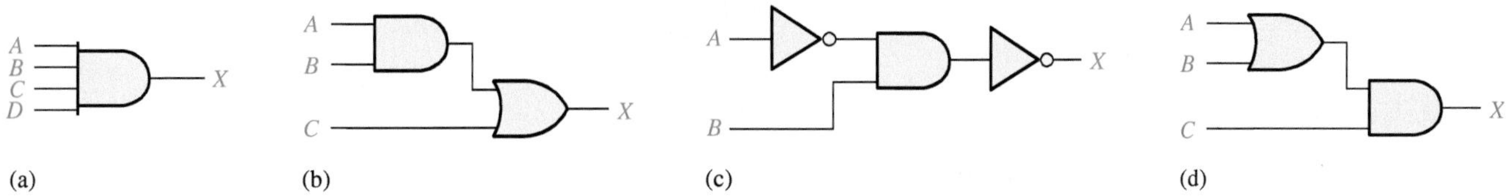

(a)

(b)

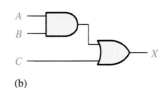

(c)

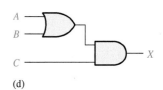

(d)

▲ FIGURE 54

14. Draw the logic circuit represented by each of the following expressions:

(a) $A + B + C$ (b) ABC

(c) $AB + C$ (d) $AB + CD$

15. Draw the logic circuit represented by each expression:

(a) $A\overline{B} + \overline{A}B$ (b) $AB + \overline{A}B + \overline{A}BC$

(c) $\overline{A}B(C + \overline{D})$ (d) $A + B[C + D(B + \overline{C})]$

16. (a) Draw a logic circuit for the case where the output, ENABLE, is LOW only if the inputs, ASSERT and READY, are both HIGH.

(b) Draw a logic circuit for the case where the output, HOLD, is LOW only if the input, LOAD, is HIGH and the input, READY, is LOW.

17. Develop the truth table for each of the circuits in Figure 55.

▶ FIGURE 55

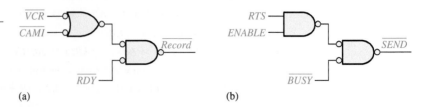

(a)   (b)

18. Construct a truth table for each of the following Boolean expressions:

    (a) $A + B$ **(b)** AB **(c)** $AB + BC$

    (d) $(A + B)C$ **(e)** $(A + B)(\overline{B} + C)$

Section 5   **Simplification Using Boolean Algebra**

19. Using Boolean algebra techniques, simplify the following expressions as much as possible:

    (a) $A(A + B)$ **(b)** $A(\overline{A} + AB)$ **(c)** $BC + \overline{B}C$

    (d) $A(A + \overline{A}B)$ **(e)** $A\overline{B}C + \overline{A}BC + \overline{A}\overline{B}C$

20. Using Boolean algebra, simplify the following expressions:

    (a) $(A + \overline{B})(A + C)$ **(b)** $\overline{A}B + \overline{A}B\overline{C} + \overline{A}BCD + \overline{A}B\overline{C}DE$

    (c) $AB + \overline{A}BC + A$ **(d)** $(A + \overline{A})(AB + AB\overline{C})$

    (e) $AB + (\overline{A} + \overline{B})C + AB$

21. Using Boolean algebra, simplify each expression:

    (a) $BD + B(D + E) + \overline{D}(D + F)$ **(b)** $\overline{A}\overline{B}C + \overline{(A + B + \overline{C})} + \overline{A}\overline{B}\overline{C}D$

    (c) $(B + BC)(B + \overline{B}C)(B + D)$ **(d)** $ABCD + AB(\overline{CD}) + (\overline{AB})CD$

    (e) $ABC[AB + \overline{C}(BC + AC)]$

22. Determine which of the logic circuits in Figure 56 are equivalent.

▶ FIGURE 56

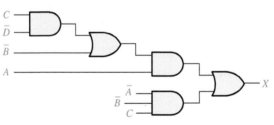

(a)   (b)

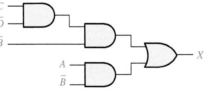

(c)   (d)

Section 6   **Standard Forms of Boolean Expressions**

23. Convert the following expressions to sum-of-product (SOP) forms:

    (a) $(A + B)(C + \overline{B})$ **(b)** $(A + \overline{B}C)C$ **(c)** $(A + C)(AB + AC)$

24. Convert the following expressions to sum-of-product (SOP) forms:

    (a) $AB + CD(A\overline{B} + CD)$ **(b)** $AB(\overline{B}\overline{C} + BD)$ **(c)** $A + B[AC + (B + \overline{C})D]$

25. Define the domain of each SOP expression in Problem 23 and convert the expression to standard SOP form.

26. Convert each SOP expression in Problem 24 to standard SOP form.

27. Determine the binary value of each term in the standard SOP expressions from Problem 25.

28. Determine the binary value of each term in the standard SOP expressions from Problem 26.

29. Convert each standard SOP expression in Problem 25 to standard POS form.

30. Convert each standard SOP expression in Problem 26 to standard POS form.

Section 7 **Boolean Expressions and Truth Tables**

31. Develop a truth table for each of the following standard SOP expressions:

(a) $A\overline{B}C + \overline{A}B\overline{C} + ABC$ (b) $\overline{X}\,\overline{Y}\,\overline{Z} + \overline{X}\,Y\overline{Z} + XY\overline{Z} + X\overline{Y}Z + \overline{X}YZ$

32. Develop a truth table for each of the following standard SOP expressions:

(a) $\overline{A}B\overline{C}D + \overline{A}BC\overline{D} + A\overline{B}CD + \overline{A}\,\overline{B}\,\overline{C}\,\overline{D}$

(b) $WXY\overline{Z} + WX\overline{Y}\overline{Z} + \overline{W}XYZ + W\overline{X}YZ + WX\overline{Y}Z$

33. Develop a truth table for each of the SOP expressions:

(a) $\overline{A}B + AB\overline{C} + \overline{A}\,\overline{C} + A\overline{B}C$ (b) $\overline{X} + Y\overline{Z} + WZ + X\overline{Y}Z$

34. Develop a truth table for each of the standard POS expressions:

(a) $(\overline{A} + \overline{B} + \overline{C})(A + B + C)(A + \overline{B} + C)$

(b) $(\overline{A} + B + \overline{C} + D)(A + \overline{B} + C + \overline{D})(A + \overline{B} + \overline{C} + D)(\overline{A} + B + C + \overline{D})$

35. Develop a truth table for each of the standard POS expressions:

(a) $(A + B)(A + C)(A + B + C)$

(b) $(A + \overline{B})(A + \overline{B} + \overline{C})(B + C + D)(\overline{A} + B + \overline{C} + D)$

36. For each truth table in Table 10, derive a standard SOP and a standard POS expression.

▶ TABLE 10

A B C	X		A B C	X
0 0 0	0		0 0 0	0
0 0 1	1		0 0 1	0
0 1 0	0		0 1 0	0
0 1 1	0		0 1 1	0
1 0 0	1		1 0 0	0
1 0 1	1		1 0 1	1
1 1 0	0		1 1 0	1
1 1 1	1		1 1 1	1
(a)			(b)	

A B C D	X		A B C D	X
0 0 0 0	1		0 0 0 0	0
0 0 0 1	1		0 0 0 1	0
0 0 1 0	0		0 0 1 0	1
0 0 1 1	1		0 0 1 1	0
0 1 0 0	0		0 1 0 0	1
0 1 0 1	1		0 1 0 1	1
0 1 1 0	1		0 1 1 0	0
0 1 1 1	0		0 1 1 1	1
1 0 0 0	0		1 0 0 0	0
1 0 0 1	1		1 0 0 1	0
1 0 1 0	0		1 0 1 0	0
1 0 1 1	0		1 0 1 1	1
1 1 0 0	1		1 1 0 0	1
1 1 0 1	0		1 1 0 1	0
1 1 1 0	0		1 1 1 0	0
1 1 1 1	0		1 1 1 1	1
(c)			(d)	

Section 8 **The Karnaugh Map**

37. Draw a 3-variable Karnaugh map and label each cell according to its binary value.

38. Draw a 4-variable Karnaugh map and label each cell according to its binary value.

39. Write the standard product term for each cell in a 3-variable Karnaugh map.

Section 9   **Karnaugh MAP SOP Minimization**

40. Use a Karnaugh map to find the minimum SOP form for each expression:

    (a) $\overline{A}\,\overline{B}\,\overline{C} + \overline{A}\,\overline{B}C + A\overline{B}C$ (b) $AC(\overline{B} + C)$

    (c) $\overline{A}(BC + B\overline{C}) + A(BC + B\overline{C})$ (d) $\overline{A}\,\overline{B}\,\overline{C} + A\overline{B}\,\overline{C} + \overline{A}B\overline{C} + AB\overline{C}$

41. Use a Karnaugh map to simplify each expression to a minimum SOP form:

    (a) $\overline{A}\,\overline{B}\,\overline{C} + A\overline{B}\,\overline{C} + \overline{A}B\overline{C} + AB\overline{C}$ (b) $AC[\overline{B} + B(B + \overline{C})]$

    (c) $DE\overline{F} + \overline{D}E\overline{F} + \overline{D}\,\overline{E}\,\overline{F}$

42. Expand each expression to a standard SOP form:

    (a) $AB + A\overline{B}C + ABC$ (b) $A + BC$

    (c) $A\overline{B}\,\overline{C}D + AC\overline{D} + \overline{B}CD + \overline{A}BCD$ (d) $A\overline{B} + A\overline{B}CD + CD + B\overline{C}D + ABCD$

43. Minimize each expression in Problem 42 with a Karnaugh map.

44. Use a Karnaugh map to reduce each expression to a minimum SOP form:

    (a) $A + B\overline{C} + CD$

    (b) $\overline{A}\,\overline{B}\,\overline{C}D + \overline{A}\,\overline{B}C\overline{D} + ABCD + AB\overline{C}\,\overline{D}$

    (c) $\overline{A}B(\overline{C}\,\overline{D} + \overline{C}D) + AB(\overline{C}\,\overline{D} + \overline{C}D) + A\overline{B}\,\overline{C}D$

    (d) $(\overline{A}\,\overline{B} + A\overline{B})(CD + C\overline{D})$

    (e) $\overline{A}\,\overline{B} + A\overline{B} + \overline{C}\,\overline{D} + C\overline{D}$

45. Reduce the function specified in truth Table 11 to its minimum SOP form by using a Karnaugh map.

46. Use the Karnaugh map method to implement the minimum SOP expression for the logic function specified in truth Table 12.

47. Solve Problem 46 for a situation in which the last six binary combinations are not allowed.

▼ TABLE 11

INPUTS	OUTPUT
A B C	X
0 0 0	1
0 0 1	1
0 1 0	0
0 1 1	1
1 0 0	1
1 0 1	1
1 1 0	0
1 1 1	1

▼ TABLE 12

INPUTS	OUTPUT
A B C D	X
0 0 0 0	0
0 0 0 1	1
0 0 1 0	1
0 0 1 1	0
0 1 0 0	0
0 1 0 1	0
0 1 1 0	1
0 1 1 1	1
1 0 0 0	1
1 0 0 1	0
1 0 1 0	1
1 0 1 1	0
1 1 0 0	1
1 1 0 1	1
1 1 1 0	0
1 1 1 1	1

Section 10   **Five-Variable Karnaugh Maps**

48. Plot the expression $A\overline{B}\,\overline{C}DE + \overline{A}\,\overline{B}C\overline{D}E$ and simplify if possible.

49. Minimize the following SOP expression using a Karnaugh map:

$$X = \overline{A}B\overline{C}D\overline{E} + \overline{A}\,\overline{B}\,\overline{C}DE + A\overline{B}\,\overline{C}DE + AB\overline{C}D\overline{E} + \overline{A}BCD\overline{E} + \overline{A}B\overline{C}\,\overline{D}E$$
$$+ \overline{A}\,\overline{B}\,\overline{C}D\overline{E} + \overline{A}\,\overline{B}CDE + AB\overline{C}D\overline{E} + A\overline{B}CDE$$

50. Apply the Karnaugh map method to minimize the following SOP expression:

$$A = \overline{V}WXYZ + V\overline{W}XYZ + VW\overline{X}YZ + VWX\overline{Y}Z + VWXY\overline{Z} + \overline{V}\overline{W}\overline{X}YZ$$
$$+ \overline{V}\overline{W}X\overline{Y}\overline{Z} + \overline{V}\overline{W}XY\overline{Z} + \overline{V}W\overline{X}\overline{Y}\overline{Z}$$

Section 11 **Describing Logic with an HDL**

51. Write a VHDL program for the logic circuit in Figure 57.

▶ FIGURE 57

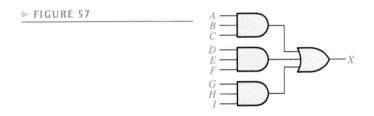

52. Write a program in VHDL for the expression

$$Y = A\overline{B}C + \overline{A}\overline{B}C + A\overline{B}\overline{C} + \overline{A}BC$$

System Application Activity

53. If you are required to choose a type of digital display for low light conditions, will you select LED or LCD 7-segment displays? Why?

54. Explain the purpose of the invalid code detector.

55. For segment c, how many fewer gates and inverters does it take to implement the minimum SOP expression than the standard SOP expression?

56. Repeat Problem 55 for the logic for segments d through g.

Special Design Problems

57. The logic for segments b and c in Figure 49 produces LOW outputs to activate the segments. If a type of 7-segment display is used that requires a HIGH to activate a segment, modify the logic accordingly.

58. Redesign the logic for segment a in the application activity to include the letter F in the display.

59. Repeat Problem 58 for segments b through g.

60. Design the invalid code detector.

Multisim Troubleshooting Practice

61. Open file P04-61 on www.pearsoned.com/electronics, apply input signals, and observe the operation of the logic circuit. Determine whether or not a fault exists.

62. Open file P04-62, apply input signals, and observe the operation of the logic circuit. Determine whether or not a fault exists.

63. Open file P04-63, apply input signals, and observe the operation of the logic circuit. Determine whether or not a fault exists.

ANSWERS

SECTION CHECKUPS

Section 1 **Boolean Operations and Expressions**

1. $\overline{A} = \overline{0} = 1$ **2.** $A = 1, B = 1, C = 0; \overline{A} + \overline{B} + C = \overline{1} + \overline{1} + 0 = 0 + 0 + 0 = 0$

3. $A = 1, B = 0, C = 1; A\overline{B}C = 1 \cdot \overline{0} \cdot 1 = 1 \cdot 1 \cdot 1 = 1$

Section 2 **Laws and Rules of Boolean Algebra**

1. $A + (B + C + D) = (A + B + C) + D$ **2.** $A(B + C + D) = AB + AC + AD$

Section 3 **DeMorgan's Theorems**

1. (a) $\overline{ABC} + \overline{(\overline{D} + E)} = \overline{A} + \overline{B} + \overline{C} + D\overline{E}$ **(b)** $\overline{(A + B)C} = \overline{A}\overline{B} + \overline{C}$

(c) $\overline{A + B + C + \overline{DE}} = \overline{A}\overline{B}\overline{C} + D + \overline{E}$

Section 4 **Boolean Analysis of Logic Circuits**

1. $(C + D)B + A$

2. Abbreviated truth table: The expression is a 1 when A is 1 or when B and C are 1s or when B and D are 1s. The expression is 0 for all other variable combinations.

Section 5 **Simplification Using Boolean Algebra**

1. (a) $A + AB + A\overline{B}C = A$ **(b)** $(\overline{A} + B)C + ABC = C(\overline{A} + B)$

(c) $A\overline{B}C(BD + CDE) + A\overline{C} = A(\overline{C} + \overline{B}DE)$

2. (a) *Original:* 2 AND gates, 1 OR gate, 1 inverter; *Simplified:* No gates (straight connection)

(b) *Original:* 2 OR gates, 2 AND gates, 1 inverter; *Simplified:* 1 OR gate, 1 AND gate, 1 inverter

(c) *Original:* 5 AND gates, 2 OR gates, 2 inverters; *Simplified:* 2 AND gates, 1 OR gate, 2 inverters

Section 6 **Standard Forms of Boolean Expressions**

1. (a) SOP   **(b)** standard POS   **(c)** standard SOP   **(d)** POS

2. (a) $AB\overline{C}\overline{D} + AB\overline{C}D + ABC\overline{D} + ABCD + \overline{A}B\overline{C}D + \overline{A}BCD + \overline{A}\,\overline{B}C\overline{D} + \overline{A}BC\overline{D}$

(c) Already standard

3. (b) Already standard

(d) $(A + \overline{B} + \overline{C})(A + \overline{B} + C)(A + B + \overline{C})(A + B + C)$

Section 7 **Boolean Expressions and Truth Tables**

1. $2^5 = 32$ **2.** $0110 \longrightarrow \overline{W}X Y\overline{Z}$ **3.** $1100 \longrightarrow \overline{W} + \overline{X} + Y + Z$

Section 8 **The Karnaugh Map**

1. (a) upper left cell: 000   **(b)** lower right cell: 101   **(c)** lower left cell: 100

(d) upper right cell: 001

2. (a) upper left cell: $\overline{X}\,\overline{Y}\,\overline{Z}$ **(b)** lower right cell: $X\overline{Y}Z$ **(c)** lower left cell: $X\overline{Y}\,\overline{Z}$

(d) upper right cell: $\overline{X}\,\overline{Y}Z$

3. (a) upper left cell: 0000   **(b)** lower right cell: 1010   **(c)** lower left cell: 1000

(d) upper right cell: 0010

4. (a) upper left cell: $\overline{W}\,\overline{X}\,\overline{Y}\,\overline{Z}$ **(b)** lower right cell: $W\overline{X}Y\overline{Z}$ **(c)** lower left cell: $W\overline{X}\,\overline{Y}\,\overline{Z}$

(d) upper right cell: $\overline{W}\,\overline{X}\,\overline{Y}Z$

Section 9 **Karnaugh Map SOP Minimization**

1. 8-cell map for 3 variables; 16-cell map for 4 variables

2. $AB + B\overline{C} + \overline{A}\,\overline{B}C$

3. (a) $\overline{A}\,\overline{B}\,\overline{C} + \overline{A}BC + ABC + AB\overline{C}$

(b) $\overline{A}\,\overline{B}\,\overline{C} + \overline{A}\,\overline{B}C + \overline{A}B\overline{C} + ABC + A\overline{B}\,\overline{C} + A\overline{B}C$

(c) $\overline{A}\,\overline{B}\,\overline{C}\,\overline{D} + \overline{A}\,\overline{B}CD + \overline{A}B\overline{C}D + \overline{A}BC\overline{D} + \overline{A}BCD + A\overline{B}\,\overline{C}D + A\overline{B}C\overline{D} + A\overline{B}CD$

(d) $\overline{A}\,\overline{B}\,\overline{C}\overline{D} + \overline{A}\,\overline{B}C\overline{D} + \overline{A}B\overline{C}\overline{D} + \overline{A}B\overline{C}D + \overline{A}BC\overline{D} + AB\overline{C}D + ABC\overline{D} + A\overline{B}C\overline{D} + A\overline{B}CD + AB\overline{C}\overline{D} + A\overline{B}\,\overline{C}\overline{D}$

Section 10 **Five-Variable Karnaugh Maps**

1. There are 32 combinations of 5 variables ($2^5 = 32$).

2. $X = 1$ because the function is 1 for all possible combinations of 5 variables.

Section 11 **Describing Logic with an HDL**

1. An HDL is a hardware description language for programmable logic.

2. Entity and architecture

3. The entity specifies the inputs and outputs of a logic function.
4. The architecture specifies operation of a logic function.

RELATED PROBLEMS FOR EXAMPLES

1 $\overline{A} + B = 0$ when $A = 1$ and $B = 0$.

2 $\overline{A}\overline{B} = 1$ when $A = 0$ and $B = 0$. **3** XYZ

4 $W + X + Y + Z$ **5** $ABC\overline{D}\overline{E}$ **6** $(A + \overline{B} + \overline{C}D)\overline{E}$

7 $\overline{ABCD} = \overline{A} + \overline{B} + \overline{C} + \overline{D}$ **8** Results should be same as example.

9 $A\overline{B}$ **10** CD **11** $AB\overline{C} + \overline{A}C + \overline{A}\overline{B}$ **12** $\overline{A} + \overline{B} + \overline{C}$

13 Results should be same as example. **14** $\overline{A}B\overline{C} + AB + A\overline{C} + A\overline{B} + \overline{B}\overline{C}$

15 $W\overline{X}YZ + W\overline{X}Y\overline{Z} + W\overline{X}Y\overline{Z} + \overline{W}\overline{X}Y\overline{Z} + WX\overline{Y}Z + WX\overline{Y}\overline{Z}$

16 011, 101, 110, 010, 111. Yes

17 $(A + \overline{B} + C)(A + \overline{B} + \overline{C})(A + B + C)(\overline{A} + B + C)$

18 010, 100, 001, 111, 011. Yes **19** SOP and POS expressions are equivalent.

20 See Table 13. **21** See Table 14.

TABLE 13

A	*B*	*C*	*X*
0	0	0	0
0	0	1	0
0	1	0	1
0	1	1	0
1	0	0	0
1	0	1	1
1	1	0	0
1	1	1	0

TABLE 14

A	*B*	*C*	*X*
0	0	0	1
0	0	1	0
0	1	0	0
0	1	1	1
1	0	0	1
1	0	1	1
1	1	0	1
1	1	1	0

22 The SOP and POS expressions are equivalent. **23** See Figure 58.

24 See Figure 59. **25** See Figure 60. **26** See Figure 61.

27 No other ways **28** $X = B + \overline{A}C + A\overline{C}D + C\overline{D}$

29 $X = \overline{D} + A\overline{B}C + B\overline{C} + \overline{A}B$

30 $Q = X + Y$ **31** $Q = \overline{X}\overline{Y}\overline{Z} + W\overline{X}Z + \overline{W}YZ$

AB \ *C*	0	1
00		
01		1
11		
10	1	1

FIGURE 58

AB \ *CD*	00	01	11	10
00				
01				1
11	1		1	1
10				

FIGURE 59

AB \ *C*	0	1
00	1	
01	1	1
11		1
10		

FIGURE 60

AB \ *CD*	00	01	11	10
00		1		
01		1		1
11	1	1	1	1
10	1	1	1	1

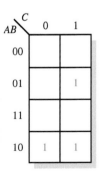

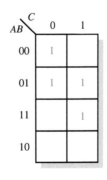

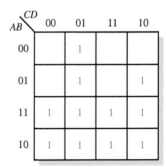

FIGURE 61

32 See Figure 62.

▶ FIGURE 62

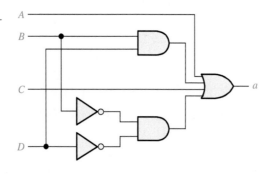

33 $Y = \overline{DE} + \overline{AE} + \overline{B}\overline{C}\overline{E}$

34 $X \Leftarrow (A \text{ and } B) \text{ nor } (C \text{ and } D);$

TRUE/FALSE QUIZ

1. T	**2.** T	**3.** F	**4.** T	**5.** T
6. F	**7.** T	**8.** F	**9.** T	**10.** F

SELF-TEST

1. (d)	**2.** (a)	**3.** (b)	**4.** (c)	**5.** (d)	**6.** (b)	**7.** (a)	**8.** (b)	**9.** (d)	**10.** (d)
11. (c)	**12.** (b)	**13.** (b)	**14.** (c)	**15.** (a)	**16.** (c)	**17.** (b)	**18.** (c)	**19.** (b)	**20.** (c)

ANSWERS TO ODD-NUMBERED PROBLEMS

1. $X = A + B + C + D$

3. $X = \overline{A} + \overline{B} + \overline{C}$

5. **(a)** $AB = 1$ when $A = 1, B = 1$

(b) $A\overline{B}C = 1$ when $A = 1, B = 0, C = 1$

(c) $A + B = 0$ when $A = 0, B = 0$

(d) $\overline{A} + B + \overline{C} = 0$ when $A = 1, B = 0, C = 1$

(e) $\overline{A} + \overline{B} + C = 0$ when $A = 1, B = 1, C = 0$

(f) $\overline{A} + B = 0$ when $A = 1, B = 0$

(g) $A\overline{B}\,\overline{C} = 1$ when $A = 1, B = 0, C = 0$

7. **(a)** Commutative

(b) Commutative

(c) Distributive

9. **(a)** $\overline{AB}$ **(b)** $A + \overline{B}$

(c) $\overline{A}\,\overline{B}\,\overline{C}$ **(d)** $\overline{A} + \overline{B} + \overline{C}$

(e) $\overline{A} + \overline{B}\,\overline{C}$ **(f)** $\overline{A} + \overline{B} + \overline{C} + \overline{D}$

(g) $(\overline{A} + \overline{B})(\overline{C} + \overline{D})$ **(h)** $\overline{AB} + \overline{CD}$

11. **(a)** $(\overline{A} + \overline{B} + \overline{C})(\overline{E} + \overline{F} + \overline{G})(\overline{H} + \overline{I} + \overline{J})(\overline{K} + \overline{L} + \overline{M})$

(b) $\overline{AB}\overline{C} + BC$

(c) $\overline{A}\,\overline{B}\,\overline{C}\,\overline{D}\,\overline{E}\,\overline{F}\,\overline{G}\,\overline{H}$

13. **(a)** $X = ABCD$ **(b)** $X = AB + C$

(c) $X = \overline{\overline{A}B}$ **(d)** $X = (A + B)C$

15. See Figure 63.

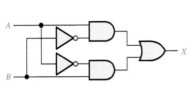

(a) $X = A\overline{B} + \overline{A}B$

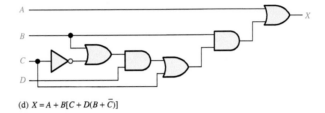

(b) $X = AB + \overline{A}\,\overline{B} + \overline{A}BC$

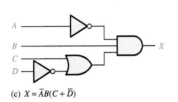

(c) $X = \overline{A}B(C + \overline{D})$

(d) $X = A + B[C + D(B + \overline{C})]$

▲ FIGURE 63

17. (a) See Table 15.

▼ TABLE 15

INPUTS			OUTPUT
VCR	CAMI	$\overline{RDY}$	RECORD
0	0	0	0
0	0	1	1
0	1	0	0
0	1	1	1
1	0	0	0
1	0	1	1
1	1	0	1
1	1	1	1

17. (b) See Table 16.

▼ TABLE 16

INPUTS			OUTPUT
RTS	ENABLE	$\overline{BUSY}$	$\overline{SEND}$
0	0	0	1
0	0	1	1
0	1	0	1
0	1	1	1
1	0	0	1
1	0	1	1
1	1	0	0
1	1	1	1

19. (a) A (b) AB (c) C
    (d) A (e) $\overline{A}C + \overline{B}C$

21. (a) $BD + BE + \overline{D}F$ (b) $\overline{A}\,\overline{B}C + \overline{A}\,\overline{B}D$
    (c) B (d) $AB + CD$
    (e) ABC

23. (a) $A\overline{B} + AC + BC$
    (b) $AC + \overline{B}C$
    (c) $AB + AC$

25. (a) Domain: A, B, C
       Standard SOP: $A\overline{B}C + A\overline{B}\,\overline{C} + ABC + \overline{A}BC$
    (b) Domain: A, B, C
       Standard SOP: $ABC + A\overline{B}C + \overline{A}\,\overline{B}C$
    (c) Domain: A, B, C
       Standard SOP: $ABC + AB\overline{C} + A\overline{B}C$

27. (a) $101 + 100 + 111 + 011$
    (b) $111 + 101 + 001$
    (c) $111 + 110 + 101$

29. (a) $(A + B + C)(A + B + \overline{C})(\overline{A} + \overline{B} + C)(\overline{A} + \overline{B} + C)$
    (b) $(A + B + C)(A + \overline{B} + C)(A + \overline{B} + \overline{C})$
       $(\overline{A} + B + C)(\overline{A} + \overline{B} + C)$
    (c) $(A + B + C)(A + B + \overline{C})(A + \overline{B} + C)$
       $(A + \overline{B} + \overline{C})(\overline{A} + B + C)$

31. (a) See Table 17.

▼ TABLE 17

A	B	C	X
0	0	0	0
0	0	1	0
0	1	0	1
0	1	1	0
1	0	0	0
1	0	1	1
1	1	0	0
1	1	1	1

31. (b) See Table 18.

▼ TABLE 18

X	Y	Z	Q
0	0	0	1
0	0	1	1
0	1	0	0
0	1	1	1
1	0	0	0
1	0	1	1
1	1	0	1
1	1	1	0

33. (a) See Table 19.

▼ TABLE 19

A	B	C	X
0	0	0	1
0	0	1	0
0	1	0	1
0	1	1	1
1	0	0	0
1	0	1	1
1	1	0	1
1	1	1	0

33. (b) See Table 20.

▼ TABLE 20

W	X	Y	Z	Q
0	0	0	0	1
0	0	0	1	1
0	0	1	0	1
0	0	1	1	1
0	1	0	0	0
0	1	0	1	1
0	1	1	0	1
0	1	1	1	0
1	0	0	0	1
1	0	0	1	1
1	0	1	0	1
1	0	1	1	1
1	1	0	0	0
1	1	0	1	1
1	1	1	0	1
1	1	1	1	1

35. (a) See Table 21.

▼ TABLE 21

A	B	C	X
0	0	0	0
0	0	1	0
0	1	0	0
0	1	1	1
1	0	0	1
1	0	1	1
1	1	0	1
1	1	1	1

35. (b) See Table 22.

▼ TABLE 22

A	B	C	D	X
0	0	0	0	1
0	0	0	1	0
0	0	1	0	1
0	0	1	1	1
0	1	0	0	0
0	1	0	1	0
0	1	1	0	0
0	1	1	1	0
1	0	0	0	1
1	0	0	1	0
1	0	1	0	0
1	0	1	1	1
1	1	0	0	1
1	1	0	1	1
1	1	1	0	1
1	1	1	1	1

37. See Figure 64.

▶ FIGURE 64

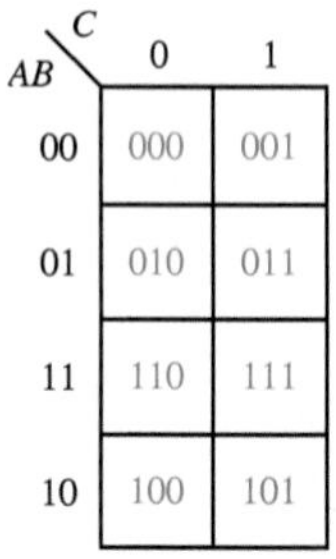

AB \ C	0	1
00	000	001
01	010	011
11	110	111
10	100	101

39. See Figure 65.

▶ FIGURE 65

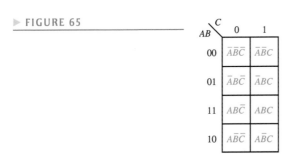

41. (a) No simplification (b) AC
(c) $\overline{D}\,\overline{F} + E\overline{F}$

43. (a) $AB + AC$
(b) $A + BC$
(c) $B\overline{C}D + A\overline{C}D + BC\overline{D} + AC\overline{D}$
(d) $A\overline{B} + CD$

45. $\overline{B} + C$

47. $\overline{A}\,\overline{B}\,CD + C\overline{D} + BC + A\overline{D}$

49. $X = \overline{A}\,\overline{B}\,\overline{C}\,\overline{D}\,\overline{E} + \overline{A}BCDE + AB\overline{C}\,\overline{D}\,\overline{E} + \overline{A}\,\overline{B}DE + \overline{A}BD\overline{E} + \overline{B}\,\overline{C}DE + ABCD$

51. **entity** AND_OR **is**
    port (A, B, C, D, E, F, G, H, I: **in** bit; X: **out** bit);
    end entity AND_OR;
    architecture Logic **of** AND_OR **is**
    begin
        X <= (A **and** B **and** C) **or** (D **and** E **and** F) **or** (G **and** H **and** I);
    end architecture Logic;

53. LED. LEDs emit light, LCDs do not.

55. One less inverter and one less gate.

57. Change the OR gates to NOR gates.

59. See Figure 66.

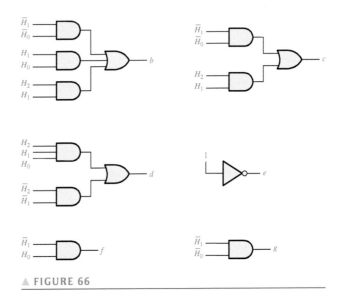

▲ FIGURE 66

61. Inverter output open

63. b-segment OR gate output open.

COMBINATIONAL LOGIC ANALYSIS

CHAPTER OBJECTIVES

◆ Analyze basic combinational logic circuits, such as AND-OR, AND-OR-Invert, exclusive-OR, and exclusive-NOR

◆ Use AND-OR and AND-OR-Invert circuits to implement sum-of-products (SOP) and product-of-sums (POS) expressions

◆ Write the Boolean output expression for any combinational logic circuit

◆ Develop a truth table from the output expression for a combinational logic circuit

◆ Use the Karnaugh map to expand an output expression containing terms with missing variables into a full SOP form

◆ Design a combinational logic circuit for a given Boolean output expression

◆ Design a combinational logic circuit for a given truth table

◆ Simplify a combinational logic circuit to its minimum form

◆ Use NAND gates to implement any combinational logic function

◆ Use NOR gates to implement any combinational logic function

◆ Troubleshoot faulty logic circuits

◆ Troubleshoot logic circuits by using signal tracing and waveform analysis

◆ Write VHDL programs for simple logic circuits

◆ Apply combinational logic to a system application

KEY TERMS

◆ Universal gate
◆ Negative-OR
◆ Negative-AND
◆ Node
◆ Signal tracing
◆ Component
◆ Signal

INTRODUCTION

When logic gates are connected together to produce a specified output for certain specified combinations of input variables, with no storage involved, the resulting circuit is in the category of **combinational logic.** In combinational logic, the output level is at all times dependent on the combination of input levels. This chapter expands on the material introduced in earlier chapters with a coverage of the analysis, design, and troubleshooting of various combinational logic circuits. The VHDL structural approach is introduced and applied to combinational logic.

SYSTEM APPLICATION ACTIVITY PREVIEW

The System Application Activity illustrates the concepts taught in this chapter by demonstrating how combinational logic can be used for a specific purpose in a practical application. A logic circuit is used to control the level and temperature of a fluid in a storage tank. By operating inlet and outlet valves, the inflow and outflow are controlled based on level-sensor inputs. The fluid temperature is controlled by turning a heating element on or off based on a temperature-sensor input. The Multisim activities are optional.

1   BASIC COMBINATIONAL LOGIC CIRCUITS

SOP expressions are implemented with an AND gate for each product term and one OR gate for summing all of the product terms. As you know, this SOP implementation is called AND-OR logic and is the basic form forrealizing standard Boolean functions. In this section, the AND-OR and the AND-OR-Invert are examined; the exclusive-OR and exclusive-NOR gates, which are actually a form of AND-OR logic, are also covered.

After completing this section, you should be able to

* ◆   Analyze and apply AND-OR circuits
* ◆   Analyze and apply AND-OR-Invert circuits
* ◆   Analyze and apply exclusive-OR gates
* ◆   Analyze and apply exclusive-NOR gates

AND-OR Logic

AND-OR logic produces an SOP expression.

Figure 1(a) shows an AND-OR circuit consisting of two 2-input AND gates and one 2-input OR gate; Figure 1(b) is the ANSI standard rectangular outline symbol. The Boolean expressions for the AND gate outputs and the resulting SOP expression for the output X are shown on the diagram. In general, an AND-OR circuit can have any number of AND gates, each with any number of inputs.

The truth table for a 4-input AND-OR logic circuit is shown in Table 1. The intermediate AND gate outputs (the AB and CD columns) are also shown in the table.

▶ FIGURE 1

An example of AND-OR logic. Open file F05-01 on www.pearsoned.com/electronics to verify the operation.

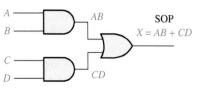

(a) Logic diagram (ANSI standard distinctive shape symbols)

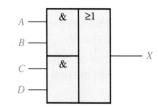

(b) ANSI standard rectangular outline symbol

▶ TABLE 1

Truth table for the AND-OR logic in Figure 1.

INPUTS						OUTPUT
A	B	C	D	AB	CD	X
0	0	0	0	0	0	0
0	0	0	1	0	0	0
0	0	1	0	0	0	0
0	0	1	1	0	1	1
0	1	0	0	0	0	0
0	1	0	1	0	0	0
0	1	1	0	0	0	0
0	1	1	1	0	1	1
1	0	0	0	0	0	0
1	0	0	1	0	0	0
1	0	1	0	0	0	0
1	0	1	1	0	1	1
1	1	0	0	1	0	1
1	1	0	1	1	0	1
1	1	1	0	1	0	1
1	1	1	1	1	1	1

An AND-OR circuit directly implements an SOP expression, assuming the complements (if any) of the variables are available. The operation of the AND-OR circuit in Figure 1 is stated as follows:

For a 4-input AND-OR logic circuit, the output X is HIGH (1) if both input A and input B are HIGH (1) or both input C and input D are HIGH (1).

EXAMPLE 1

In a certain chemical-processing plant, a liquid chemical is used in a manufacturing process. The chemical is stored in three different tanks. A level sensor in each tank produces a HIGH voltage when the level of chemical in the tank drops below a specified point.

Design a circuit that monitors the chemical level in each tank and indicates when the level in any two of the tanks drops below the specified point.

Solution The AND-OR circuit in Figure 2 has inputs from the sensors on tanks A, B, and C as shown. The AND gate G_1 checks the levels in tanks A and B, gate G_2 checks tanks A and C, and gate G_3 checks tanks B and C. When the chemical level in any two of the tanks gets too low, one of the AND gates will have HIGHs on both of its inputs, causing its output to be HIGH; and so the final output X from the OR gate is HIGH. This HIGH input is then used to activate an indicator such as a lamp or audible alarm, as shown in the figure.

▶ FIGURE 2

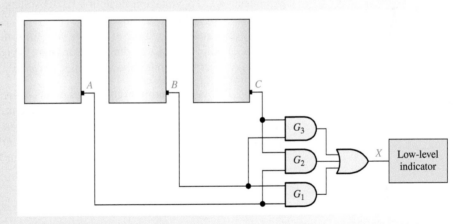

Related Problem Write the Boolean SOP expression for the AND-OR logic in Figure 2.

———————

*Answers are at the end of the chapter.

AND-OR-Invert Logic

When the output of an AND-OR circuit is complemented (inverted), it results in an AND-OR-Invert circuit. Recall that AND-OR logic directly implements SOP expressions. POS expressions can be implemented with AND-OR-Invert logic. This is illustrated as follows, starting with a POS expression and developing the corresponding AND-OR-Invert (AOI) expression.

$$X = (\overline{A} + \overline{B})(\overline{C} + \overline{D}) = (\overline{AB})(\overline{CD}) = \overline{(\overline{AB})(\overline{CD})} = \overline{\overline{AB} + \overline{CD}} = \overline{AB + CD}$$

The logic diagram in Figure 3(a) shows an AND-OR-Invert circuit with four inputs and the development of the POS output expression. The ANSI standard rectangular outline symbol is shown in part (b). In general, an AND-OR-Invert circuit can have any number of AND gates, each with any number of inputs.

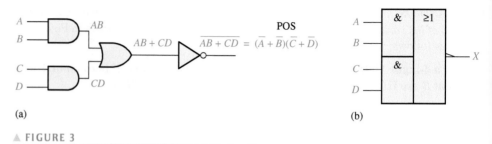

(a)   (b)

▲ FIGURE 3

An AND-OR-Invert circuit produces a POS output. Open file F05-03 to verify the operation.

The operation of the AND-OR-Invert circuit in Figure 3 is stated as follows:

For a 4-input AND-OR-Invert logic circuit, the output X is LOW (0) if both input A and input B are HIGH (1) or both input C and input D are HIGH (1).

A truth table can be developed from the AND-OR truth table in Table 1 by simply changing all 1s to 0s and all 0s to 1s in the output column.

EXAMPLE 2

The sensors in the chemical tanks of Example 1 are being replaced by a new model that produces a LOW voltage instead of a HIGH voltage when the level of the chemical in the tank drops below a critical point.

Modify the circuit in Figure 2 to operate with the different input levels and still produce a HIGH output to activate the indicator when the level in any two of the tanks drops below the critical point. Show the logic diagram.

Solution   The AND-OR-Invert circuit in Figure 4 has inputs from the sensors on tanks A, B, and C as shown. The AND gate G_1 checks the levels in tanks A and B, gate G_2 checks tanks A and C, and gate G_3 checks tanks B and C. When the chemical level in any two of the tanks gets too low, each AND gate will have a LOW on at least one input, causing its output to be LOW and, thus, the final output X from the inverter is HIGH. This HIGH output is then used to activate an indicator.

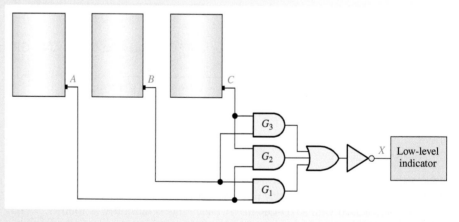

▲ FIGURE 4

Related Problem   Write the Boolean expression for the AND-OR-Invert logic in Figure 4 and show that the output is HIGH (1) when any two of the inputs A, B, and C are LOW (0).

Exclusive-OR Logic

Although, because of its importance, this circuit is considered a type of logic gate with its own unique symbol, it is actually a combination of two AND gates, one OR gate, and two inverters, as shown in Figure 5(a). The two ANSI standard exclusive-OR logic symbols are shown in parts (b) and (c).

The XOR gate is actually a combination of other gates.

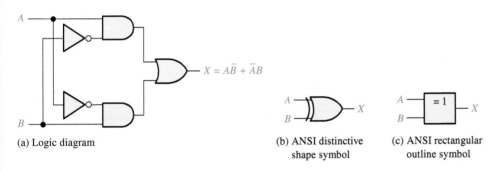

(a) Logic diagram

(b) ANSI distinctive shape symbol

(c) ANSI rectangular outline symbol

▲ FIGURE 5

Exclusive-OR logic diagram and symbols. Open file F05-05 to verify the operation.

The output expression for the circuit in Figure 5 is

$$X = A\bar{B} + \bar{A}B$$

Evaluation of this expression results in the truth table in Table 2. Notice that the output is HIGH only when the two inputs are at opposite levels. A special exclusive-OR operator $\oplus$ is often used, so the expression $X = A\bar{B} + \bar{A}B$ can be stated as "X is equal to A exclusive-OR B" and can be written as

$$X = A \oplus B$$

▼ TABLE 2

Truth table for an exclusive-OR.

A	B	X
0	0	0
0	1	1
1	0	1
1	1	0

Exclusive-NOR Logic

As you know, the complement of the exclusive-OR function is the exclusive-NOR, which is derived as follows:

$$X = \overline{A\bar{B} + \bar{A}B} = (\overline{A\bar{B}})(\overline{\bar{A}B}) = (\bar{A} + B)(A + \bar{B}) = \bar{A}\bar{B} + AB$$

Notice that the output X is HIGH only when the two inputs, A and B, are at the same level.

The exclusive-NOR can be implemented by simply inverting the output of an exclusive-OR, as shown in Figure 6(a), or by directly implementing the expression $\bar{A}\bar{B} + AB$, as shown in part (b).

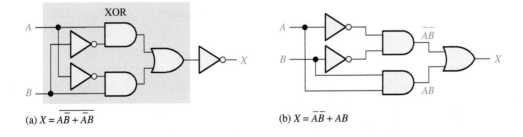

(a) $X = \overline{A\bar{B} + \bar{A}B}$

(b) $X = \bar{A}\bar{B} + AB$

▲ FIGURE 6

Two equivalent ways of implementing the exclusive-NOR. Open files F05-06 (a) and (b) to verify the operation.

EXAMPLE 3

Use exclusive-OR gates to implement an even-parity code generator for an original 4-bit code.

Solution A parity bit is added to a binary code in order to provide error detection. For even parity, a parity bit is added to the original code to make the total number of 1s in the code even. The circuit in Figure 7 produces a 1 output when there is an odd number of 1s on the inputs in order to make the total number of 1s in the output code even. A 0 output is produced when there is an even number of 1s on the inputs.

▶ FIGURE 7

Even-parity generator.

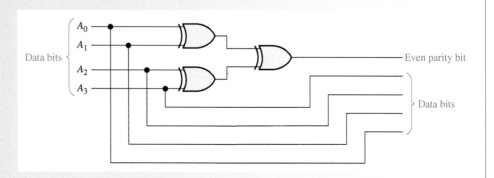

Related Problem How would you verify that a correct even-parity bit is generated for each combination of the four data bits?

EXAMPLE 4

Use exlusive-OR gates to implement an even-parity checker for the 5-bit code generated by the circuit in Example 3.

Solution The circuit in Figure 8 produces a 1 output when there is an error in the five-bit code and a 0 when there is no error.

▶ FIGURE 8

Even-parity checker.

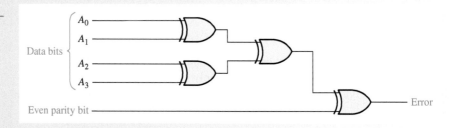

Related Problem How would you verify that an error is indicated when the input code is incorrect?

SECTION 1 CHECKUP
Answers are at the end of the chapter.

1. Determine the output (1 or 0) of a 4-variable AND-OR-Invert circuit for each of the following input conditions:
   (a) $A = 1, B = 0, C = 1, D = 0$
   (b) $A = 1, B = 1, C = 0, D = 1$
   (c) $A = 0, B = 1, C = 1, D = 1$

2. Determine the output (1 or 0) of an exclusive-OR gate for each of the following input conditions:

   (a) $A = 1, B = 0$ (b) $A = 1, B = 1$

   (c) $A = 0, B = 1$ (d) $A = 0, B = 0$

3. Develop the truth table for a certain 3-input logic circuit with the output expression $X = AB\overline{C} + \overline{A}B\overline{C} + \overline{A}\,\overline{B}\,\overline{C} + A\overline{B}\,\overline{C} + ABC$.

4. Draw the logic diagram for an exclusive-NOR circuit.

2   IMPLEMENTING COMBINATIONAL LOGIC

In this section, examples are used to illustrate how to implement a logic circuit from a Boolean expression or a truth table. Minimization of a logic circuit is also included.

After completing this section, you should be able to

- Implement a logic circuit from a Boolean expression
- Implement a logic circuit from a truth table
- Minimize a logic circuit

From a Boolean Expression to a Logic Circuit

Let's examine the following Boolean expression:

$$X = AB + CDE$$

A brief inspection shows that this expression is composed of two terms, AB and CDE, with a domain of five variables. The first term is formed by ANDing A with B, and the second term is formed by ANDing C, D, and E. The two terms are then ORed to form the output X. These operations are indicated in the structure of the expression as follows:

$$X = \underbrace{AB + CDE}_{}$$
AND
OR

Note that in this particular expression, the AND operations forming the two individual terms, AB and CDE, must be performed *before* the terms can be ORed.

To implement this Boolean expression, a 2-input AND gate is required to form the term AB, and a 3-input AND gate is needed to form the term CDE. A 2-input OR gate is then required to combine the two AND terms. The resulting logic circuit is shown in Figure 9.

> For every Boolean expression there is a logic circuit, and for every logic circuit there is a Boolean expression.

COMPUTER NOTE

Many control programs require logic operations to be performed by a computer. A driver program is a control program that is used with computer peripherals. For example, a mouse driver requires logic tests to determine if a button has been pressed and further logic operations to determine if it has moved, either horizontally or vertically. Within the heart of a microprocessor is the arithmetic logic unit (ALU), which performs these logic operations as directed by program instructions. All of the logic described in this chapter can also be performed by the ALU, given the proper instructions.

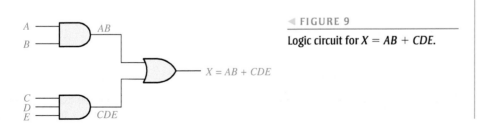

◄ FIGURE 9

Logic circuit for $X = AB + CDE$.

As another example, let's implement the following expression:

$$X = AB(\overline{CD} + EF)$$

A breakdown of this expression shows that the terms AB and $(\overline{CD} + EF)$ are ANDed. The term $\overline{CD} + EF$ is formed by first ANDing C and $\overline{D}$ and ANDing E and F, and then ORing these two terms. This structure is indicated in relation to the expression as follows:

$$X = AB(\overline{CD} + EF)$$

AND
NOT
OR

AND

Before you can implement the final expression, you must create the sum term $\overline{CD} + EF$; but before you can get this term; you must create the product terms $\overline{CD}$ and EF; but before you can get the term $\overline{CD}$, you must create $\overline{D}$. So, as you can see, the logic operations must be done in the proper order.

The logic gates required to implement $X = AB(\overline{CD} + EF)$ are as follows:

1. One inverter to form $\overline{D}$

2. Two 2-input AND gates to form $\overline{CD}$ and EF

3. One 2-input OR gate to form $\overline{CD} + EF$

4. One 3-input AND gate to form X

The logic circuit for this expression is shown in Figure 10(a). Notice that there is a maximum of four gates and an inverter between an input and output in this circuit (from input D to output). Often the total propagation delay time through a logic circuit is a major consideration. Propagation delays are additive, so the more gates or inverters between input and output, the greater the propagation delay time.

Unless an intermediate term, such as $\overline{CD} + EF$ in Figure 10(a), is required as an output for some other purpose, it is usually best to reduce a circuit to its SOP form in order to reduce the overall propagation delay time. The expression is converted to SOP as follows, and the resulting circuit is shown in Figure 10(b).

$$AB(\overline{CD} + EF) = ABC\overline{D} + ABEF$$

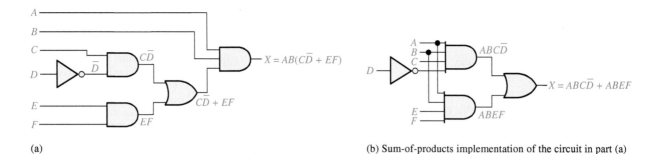

(a)

(b) Sum-of-products implementation of the circuit in part (a)

▲ FIGURE 10

Logic circuits for $X = AB(\overline{CD} + EF) = ABC\overline{D} + ABEF$.

From a Truth Table to a Logic Circuit

If you begin with a truth table instead of an expression, you can write the SOP expression from the truth table and then implement the logic circuit. Table 3 specifies a logic function.

◀ TABLE 3

INPUTS			OUTPUT	
A	B	C	X	PRODUCT TERM
0	0	0	0	
0	0	1	0	
0	1	0	0	
0	1	1	1	$\overline{A}BC$
1	0	0	1	$A\overline{B}\,\overline{C}$
1	0	1	0	
1	1	0	0	
1	1	1	0	

The Boolean SOP expression obtained from the truth table by ORing the product terms for which $X = 1$ is

$$X = \overline{A}BC + A\overline{B}\,\overline{C}$$

The first term in the expression is formed by ANDing the three variables $\overline{A}$, B, and C. The second term is formed by ANDing the three variables A, $\overline{B}$, and $\overline{C}$.

The logic gates required to implement this expression are as follows: three inverters to form the $\overline{A}$, $\overline{B}$, and $\overline{C}$ variables; two 3-input AND gates to form the terms $\overline{A}BC$ and $A\overline{B}\,\overline{C}$; and one 2-input OR gate to form the final output function, $\overline{A}BC + A\overline{B}\,\overline{C}$.

The implementation of this logic function is illustrated in Figure 11.

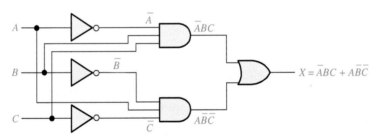

◀ FIGURE 11

Logic circuit for $X = \overline{A}BC + A\overline{B}\,\overline{C}$. Open file F05-11 to verify the operation.

EXAMPLE 5

Design a logic circuit to implement the operation specified in the truth table of Table 4.

▼ TABLE 4

INPUTS			OUTPUT	
A	B	C	X	PRODUCT TERM
0	0	0	0	
0	0	1	0	
0	1	0	0	
0	1	1	1	$\overline{A}BC$
1	0	0	0	
1	0	1	1	$A\overline{B}C$
1	1	0	1	$AB\overline{C}$
1	1	1	0	

Solution   Notice that $X = 1$ for only three of the input conditions. Therefore, the logic expression is

$$X = \overline{A}BC + A\overline{B}C + AB\overline{C}$$

The logic gates required are three inverters, three 3-input AND gates and one 3-input OR gate. The logic circuit is shown in Figure 12.

▶ FIGURE 12

Open file F05-12 to verify the operation.

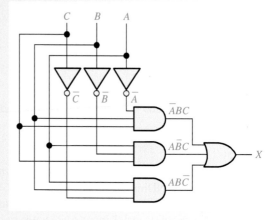

Related Problem   Determine if the logic circuit of Figure 12 can be simplified.

EXAMPLE 6

Develop a logic circuit with four input variables that will only produce a 1 output when exactly three input variables are 1s.

Solution   Out of sixteen possible combinations of four variables, the combinations in which there are exactly three 1s are listed in Table 5, along with the corresponding product term for each.

▼ TABLE 5

A	B	C	D	PRODUCT TERM
0	1	1	1	$\overline{A}BCD$
1	0	1	1	$A\overline{B}CD$
1	1	0	1	$AB\overline{C}D$
1	1	1	0	$ABC\overline{D}$

The product terms are ORed to get the following expression:

$$X = \overline{A}BCD + A\overline{B}CD + AB\overline{C}D + ABC\overline{D}$$

This expression is implemented in Figure 13 with AND-OR logic.

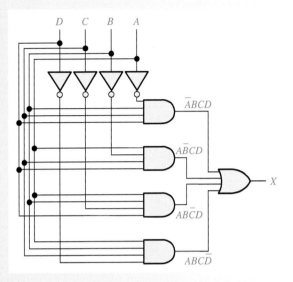

► FIGURE 13

Open file F05-13 to verify the operation.

Related Problem   Determine if the logic circuit of Figure 13 can be simplified.

EXAMPLE 7

Reduce the combinational logic circuit in Figure 14 to a minimum form.

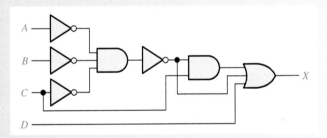

► FIGURE 14

Open file F05-14 to verify that this circuit is equivalent to the circuit in Figure 15.

Solution   The expression for the output of the circuit is

$$X = (\overline{\overline{A}\,\overline{B}\,\overline{C}})C + \overline{\overline{A}\,\overline{B}\,\overline{C}} + D$$

Applying DeMorgan's theorem and Boolean algebra,

$$X = (\overline{\overline{A}} + \overline{\overline{B}} + \overline{\overline{C}})C + \overline{\overline{A}} + \overline{\overline{B}} + \overline{\overline{C}} + D$$
$$= AC + BC + CC + A + B + C + D$$
$$= AC + BC + C + A + B + \mathcal{C} + D$$
$$= C(A + B + 1) + A + B + D$$
$$X = A + B + C + D$$

The simplified circuit is a 4-input OR gate as shown in Figure 15.

► FIGURE 15

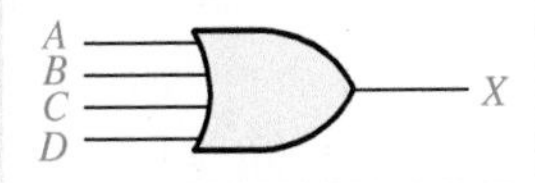

$$\begin{array}{c} A \\ B \\ C \\ D \end{array} \!\!\!\!\! \supset\!\!\!\!-\!\!\!\!- X$$

Related Problem   Verify the minimized expression $A + B + C + D$ using a Karnaugh map.

EXAMPLE 8

Minimize the combinational logic circuit in Figure 16. Inverters for the complemented variables are not shown.

▶ FIGURE 16

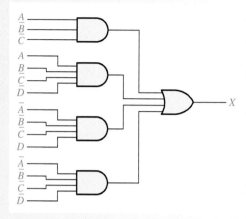

Solution   The output expression is

$$X = A\overline{B}\,\overline{C} + AB\overline{C}\overline{D} + \overline{A}\,\overline{B}CD + \overline{A}BC\overline{D}$$

Expanding the first term to include the missing variables D and $\overline{D}$,

$$X = A\overline{B}\,\overline{C}(D + \overline{D}) + AB\overline{C}\overline{D} + \overline{A}\,\overline{B}CD + \overline{A}BC\overline{D}$$
$$= A\overline{B}\,\overline{C}D + A\overline{B}\,\overline{C}\overline{D} + AB\overline{C}\overline{D} + \overline{A}\,\overline{B}CD + \overline{A}BC\overline{D}$$

This expanded SOP expression is mapped and simplified on the Karnaugh map in Figure 17(a). The simplified implementation is shown in part (b). Inverters are not shown.

◀ FIGURE 17

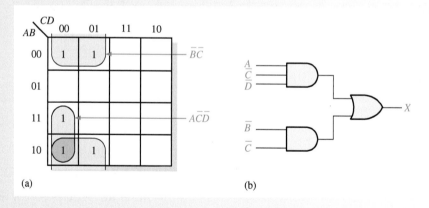

(a)   (b)

Related Problem   Develop the POS equivalent of the circuit in Figure 17(b).

SECTION 2
CHECKUP

1. Implement the following Boolean expressions as they are stated:
   (a) $X = ABC + AB + AC$ (b) $X = AB(C + DE)$
2. Develop a logic circuit that will produce a 1 on its output only when all three inputs are 1s or when all three inputs are 0s.
3. Reduce the circuits in Question 1 to minimum SOP form.

254

3   THE UNIVERSAL PROPERTY OF NAND AND NOR GATES

Up to this point, you have studied combinational circuits implemented with AND gates, OR gates, and inverters. In this section, the universal property of the NAND gate and the NOR gate is discussed. The universality of the NAND gate means that it can be used as an inverter and that combinations of NAND gates can be used to implement the AND, OR, and NOR operations. Similarly, the NOR gate can be used to implement the inverter (NOT), AND, OR, and NAND operations.

After completing this section, you should be able to

♦ Use NAND gates to implement the inverter, the AND gate, the OR gate, and the NOR gate

♦ Use NOR gates to implement the inverter, the AND gate, the OR gate, and the NAND gate

The NAND Gate as a Universal Logic Element

The NAND gate is a **universal gate** because it can be used to produce the NOT, the AND, the OR, and the NOR functions. An inverter can be made from a NAND gate by connecting all of the inputs together and creating, in effect, a single input, as shown in Figure 18(a) for a 2-input gate. An AND function can be generated by the use of NAND gates alone, as shown in Figure 18(b). An OR function can be produced with only NAND gates, as illustrated in part (c). Finally, a NOR function is produced as shown in part (d).

Combinations of NAND gates can be used to produce any logic function.

(a) One NAND gate used as an inverter

(b) Two NAND gates used as an AND gate

(c) Three NAND gates used as an OR gate

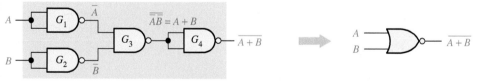

(d) Four NAND gates used as a NOR gate

▲ FIGURE 18

Universal application of NAND gates. Open files F05-18(a), (b), (c), and (d) to verify each of the equivalencies.

In Figure 18(b), a NAND gate is used to invert (complement) a NAND output to form the AND function, as indicated in the following equation:

$$X = \overline{\overline{AB}} = AB$$

In Figure 18(c), NAND gates G_1 and G_2 are used to invert the two input variables before they are applied to NAND gate G_3. The final OR output is derived as follows by application of DeMorgan's theorem:

$$X = \overline{\overline{A}\,\overline{B}} = A + B$$

In Figure 18(d), NAND gate G_4 is used as an inverter connected to the circuit of part (c) to produce the NOR operation $\overline{A + B}$.

The NOR Gate as a Universal Logic Element

Combinations of NOR gates can be used to produce any logic function.

Like the NAND gate, the NOR gate can be used to produce the NOT, AND, OR, and NAND functions. A NOT circuit, or inverter, can be made from a NOR gate by connecting all of the inputs together to effectively create a single input, as shown in Figure 19(a) with a 2-input example. Also, an OR gate can be produced from NOR gates, as illustrated in Figure 19(b). An AND gate can be constructed by the use of NOR gates, as shown in Figure 19(c). In this case the NOR gates G_1 and G_2 are used as inverters, and the final output is derived by the use of DeMorgan's theorem as follows:

$$X = \overline{\overline{A} + \overline{B}} = AB$$

Figure 19(d) shows how NOR gates are used to form a NAND function.

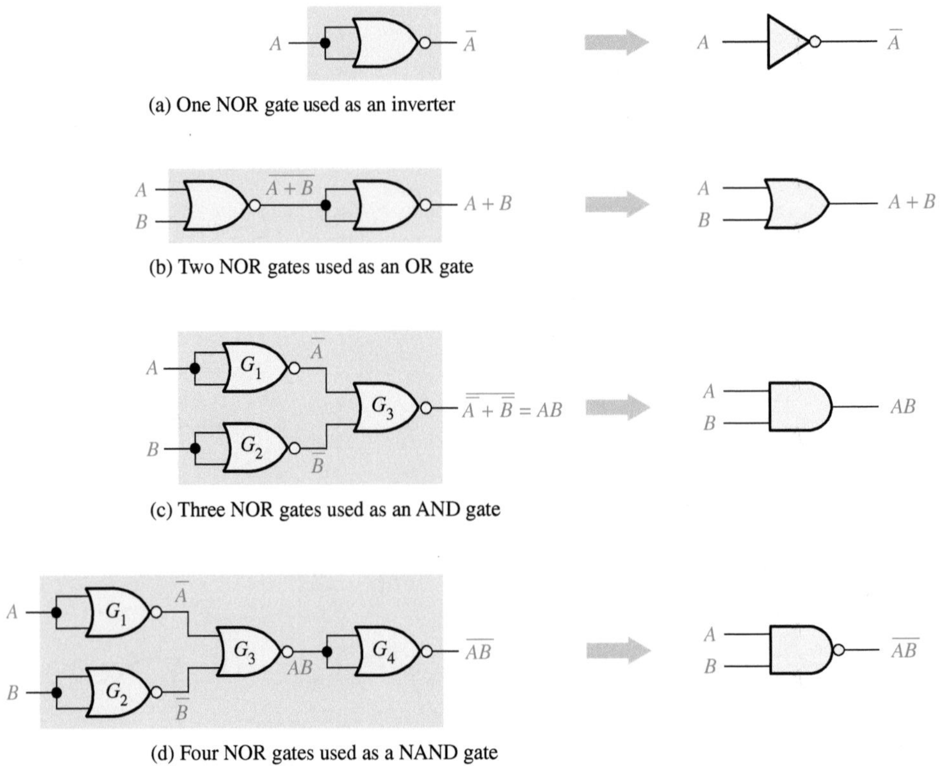

(a) One NOR gate used as an inverter

(b) Two NOR gates used as an OR gate

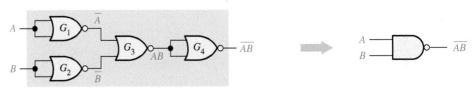

(c) Three NOR gates used as an AND gate

(d) Four NOR gates used as a NAND gate

▲ FIGURE 19

Universal application of NOR gates. Open files F05-19(a), (b), (c), and (d) to verify each of the equivalencies.

SECTION 3
CHECKUP

1. Use NAND gates to implement each expression:
   (a) $X = \overline{A} + B$ (b) $X = A\overline{B}$
2. Use NOR gates to implement each expression:
   (a) $X = \overline{A} + B$ (b) $X = A\overline{B}$

4 COMBINATIONAL LOGIC USING NAND AND NOR GATES

In this section, you will see how NAND and NOR gates can be used to implement a logic function. The NAND gate also exhibits an equivalent operation called the negative-OR and that the NOR gate exhibits an equivalent operation called the negative-AND. You will see how the use of the appropriate symbols to represent the equivalent operations makes "reading" a logic diagram easier.

After completing this section, you should be able to

♦ Use NAND gates to implement a logic function

♦ Use NOR gates to implement a logic function

♦ Use the appropriate dual symbol in a logic diagram

NAND Logic

As you have learned, a NAND gate can function as either a NAND or a negative-OR because, by DeMorgan's theorem,

$$\overline{AB} = \overline{A} + \overline{B}$$

NAND ⟶   ⟵ negative-OR

Consider the NAND logic in Figure 20. The output expression is developed in the following steps:

$$X = \overline{(\overline{AB})(\overline{CD})}$$
$$= \overline{(\overline{A} + \overline{B})(\overline{C} + \overline{D})}$$
$$= \overline{(\overline{A} + \overline{B})} + \overline{(\overline{C} + \overline{D})}$$
$$= \overline{\overline{A}}\,\overline{\overline{B}} + \overline{\overline{C}}\,\overline{\overline{D}}$$
$$= AB + CD$$

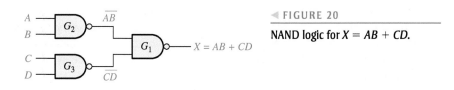

◀ FIGURE 20

NAND logic for $X = AB + CD$.

As you can see in Figure 20, the output expression, $AB + CD$, is in the form of two AND terms ORed together. This shows that gates G_2 and G_3 act as AND gates and that gate G_1 acts as an OR gate, as illustrated in Figure 21(a). This circuit is redrawn in part (b) with NAND symbols for gates G_2 and G_3 and a negative-OR symbol for gate G_1.

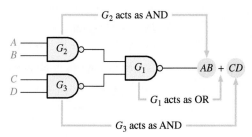

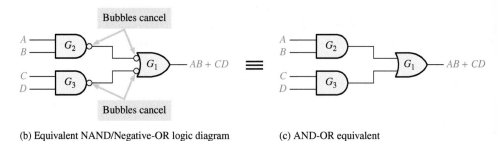

(a) Original NAND logic diagram showing effective gate operation relative to the output expression

(b) Equivalent NAND/Negative-OR logic diagram   (c) AND-OR equivalent

▲ FIGURE 21

Development of the AND-OR equivalent of the circuit in Figure 20.

Notice in Figure 21(b) the bubble-to-bubble connections between the outputs of gates G_2 and G_3 and the inputs of gate G_1. *Since a bubble represents an inversion, two connected bubbles represent a double inversion and therefore cancel each other.* This inversion cancellation can be seen in the previous development of the output expression $AB + CD$ and is indicated by the absence of barred terms in the output expression. Thus, the circuit in Figure 21(b) is *effectively* an AND-OR circuit, as shown in Figure 21(c).

NAND Logic Diagrams Using Dual Symbols   All logic diagrams using NAND gates should be drawn with each gate represented by either a NAND symbol or the equivalent negative-OR symbol to reflect the operation of the gate within the logic circuit. The NAND symbol and the **negative-OR** symbol are called *dual symbols*. When drawing a NAND logic diagram, always use the gate symbols in such a way that every connection between

a gate output and a gate input is either bubble-to-bubble or nonbubble-to-nonbubble. In general, a bubble output should not be connected to a nonbubble input or vice versa in a logic diagram.

Figure 22 shows an arrangement of gates to illustrate the procedure of using the appropriate dual symbols for a NAND circuit with several gate levels. Although using all NAND symbols as in Figure 22(a) is correct, the diagram in part (b) is much easier to "read" and is the preferred method. As shown in Figure 22(b), the output gate is represented with a negative-OR symbol. Then the NAND symbol is used for the level of gates right before the output gate and the symbols for successive levels of gates are alternated as you move away from the output.

The shape of the gate indicates the way its inputs will appear in the output expression and thus shows how the gate functions within the logic circuit. For a NAND symbol, the inputs appear ANDed in the output expression; and for a negative-OR symbol, the inputs appear ORed in the output expression, as Figure 22(b) illustrates. The dual-symbol diagram in part (b) makes it easier to determine the output expression directly from the logic diagram because each gate symbol indicates the relationship of its input variables as they appear in the output expression.

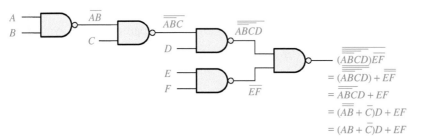

► FIGURE 22

Illustration of the use of the appropriate dual symbols in a NAND logic diagram.

$$(\overline{\overline{ABCD})\overline{EF}}$$
$$= (\overline{\overline{ABCD}}) + \overline{\overline{EF}}$$
$$= \overline{ABCD} + EF$$
$$= (\overline{AB} + \overline{C})D + EF$$
$$= (AB + \overline{C})D + EF$$

(a) Several Boolean steps are required to arrive at final output expression.

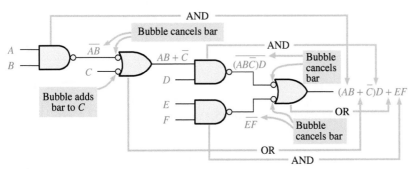

(b) Output expression can be obtained directly from the function of each gate symbol in the diagram.

EXAMPLE 9

Redraw the logic diagram and develop the output expression for the circuit in Figure 23 using the appropriate dual symbols.

▶ FIGURE 23

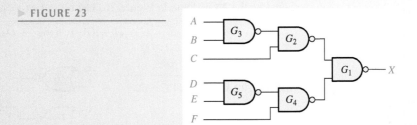

Solution Redraw the logic diagram in Figure 23 with the use of equivalent negative-OR symbols as shown in Figure 24. Writing the expression for X directly from the indicated logic operation of each gate gives $X = (\overline{A} + \overline{B})C + (\overline{D} + \overline{E})F$.

◀ FIGURE 24

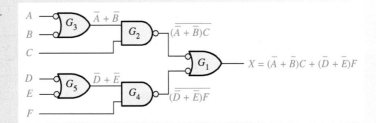

Related Problem Derive the output expression from Figure 23 and show it is equivalent to the expression in the solution.

EXAMPLE 10

Implement each expression with NAND logic using appropriate dual symbols:

(a) $ABC + DE$　　　　**(b)** $ABC + \overline{D} + \overline{E}$

Solution　See Figure 25.

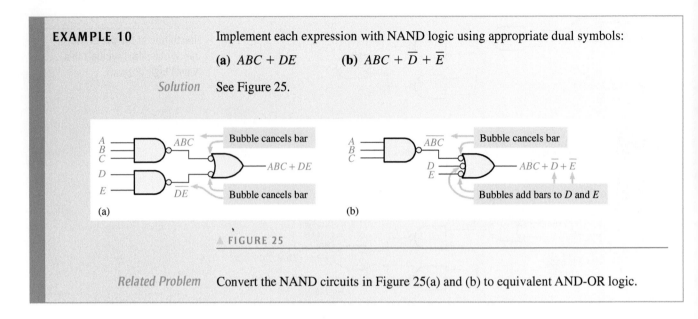

(a)　　　　　　　　　　　　　　　　　　(b)

▲ FIGURE 25

Related Problem　Convert the NAND circuits in Figure 25(a) and (b) to equivalent AND-OR logic.

NOR Logic

A NOR gate can function as either a NOR or a **negative-AND,** as shown by DeMorgan's theorem.

$$\overline{A + B} = \overline{A}\,\overline{B}$$

NOR ———↑　　　↑——— negative-AND

Consider the NOR logic in Figure 26. The output expression is developed as follows:

$$X = \overline{\overline{A + B} + \overline{C + D}} = (\overline{\overline{A + B}})(\overline{\overline{C + D}}) = (A + B)C + D)$$

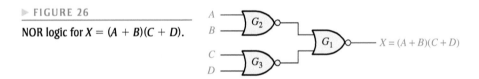

▶ FIGURE 26

NOR logic for $X = (A + B)(C + D)$.

As you can see in Figure 26, the output expression $(A + B)(C + D)$ consists of two OR terms ANDed together. This shows that gates G_2 and G_3 act as OR gates and gate G_1 acts as an AND gate, as illustrated in Figure 27(a). This circuit is redrawn in part (b) with a negative-AND symbol for gate G_1.

▶ FIGURE 27

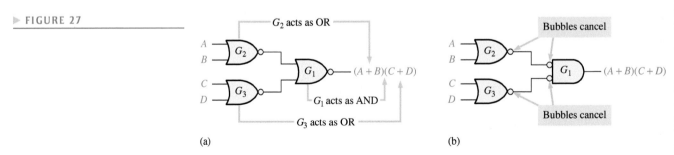

(a)　　　　　　　　　　　　　　　　　　(b)

NOR Logic Diagram Using Dual Symbols　As with NAND logic, the purpose for using the dual symbols is to make the logic diagram easier to read and analyze, as illustrated in the NOR logic circuit in Figure 28. When the circuit in part (a) is redrawn with dual

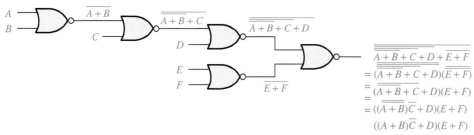

FIGURE 28

Illustration of the use of the appropriate dual symbols in a NOR logic diagram.

$$\overline{\overline{\overline{A+B+C+D} + \overline{E+F}}}$$
$$= \overline{(A+B+C+D)}\overline{(\overline{E+F})}$$
$$= \overline{(A+\overline{B}+C+D)}(E+F)$$
$$= ((\overline{A+B})\overline{C}+D)(E+F)$$
$$((A+B)\overline{C}+D)(E+F)$$

(a) Final output expression is obtained after several Boolean steps.

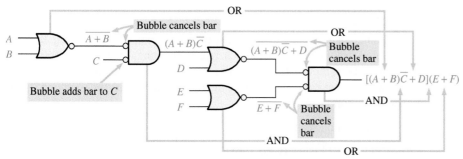

(b) Output expression can be obtained directly from the function of each gate symbol in the diagram.

symbols in part (b), notice that all output-to-input connections between gates are bubble-to-bubble or nonbubble-to-nonbubble. Again, you can see that the shape of each gate symbol indicates the type of term (AND or OR) that it produces in the output expression, thus making the output expression easier to determine and the logic diagram easier to analyze.

EXAMPLE 11

Using appropriate dual symbols, redraw the logic diagram and develop the output expression for the circuit in Figure 29.

▶ FIGURE 29

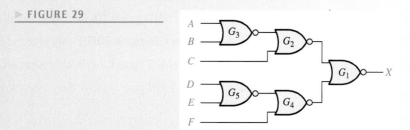

Solution   Redraw the logic diagram with the equivalent negative-AND symbols as shown in Figure 30. Writing the expression for X directly from the indicated operation of each gate,

$$X = (\overline{A}\overline{B} + C)(\overline{D}\overline{E} + F)$$

▶ FIGURE 30

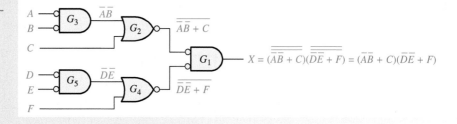

Related Problem   Prove that the output of the NOR circuit in Figure 29 is the same as for the circuit in Figure 30.

SECTION 4
CHECKUP

1. Implement the expression $X = \overline{(\overline{A} + \overline{B} + \overline{C})DE}$ by using NAND logic.
2. Implement the expression $X = \overline{\overline{A}\,\overline{B}\,\overline{C}} + (D + E)$ with NOR logic.

---

5   LOGIC CIRCUIT OPERATION WITH PULSE WAVEFORM INPUTS

General combinational logic circuits with pulse waveform inputs are examined in this section. Keep in mind that the operation of each gate is the same for pulse waveform inputs as for constant-level inputs. The output of a logic circuit at any given time depends on the inputs at that particular time, so the relationship of the time-varying inputs is of primary importance.

After completing this section, you should be able to

+   Analyze combinational logic circuits with pulse waveform inputs

+   Develop a timing diagram for any given combinational logic circuit with specified inputs

The operation of any gate is the same regardless of whether its inputs are pulsed or constant levels. The nature of the inputs (pulsed or constant levels) does not alter the truth table of a circuit. The examples in this section illustrate the analysis of combinational logic circuits with pulse waveform inputs.

The following is a review of the operation of individual gates for use in analyzing combinational circuits with pulse waveform inputs:

1. The output of an AND gate is HIGH only when all inputs are HIGH at the same time.

2. The output of an OR gate is HIGH only when at least one of its inputs is HIGH.

3. The output of a NAND gate is LOW only when all inputs are HIGH at the same time.

4. The output of a NOR gate is LOW only when at least one of its inputs is HIGH.

EXAMPLE 12

Determine the final output waveform X for the circuit in Figure 31, with input waveforms A, B, and C as shown.

FIGURE 31

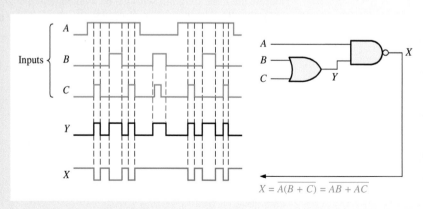

$X = \overline{A(B + C)} = \overline{AB + AC}$

Solution The output expression, $\overline{AB + AC}$, indicates that the output X is LOW when both A and B are HIGH or when both A and C are HIGH or when all inputs are HIGH. The output waveform X is shown in the timing diagram of Figure 31. The intermediate waveform Y at the output of the OR gate is also shown.

Related Problem Determine the output waveform if input A is a constant HIGH level.

EXAMPLE 13

Draw the timing diagram for the circuit in Figure 32 showing the outputs of G_1, G_2, and G_3 with the input waveforms, A, and B, as indicated.

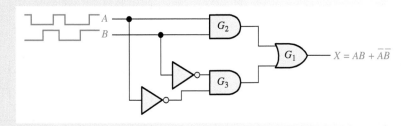

▲ FIGURE 32

Solution When both inputs are HIGH or when both inputs are LOW, the output X is HIGH as shown in Figure 31. Notice that this is an exclusive-NOR circuit. The intermediate outputs of gates G_2 and G_3 are also shown in Figure 33.

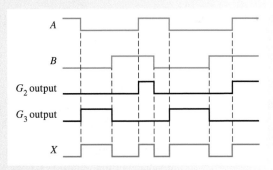

▲ FIGURE 33

Related Problem Determine the output X in Figure 32 if input B is inverted.

EXAMPLE 14

Determine the output waveform X for the logic circuit in Figure 34(a) by first finding the intermediate waveform at each of points Y_1, Y_2, Y_3, and Y_4. The input waveforms are shown in Figure 34(b).

FIGURE 34

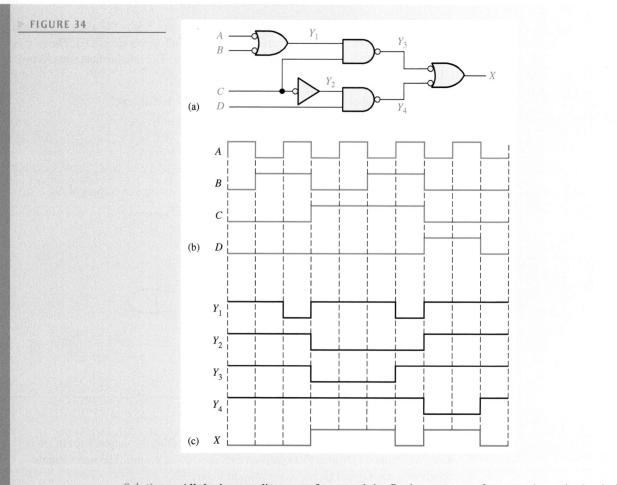

(a)

(b)

(c)

Solution   All the intermediate waveforms and the final output waveform are shown in the timing diagram of Figure 34(c).

Related Problem   Determine the waveforms Y_1, Y_2, Y_3, Y_4 and X if input waveform A is inverted.

EXAMPLE 15   Determine the output waveform X for the circuit in Example 14, Figure 34(a), directly from the output expression.

Solution   The output expression for the circuit is developed in Figure 35. The SOP form indicates that the output is HIGH when A is LOW and C is HIGH or when B is LOW and C is HIGH or when C is LOW and D is HIGH.

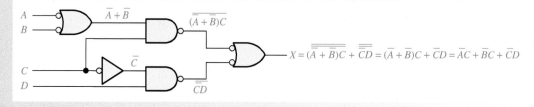

$$X = \overline{\overline{(\overline{A} + \overline{B})C} + \overline{\overline{CD}}} = (\overline{A} + \overline{B})C + \overline{CD} = \overline{A}C + \overline{B}C + \overline{C}D$$

▲ FIGURE 35

264

The result is shown in Figure 36 and is the same as the one obtained by the intermediate-waveform method in Example 14. The corresponding product terms for each waveform condition that results in a HIGH output are indicated.

FIGURE 36

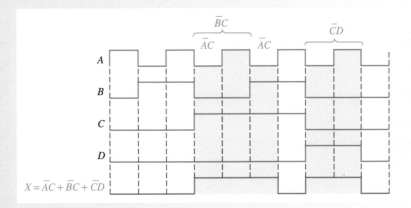

$$X = \bar{A}C + \bar{B}C + \bar{C}D$$

Related Problem   Repeat this example if all the input waveforms are inverted.

**SECTION 5
CHECKUP**

1. One pulse with $t_W = 50 \ \mu s$ is applied to one of the inputs of an exclusive-OR circuit. A second positive pulse with $t_W = 10 \ \mu s$ is applied to the other input beginning 15 μs after the leading edge of the first pulse. Show the output in relation to the inputs.

2. The pulse waveforms A and B in Figure 31 are applied to the exclusive-NOR circuit in Figure 32. Develop a complete timing diagram.

---

6   TROUBLESHOOTING

The preceding sections have given you some insight into the operation of combinational logic circuits and the relationships of inputs and outputs. This type of understanding is essential when you troubleshoot digital circuits because you must know what logic levels or waveforms to look for throughout the circuit for a given set of input conditions.

In this section, an oscilloscope is used to troubleshoot a fixed-function logic circuit when a gate output is connected to several gate inputs. Also, an example of signal tracing and waveform analysis methods is presented using a scope or logic analyzer for locating a fault in a combinational logic circuit.

After completing this section, you should be able to

* Define a circuit node

* Use an oscilloscope to find a faulty circuit node

* Use an oscilloscope to find an open gate output

* Use an oscilloscope to find a shorted gate input or output

* Use an oscilloscope or a logic analyzer for signal tracing in a combinational logic circuit

In a combinational logic circuit, the output of one gate may be connected to two or more gate inputs as shown in Figure 37. The interconnecting paths share a common electrical point known as a **node.**

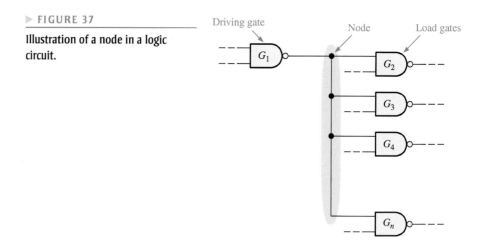

Gate G_1 in Figure 37 is driving the node, and the other gates represent loads connected to the node. A driving gate can drive a number of load gate inputs up to its specified fanout. Several types of failures are possible in this situation. Some of these failure modes are difficult to isolate to a single bad gate because all the gates connected to the node are affected. Common types of failures are the following:

1. *Open output in driving gate.* This failure will cause a loss of signal to all load gates.

2. *Open input in a load gate.* This failure will not affect the operation of any of the other gates connected to the node, but it will result in loss of signal output from the faulty gate.

3. *Shorted output in driving gate.* This failure can cause the node to be stuck in the LOW state (short to ground) or in the HIGH state (short to V_{CC}).

4. *Shorted input in a load gate.* This failure can also cause the node to be stuck in the LOW state (short to ground) or in the HIGH state (short to V_{CC}).

Troubleshooting Common Faults

Open Output in Driving Gate In this situation there is no pulse activity on the node. With circuit power on, an open node will normally result in a "floating" level, as illustrated in Figure 38.

Hands-On Tip

When troubleshooting logic circuits, begin with a visual check, looking for obvious problems. In addition to components, visual inspection should include connectors. Edge connectors are frequently used to bring power, ground, and signals to a circuit board. The mating surfaces of the connector need to be clean and have a good mechanical fit. A dirty connector can cause intermittent or complete failure of the circuit. Edge connectors can be cleaned with a common pencil eraser and wiped clean with a Q-tip soaked in alcohol. Also, all connectors should be checked for loose-fitting pins.

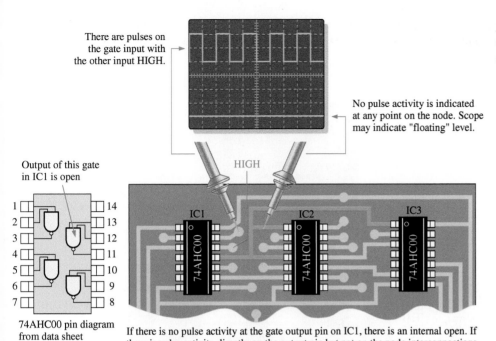

◄ FIGURE 38

Open output in driving gate. Assume a HIGH is on one gate input.

There are pulses on the gate input with the other input HIGH.

No pulse activity is indicated at any point on the node. Scope may indicate "floating" level.

Output of this gate in IC1 is open

74AHC00 pin diagram from data sheet

If there is no pulse activity at the gate output pin on IC1, there is an internal open. If there is pulse activity directly on the output pin but not on the node interconnections, the connection between the pin and the board is open.

Open Input in a Load Gate If the check for an open driver output in IC1 is negative (there is pulse activity), then a check for an open input in a load gate should be performed. Check the output of each gate for pulse activity, as illustrated in Figure 39. If one of the inputs that is normally connected to the node is open, no pulses will be detected on that gate's output.

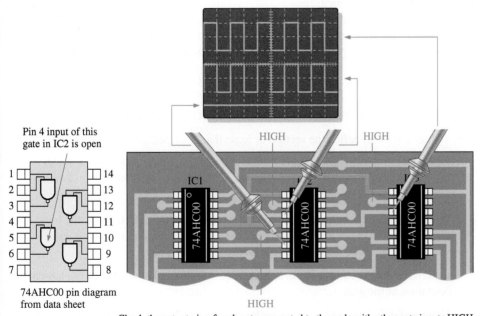

◄ FIGURE 39

Open input in a load gate.

Pin 4 input of this gate in IC2 is open

74AHC00 pin diagram from data sheet

Check the output pin of each gate connected to the node with other gate inputs HIGH. No pulse activity on an output indicates an open gate input or open gate output.

Output or Input Shorted to Ground When the output is shorted to ground in the driving gate or the input to a load gate is shorted to ground, it will cause the node to be stuck LOW, as previously mentioned. A quick check with a scope probe will indicate this, as shown in Figure 40. A short to ground in the driving gate's output or in any load gate input will cause this symptom, and further checks must therefore be made to isolate the short to a particular gate.

▷ FIGURE 40

Shorted output in the driving gate or shorted input in a load gate.

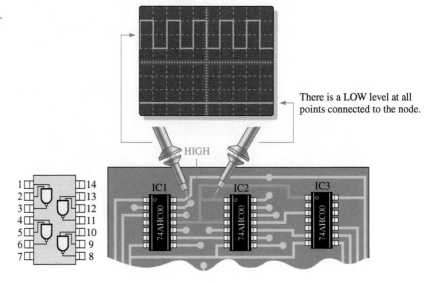

There is a LOW level at all points connected to the node.

Signal Tracing and Waveform Analysis

Although the methods of isolating an open or a short at a node point are very useful from time to time, a more general troubleshooting technique called **signal tracing** is of value in just about every troubleshooting situation. Waveform measurement is accomplished with an oscilloscope or a logic analyzer.

Basically, the signal tracing method requires that you observe the waveforms and their time relationships at all accessible points in the logic circuit. You can begin at the inputs and, from an analysis of the waveform timing diagram for each point, determine where an incorrect waveform first occurs. With this procedure you can usually isolate the fault to a specific gate. A procedure beginning at the output and working back toward the inputs can also be used.

The general procedure for signal tracing starting at the inputs is outlined as follows:

- ◆ Within a system, define the section of logic that is suspected of being faulty.

- ◆ Start at the inputs to the section of logic under examination. We assume, for this discussion, that the input waveforms coming from other sections of the system have been found to be correct.

- ◆ For each gate, beginning at the input and working toward the output of the logic circuit, observe the output waveform of the gate and compare it with the input waveforms by using the oscilloscope or the logic analyzer.

- ◆ Determine if the output waveform is correct, using your knowledge of the logical operation of the gate.

- ◆ If the output is incorrect, the gate under test may be faulty. Pull the IC containing the gate that is suspected of being faulty, and test it out-of-circuit. If the gate is found to be faulty, replace the IC. If it works correctly, the fault is in the external circuitry or in another IC to which the tested one is connected.

- ◆ If the output is correct, go to the next gate. Continue checking each gate until an incorrect waveform is observed.

Figure 41 is an example that illustrates the general procedure for a specific logic circuit in the following steps:

Step 1: Observe the output of gate G_1 (test point 5) relative to the inputs. If it is correct, check the inverter next. If the output is not correct, the gate or its connections are bad; or, if the output is LOW, the input to gate G_2 may be shorted.

Step 2: Observe the output of the inverter (TP6) relative to the input. If it is correct, check gate G_2 next. If the output is not correct, the inverter or its connections are bad; or, if the output is LOW, the input to gate G_3 may be shorted.

Step 3: Observe the output of gate G_2 (TP7) relative to the inputs. If it is correct, check gate G_3 next. If the output is not correct, the gate or its connections are bad; or, if the output is LOW, the input to gate G_4 may be shorted.

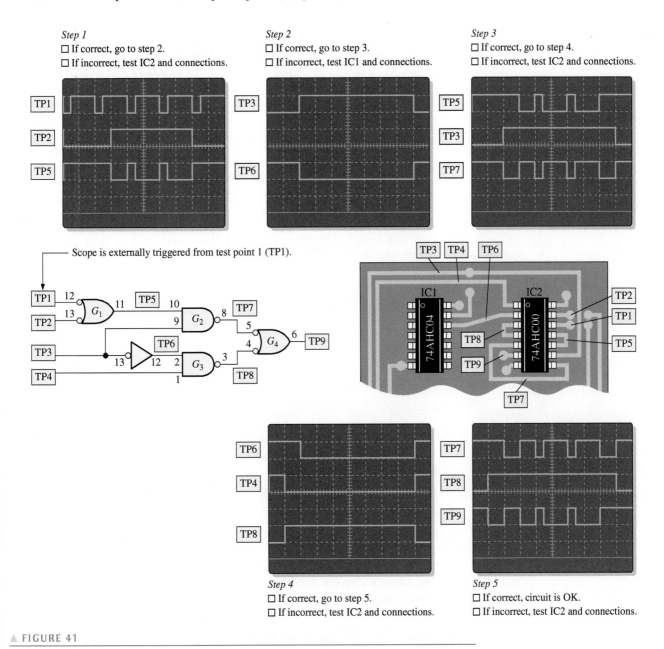

Step 1
☐ If correct, go to step 2.
☐ If incorrect, test IC2 and connections.

Step 2
☐ If correct, go to step 3.
☐ If incorrect, test IC1 and connections.

Step 3
☐ If correct, go to step 4.
☐ If incorrect, test IC2 and connections.

Scope is externally triggered from test point 1 (TP1).

Step 4
☐ If correct, go to step 5.
☐ If incorrect, test IC2 and connections.

Step 5
☐ If correct, circuit is OK.
☐ If incorrect, test IC2 and connections.

▲ FIGURE 41

Example of signal tracing and waveform analysis in a portion of a printed circuit board. TP indicates test point.

Step 4: Observe the output of gate G_3 (TP8) relative to the inputs. If it is correct, check gate G_4 next. If the output is not correct, the gate or its connections are bad; or, if the output is LOW, the input to gate G_4 (TP7) may be shorted.

Step 5: Observe the output of gate G_4 (TP9) relative to the inputs. If it is correct, the circuit is okay. If the output is not correct, the gate or its connections are bad.

EXAMPLE 16

Determine the fault in the logic circuit of Figure 42(a) by using waveform analysis. You have observed the waveforms shown in green in Figure 42(b). The red waveforms are correct and are provided for comparison.

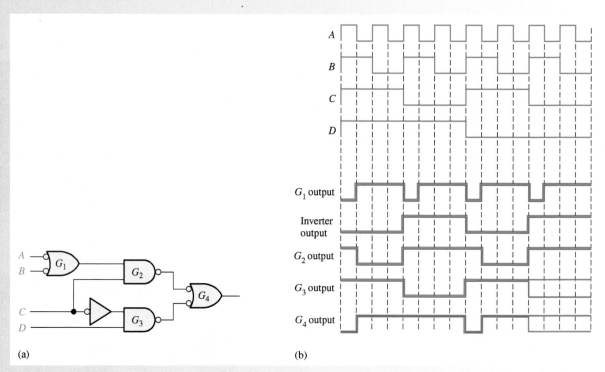

(a) (b)

△ FIGURE 42

Solution

1. Determine what the correct waveform should be for each gate. The correct waveforms are shown in red, superimposed on the actual measured waveforms, in Figure 42(b).

2. Compare waveforms gate by gate until you find a measured waveform that does not match the correct waveform.

   In this example, everything tested is correct until gate G_3 is checked. The output of this gate is not correct as the differences in the waveforms indicate. An analysis of the waveforms indicates that if the D input to gate G_3 is open and acting as a HIGH, you will get the output waveform measured (shown in red). Notice that the output of G_4 is also incorrect due to the incorrect input from G_3.

   Replace the IC containing G_3, and check the circuit's operation again.

Related Problem

For the inputs in Figure 42(b), determine the output waveform for the logic circuit (output of G_4) if the inverter has an open output.

Hands-On Tip

As you know, testing and troubleshooting logic circuits often require observing and comparing two digital waveforms simultaneously, such as an input and the output of a gate, on an oscilloscope. For digital waveforms, the scope should always be set to DC coupling on each channel input to avoid "shifting" the ground level. You should determine where the 0 V level is on the screen for both channels.

To compare the timing of the waveforms, the scope should be triggered from only one channel (don't use vertical mode or composite triggering). The channel selected for triggering should always be the one that has the lowest frequency waveform, if possible.

Troubleshooting problems that are keyed to the website (www.pearsoned.com/electronics) are available in the Multisim Troubleshooting Practice section of the end-of-chapter problems.

SECTION 6 CHECKUP

1. List four common internal failures in logic gates.
2. One input of a NOR gate is externally shorted to $+V_{CC}$. How does this condition affect the gate operation?
3. Determine the output of gate G_4 in Figure 42(a), with inputs as shown in part (b), for the following faults:
   (a) one input to G_1 shorted to ground
   (b) the inverter input shorted to ground
   (c) an open output in G_3

7   COMBINATIONAL LOGIC WITH VHDL

The purpose of describing logic using VHDL is so that it can be programmed into a PLD. In this section, both the data flow approach using Boolean expressions and the structural approach are used to develop VHDL code for describing logic circuits. The VHDL component is introduced and used to illustrate structural descriptions. Some aspects of software development tools are discussed.

After completing this section, you should be able to

* Describe a VHDL component and discuss how it is used in a program

* Apply the structural approach and the data flow approach to writing VHDL code

* Describe two basic software development tools

Structural Approach to VHDL Programming

The structural approach to writing a VHDL description of a logic function can be compared to installing IC devices on a circuit board and interconnecting them with wires. With the structural approach, you describe logic functions and specify how they are connected together. The VHDL **component** is a way to predefine a logic function for repeated use in a program or in other programs. The component can be used to describe anything from a simple logic gate to a complex logic function. The VHDL **signal** can be thought of as a way to specify a "wire" connection between components.

Figure 43 provides a simplified comparison of the structural approach to a hardware implementation on a circuit board.

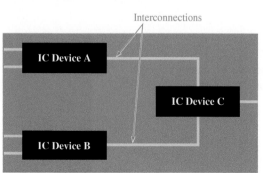 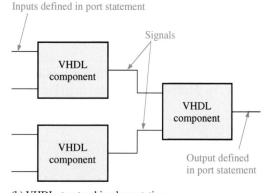

(a) Hardware implementation with fixed-function logic (b) VHDL structural implementation

▲ FIGURE 43

Simplified comparison of the VHDL structural approach to a hardware implementation. The VHDL signals correspond to the interconnections on the circuit board, and the VHDL components correspond to the IC devices.

VHDL Components

A VHDL component describes predefined logic that can be stored as a package declaration in a VHDL library and called as many times as necessary in a program. You can use components to avoid repeating the same code over and over within a program. For example, you can create a VHDL component for an AND gate and then use it as many times as you wish without having to write a program for an AND gate every time you need one.

VHDL components are stored and are available for use when you write a program. This is similar to having, for example, a storage bin of ICs available when you are constructing a circuit. Every time you need to use one in your circuit, you reach into the storage bin and place it on the circuit board.

The VHDL program for any logic function can become a component and used whenever necessary in a larger program with the use of a component declaration of the following general form. **Component** is a VHDL keyword.

> **component** name_of_component **is**
>   **port** (port definitions);
> **end component** name_of_component;

For simplicity, let's assume that there are predefined VHDL data flow descriptions of a 2-input AND gate with the entity name AND_gate and a 2-input OR gate with the entity name OR_gate, as shown in Figure 44.

Next, assume that you are writing a program for a logic circuit that has several AND gates. Instead of rewriting the program in Figure 44 over and over, you can use a

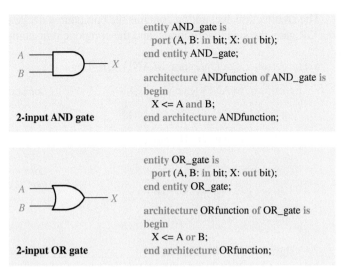

Predefined programs for a 2-input AND gate and a 2-input OR gate to be used as components in the data flow approach.

component declaration to specify the AND gate. The port statement in the component declaration must correspond to the port statement in the entity declaration of the AND gate.

component AND_gate is

    port (A, B: in bit; X: out bit);

end component AND_gate;

Using Components in a Program   To use a component in a program, you must write a component instantiation statement for each instance in which the component is used. You can think of a component instantiation as a request or call for the component to be used in the main program. For example, the simple SOP logic circuit in Figure 45 has two AND gates and one OR gate. Therefore, the VHDL program for this circuit will have two components and three component instantiations or calls.

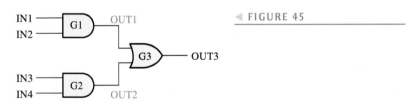

Signals   In VHDL, signals are analogous to wires that interconnect components on a circuit board. The signals in Figure 45 are named OUT1 and OUT2. Signals are the *internal* connections in the logic circuit and are treated differently than the inputs and outputs. Whereas the inputs and outputs are declared in the entity declaration using the port statement, the signals are declared within the architecture using the signal statement. **Signal** is a VHDL keyword.

The Program   The program for the logic in Figure 45 begins with an entity declaration as follows:

--Program for the logic circuit in Figure 45

entity AND_OR_Logic is

    port (IN1, IN2, IN3, IN4: in bit; OUT3: out bit);

end entity AND_OR_Logic;

The architecture declaration contains the component declarations for the AND gate and the OR gate, the signal definitions, and the component instantiations.

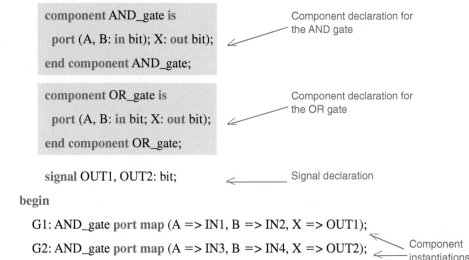

architecture LogicOperation of AND_OR_Logic is

    component AND_gate is

      port (A, B: in bit); X: out bit);   Component declaration for the AND gate

    end component AND_gate;

    component OR_gate is

      port (A, B: in bit; X: out bit);   Component declaration for the OR gate

    end component OR_gate;

    signal OUT1, OUT2: bit;   Signal declaration

begin

    G1: AND_gate port map (A => IN1, B => IN2, X => OUT1);

    G2: AND_gate port map (A => IN3, B => IN4, X => OUT2);   Component instantiations

    G3: OR_gate port map (A => OUT1, B => OUT2, X => OUT3);

    end architecture LogicOperation;

Component Instantiations Let's look at the component instantiations. First, notice that the component instantiations appear between the keyword **begin** and the **end** statement. For each instantiation an identifier is defined, such as G1, G2, and G3 in this case. Then the component name is specified. The port map essentially makes all the connections for the logic function using the operator =>. For example, the first instantiation,

    G1: AND_gate **port map** (A => IN1, B => IN2, X => OUT1);

can be explained as follows: *Input A of AND gate G1 is connected to input IN1, input B of the gate is connected to input IN2, and the output X of the gate is connected to the signal OUT1.*

The three instantiation statements together completely describe the logic circuit in Figure 45, as illustrated in Figure 46.

▶ FIGURE 46

Illustration of the instantiation statements and port mapping applied to the AND-OR logic. Signals are shown in red.

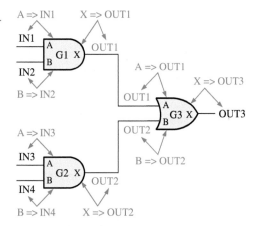

Although the data flow approach using Boolean expressions would have been easier and probably the best way to describe this particular circuit, we have used this simple circuit to explain the concept of the structural approach. Example 17 compares the structural and data flow approaches to writing a VHDL program for an SOP logic circuit.

EXAMPLE 17

Write a VHDL program for the SOP logic circuit in Figure 47 using the structural approach. Assume that VHDL components for a 3-input NAND gate and for a 2-input NAND are available. Notice the NAND gate G4 is shown as a negative-OR.

▶ FIGURE 47

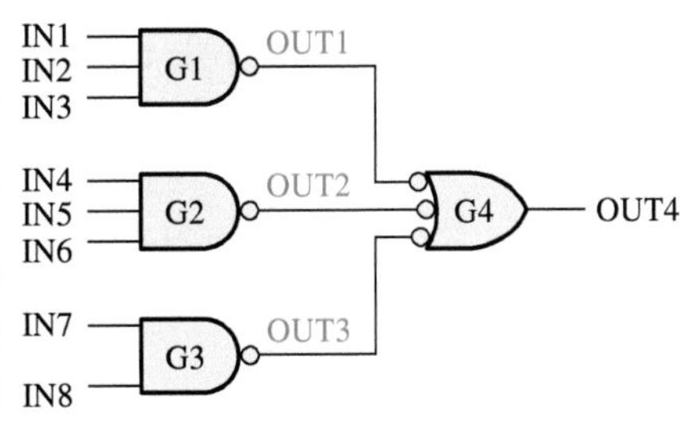

Solution The components and component instantiations are highlighted.

--Program for the logic circuit in Figure 47

entity SOP_Logic is

    port (IN1, IN2, IN3, IN4, IN5, IN6, IN7, IN8: in bit; OUT4: out bit);

end entity SOP_Logic;

architecture LogicOperation of SOP_Logic is

--component declaration for 3-input NAND gate

    component NAND_gate3 is
      port (A, B, C: in bit X: out bit);
    end component NAND_gate3;

--component declaration for 2-input NAND gate

    component NAND_gate2 is
      port (A, B: in bit; X: out bit);
    end component NAND_gate;

    signal OUT1, OUT2, OUT3: bit;
begin

    G1: NAND_gate3 port map (A => IN1, B => IN2, C => IN3, X => OUT1);
    G2: NAND_gate3 port map (A => IN4, B => IN5, C => IN6, X => OUT2);
    G3: NAND_gate2 port map (A => IN7, B => IN8, X => OUT3);
    G4: NAND_gate3 port map   (A => OUT1, B => OUT2, C => OUT3, X => OUT4);

end architecture LogicOperation;

For comparison purposes, let's write the program for the logic circuit in Figure 47 using the data flow approach.

entity SOP_Logic is

    port (IN1, IN2, IN3, IN4, IN5, IN6, IN7, IN8: in bit; OUT4: out bit);

end entity SOP_Logic;

275

```
architecture LogicOperation of SOP_Logic is
begin
    OUT4 <= (IN1 and IN2 and IN3) or (IN4 and IN5 and IN6) or (IN7 and IN8);
end architecture LogicOperation;
```

As you can see, the data flow approach results in a much simpler code for this particular logic function. However, in situations where a logic function consists of many blocks of complex logic, the structural approach might have an advantage over the data flow approach.

Related Problem   If another NAND gate is added to the circuit in Figure 47 with inputs IN9 and IN10, write a component instantiation to add to the program.

Applying Software Development Tools

As you have learned, a software development package must be used to implement an HDL design in a target device. Once the logic has been described using an HDL and entered via a software tool called a code or text editor, it can be tested using a simulation to verify that it performs properly before actually programming the target device. Using software development tools allows for the design, development, and testing of combinational logic before it is committed to hardware.

Typical software development tools allow you to input VHDL code on a text-based editor specific to the particular development tool that you are using. The VHDL code for a combinational logic circuit has been written using a generic text-based editor for illustration and appears on the computer screen as shown in Figure 48. As shown, many code editors provide enhanced features such as the highlighting of keywords.

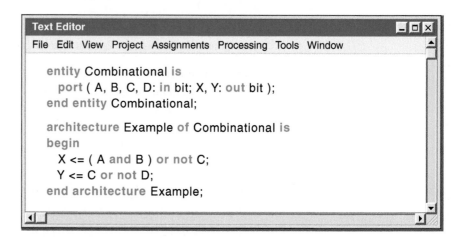

▲ FIGURE 48

A VHDL program for a combinational logic circuit after entry on a generic text editor screen that is part of a software development tool.

After the program has been written into the text editor, it is passed to the compiler. The compiler takes the high-level VHDL code and converts it into a file that can be downloaded to the target device. Once the program has been compiled, you can create a simulation for testing. Simulated input values are inserted into the logic design and allow for verification of the output(s).

You specify the input waveforms on a software tool called a waveform editor, as shown in Figure 49. The output waveforms are generated by a simulation of the VHDL code that you entered on the text editor in Figure 48. The waveform simulation provides the resulting outputs X and Y for the inputs A, B, C, and D in all sixteen combinations from $0\,0\,0\,0_2$ to $1\,1\,1\,1_2$.

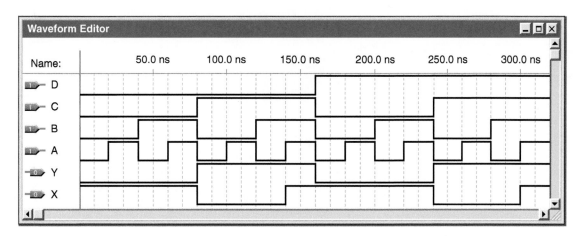

▲ FIGURE 49

A typical waveform editor tool showing the simulated waveforms for the logic circuit described by the VHDL code in Figure 48.

There are several performance characteristics of logic circuits to be considered in the creation of any digital system. Propagation delay, for example, determines the speed or frequency at which a logic circuit can operate. A timing simulation can be used to mimic the propagation delay through the logic design in the target device.

SECTION 7 CHECKUP	1. What is a VHDL component?
	2. State the purpose of a component instantiation in a program architecture.
	3. How are interconnections made between components in VHDL?
	4. The use of components in a VHDL program represents what approach?

System Application Activity

Tank Control Logic

A storage tank system for a pancake syrup manufacturing company is shown in Figure 50. The control logic allows a volume of corn syrup to be preheated to a specified temperature to achieve the proper viscosity prior to being sent to a mixing vat where ingredients such as sugar, flavoring, preservative, and coloring are added. Level and temperature sensors in the tank and the flow sensor provide the inputs for the logic.

FIGURE 50

Tank with level and temperature sensors and controls.

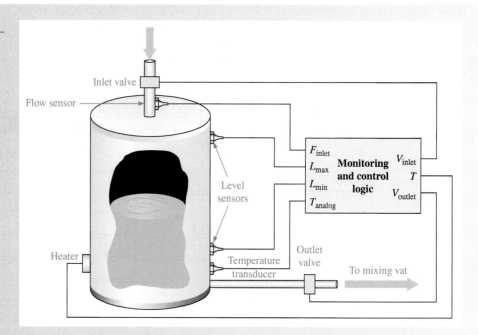

System Operation and Analysis

The tank holds corn syrup for use in a pancake syrup manufacturing process. In preparation for mixing, the temperature of the corn syrup when released from the tank into a mixing vat must be at a specified value for proper viscosity to produce required flow characteristics. This temperature can be selected via a keypad input. The control logic maintains the temperature at this value by turning a heater *on* and *off*. The analog output from the temperature transducer (T_{analog}) is converted to an 8-bit binary code by an analog-to-digital converter and then to an 8-bit BCD code. A temperature controller detects when the temperature falls below the specified value and turns the heater *on*. When the temperature reaches the specified value, the heater is turned *off*.

The level sensors produce a HIGH when the corn syrup is at or above the minimum or at the maximum level. The valve control logic detects when the maximum level (L_{max}) or minimum level (L_{min}) has been reached and when solution is flowing into the tank (F_{inlet}). Based on these inputs, the control logic opens or closes each valve (V_{inlet} and V_{outlet}). New corn syrup can be added to the tank via the inlet valve only when the minimum level is reached. Once the inlet valve is opened, the level in the tank must reach the maximum point before the inlet valve is closed. Also, once the outlet valve is opened, the level must reach the minimum point before the outlet valve is closed. New syrup is always cooler than the syrup in the tank. Syrup cannot be released from the tank while it is being filled or its temperature is below the specified value.

Inlet Valve Control   The conditions for which the inlet valve is open, allowing the tank to fill, are

- The solution level is at minimum (L_{min}).
- The tank is filling (F_{inlet}) but the maximum level has not been reached ($\overline{L}_{max}$).

Table 6 is the truth table for the inlet valve. A HIGH (1) is the active level for the inlet valve to be open (*on*).

1. Explain why the two conditions indicated in the truth table cannot occur.
2. Under how many input conditions is the inlet valve open?
3. Once the level drops below minimum and the tank starts refilling, when does the inlet valve turn *off*?

From the truth table, an expression for the inlet valve control output can be written.

$$V_{inlet} = \overline{L}_{max}\overline{L}_{min}\overline{F}_{inlet} + \overline{L}_{max}\overline{L}_{min}F_{inlet} + \overline{L}_{max}L_{min}F_{inlet}$$

	INPUTS		OUTPUT	
L_{max}	L_{min}	F_{inlet}	V_{inlet}	DESCRIPTION
0	0	0	1	Level below minimum. No inlet flow.
0	0	1	1	Level below minimum. Inlet flow.
0	1	0	0	Level above min and below max. No inlet flow.
0	1	1	1	Level above min and below max. Inlet flow.
1	0	0	X	Cannot occur.
1	0	1	X	Cannot occur.
1	1	0	0	Level at maximum. No inlet flow.
1	1	1	0	Level at maximum. Inlet flow.

The SOP expression can be reduced to the following simplified expression:

$$V_{inlet} = \overline{L}_{min} + \overline{L}_{max}F_{inlet}$$

4. Using a K-map, prove that the simplified expression is correct.
5. Using the simplified expression, draw the logic diagram for the inlet valve control.

Outlet Valve Control   The conditions for which the outlet valve is open allowing the tank to drain are

♦ The syrup level is above minimum and the tank is not filling.
♦ The temperature of the syrup is at the specified value.

Table 7 is the truth table for the outlet valve. A HIGH (1) is the active level for the outlet valve to be open (*on*).

	INPUTS			OUTPUT	
L_{max}	L_{min}	F_{inlet}	T	V_{outlet}	DESCRIPTION
0	0	0	0	0	Level below minimum. No inlet flow. Temp low.
0	0	0	1	0	Level below minimum. No inlet flow. Temp correct.
0	0	1	0	0	Level below minimum. Inlet flow. Temp low.
0	0	1	1	0	Level below minimum. Inlet flow. Temp correct.
0	1	0	0	0	Level above min and below max. No inlet flow. Temp low.
0	1	0	1	1	Level above min and below max. No inlet flow. Temp correct.
0	1	1	0	0	Level above min and below max. Inlet flow. Temp low.
0	1	1	1	0	Level above min and below max. Inlet flow. Temp correct.
1	0	0	0	X	Cannot occur.
1	0	0	1	X	Cannot occur.
1	0	1	0	X	Cannot occur.
1	0	1	1	X	Cannot occur.
1	1	0	0	0	Level at maximum. No inlet flow. Temp low.
1	1	0	1	1	Level at maximum. No inlet flow. Temp correct.
1	1	1	0	0	Level at maximum. Inlet flow. Temp low.
1	1	1	1	0	Level at maximum. Inlet flow. Temp correct.

6. Why does the outlet valve control require four inputs and the inlet valve only three?
7. Under how many input conditions is the outlet valve open?
8. Once the level reaches maximum and the tank starts draining, when does the outlet valve turn off?

From the truth table, an expression for the outlet valve control output can be written.

$$V_{outlet} = \overline{L}_{max} L_{min} \overline{F}_{inlet} T + L_{max} L_{min} \overline{F}_{inlet} T$$

The SOP expression can be reduced to the following simplified expression:

$$V_{outlet} = L_{min} \overline{F}_{inlet} T$$

9. Using a K-map, prove that the simplified expression is correct.
10. Using the simplified expression, draw the logic diagram for the outlet valve control.

Simulation of the Valve Control Logic

The inlet and outlet valve control logic simulation screen is shown in Figure 51. SPDT switches are used to represent the level and flow sensor inputs and the temperature indication. Probes are used to indicate the output states.

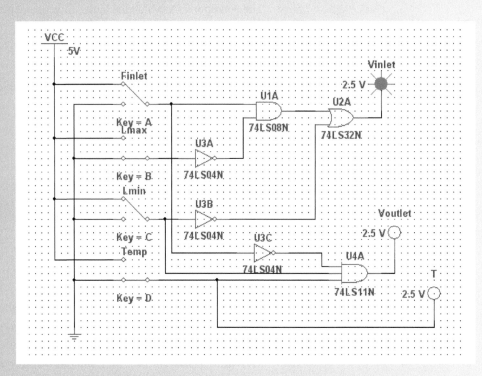

FIGURE 51

Multisim circuit screen for the valve control logic.

Temperature Control The temperature control logic accepts an 8-bit BCD code representing the measured temperature and compares it to the BCD code for the specified temperature. A block diagram is shown in Figure 52. The analog-to-digital converter and the binary-to-BCD converter are beyond the scope of this application activity.

FIGURE 52

Block diagram for temperature control circuit.

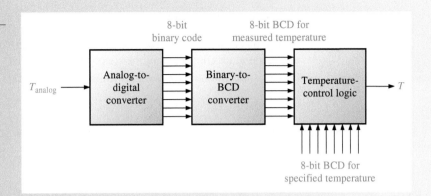

FIGURE 52

Block diagram for temperature control circuit.

When the measured temperature and the specified temperature are the same, the two BCD codes are equal and the T output is LOW (0). When the measured temperature falls below the specified value, there is a difference in the BCD codes and the T output is HIGH (1), which turns on the heater. The temperature control logic can be implemented with exclusive-OR gates, as shown in Figure 53. Each pair of corresponding bits from the two BCD codes is applied to an exclusive-OR gate. If the bits are the same, the output of the XOR gate is 0; and if they are different, the output of the XOR gate is 1. When one or more XOR outputs equal 1, the T output of the OR gate equals 1, causing the heater to turn on.

FIGURE 53

Logic diagram of the temperature control logic.

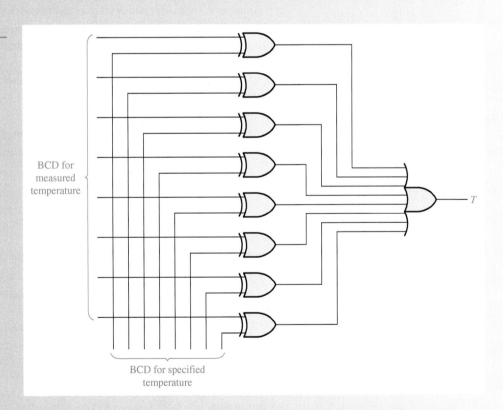

Open file SAA05 on www.pearsoned.com/electronics. Run the simulation of the valve-control logic using your Multisim software and observe the operation. Create a new Multisim file, connect the temperature control logic, and run the simulation.

Putting Your Knowledge to Work

If the temperature of the syrup can never be more than 9°C below the specified value, can the temperature control circuit be simplified? If so, how?

SUMMARY

- ◆ AND-OR logic produces an output expression in SOP form.
- ◆ AND-OR-Invert logic produces a complemented SOP form, which is actually a POS form.
- ◆ The operational symbol for exclusive-OR is $\oplus$. An exclusive-OR expression can be stated in two equivalent ways:

$$A\overline{B} + \overline{A}B = A \oplus B$$

- ◆ To do an analysis of a logic circuit, start with the logic circuit, and develop the Boolean output expression or the truth table or both.
- ◆ Implementation of a logic circuit is the process in which you start with the Boolean output expressions or the truth table and develop a logic circuit that produces the output function.
- ◆ All NAND or NOR logic diagrams should be drawn using appropriate dual symbols so that bubble outputs are connected to bubble inputs and nonbubble outputs are connected to nonbubble inputs.
- ◆ When two negation indicators (bubbles) are connected, they effectively cancel each other.
- ◆ A VHDL component is a predefined logic function stored for use throughout a program or in other programs.
- ◆ A component instantiation is used to call for a component in a program.
- ◆ A VHDL signal effectively acts as an internal interconnection in a VHDL structural description.

KEY TERMS

Component   A VHDL feature that can be used to predefine a logic function for multiple use throughout a program or programs.

Negative-AND   The dual operation of a NOR gate when the inputs are active-LOW.

Negative-OR   The dual operation of a NAND gate when the inputs are active-LOW.

Node   A common connection point in a circuit in which a gate output is connected to one or more gate inputs.

Signal   A waveform; a type of VHDL object that holds data.

Signal tracing   A troubleshooting technique in which waveforms are observed in a step-by-step manner beginning at the input and working toward the output or vice versa. At each point the observed waveform is compared with the correct signal for that point.

Universal gate   Either a NAND gate or a NOR gate. The term *universal* refers to the property of a gate that permits any logic function to be implemented by that gate or by a combination of that kind.

TRUE/FALSE QUIZ

Answers are at the end of the chapter.

1. AND-OR logic can have only two 2-input AND gates.
2. AOI is an acronym for AND-OR-Invert.

3. If the inputs of an exclusive-OR gate are the same, the output is HIGH (1).

4. If the inputs of an exclusive-NOR gate are different, the output is LOW (0).

5. A parity generator can be implemented using exclusive-OR gates.

6. NAND gates cannot be used to produce the OR function.

7. NOR gates can be used to produce the AND function.

8. Any SOP expression can be implemented using only NAND gates.

9. The dual symbol for a NAND gate is a negative-AND symbol.

10. Negative-OR is equivalent to NAND.

SELF-TEST

Answers are at the end of the chapter.

1. The output expression for an AND-OR circuit having one AND gate with inputs A, B, C, and D and one AND gate with inputs E and F is
   - (a) $ABCDEF$
   - (b) $A + B + C + D + E + F$
   - (c) $(A + B + C + D)(E + F)$
   - (d) $ABCD + EF$

2. A logic circuit with an output $X = A\overline{B}C + A\overline{C}$ consists of
   - (a) two AND gates and one OR gate
   - (b) two AND gates, one OR gate, and two inverters
   - (c) two OR gates, one AND gate, and two inverters
   - (d) two AND gates, one OR gate, and one inverter

3. To implement the expression $\overline{A}BCD + A\overline{B}CD + ABC\overline{D}$, it takes one OR gate and
   - (a) one AND gate
   - (b) three AND gates
   - (c) three AND gates and four inverters
   - (d) three AND gates and three inverters

4. The expression $\overline{A}BCD + ABC\overline{D} + A\overline{B}\,\overline{C}D$
   - (a) cannot be simplified
   - (b) can be simplified to $\overline{A}BC + A\overline{B}$
   - (c) can be simplified to $ABC\overline{D} + \overline{A}B\overline{C}$
   - (d) None of these answers is correct.

5. The output expression for an AND-OR-Invert circuit having one AND gate with inputs, A, B, C, and D and one AND gate with inputs E and F is
   - (a) $ABCD + EF$
   - (b) $\overline{A} + \overline{B} + \overline{C} + \overline{D} + \overline{E} + \overline{F}$
   - (c) $\overline{(A + B + C + D)(E + F)}$
   - (d) $(\overline{A} + \overline{B} + \overline{C} + \overline{D})(\overline{E} + \overline{F})$

6. An exclusive-OR function is expressed as
   - (a) $\overline{A}\overline{B} + AB$
   - (b) $\overline{A}B + A\overline{B}$
   - (c) $(\overline{A} + B)(A + \overline{B})$
   - (d) $(\overline{A} + \overline{B}) + (A + B)$

7. The AND operation can be produced with
   - (a) two NAND gates
   - (b) three NAND gates
   - (c) one NOR gate
   - (d) three NOR gates

8. The OR operation can be produced with
   - (a) two NOR gates
   - (b) three NAND gates
   - (c) four NAND gates
   - (d) both answers (a) and (b)

9. When using dual symbols in a logic diagram,
   - (a) bubble outputs are connected to bubble inputs
   - (b) the NAND symbols produce the AND operations
   - (c) the negative-OR symbols produce the OR operations
   - (d) All of these answers are true.
   - (e) None of these answers is true.

10. All Boolean expressions can be implemented with

    (a) NAND gates only

    (b) NOR gates only

    (c) combinations of NAND and NOR gates

    (d) combinations of AND gates, OR gates, and inverters

    (e) any of these

11. A VHDL component

    (a) can be used once in each program

    (b) is a predefined description of a logic function

    (c) can be used multiple times in a program

    (d) is part of a data flow description

    (e) answers (b) and (c)

12. A VHDL component is called for use in a program by using a

    (a) signal   **(b)** variable

    (c) component instantiation   **(d)** architecture declaration

PROBLEMS

Answers to odd-numbered problems are at the end of the chapter.

Section 1   **Basic Combinational Logic Circuits**

1. Draw the ANSI distinctive shape logic diagram for a 3-wide, 4-input AND-OR-Invert circuit. Also draw the ANSI standard rectangular outline symbol.

2. Write the output expression for each circuit in Figure 54.

3. Write the output expression for each circuit as it appears in Figure 55.

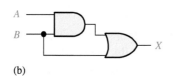

(a)

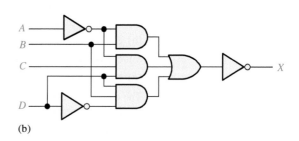

(b)

▲ FIGURE 54

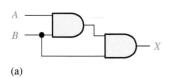

(a)

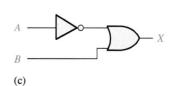

(b)

(c)

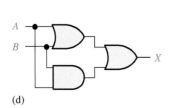

(d)

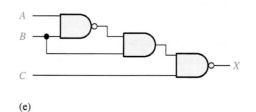

(e)

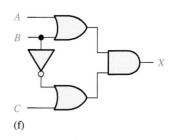

(f)

▲ FIGURE 55

4. Write the output expression for each circuit as it appears in Figure 56 and then change each circuit to an equivalent AND-OR configuration.

5. Develop the truth table for each circuit in Figure 55.

6. Develop the truth table for each circuit in Figure 56.

7. Show that an exclusive-NOR circuit produces a POS output.

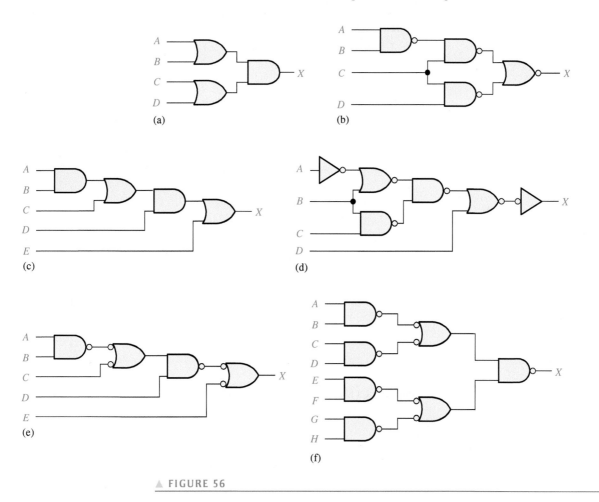

▲ FIGURE 56

Section 2   **Implementing Combinational Logic**

8. Develop an AND-OR-Invert logic circuit for a power saw that removes power (logic 0) if the guard is not in place (logic 0) and the switch is *on* (logic 1) or the switch is *on* and the motor is too hot (logic 1).

9. An AOI (AND-OR-Invert) logic chip has two 4-input AND gates connected to a 2-input NOR gate. Write the Boolean expression for the circuit (assume the inputs are labeled *A* through *H*).

10. Use AND gates, OR gates, or combinations of both to implement the following logic expressions as stated:

(a) $X = AB$

(b) $X = A + B$

(c) $X = AB + C$

(d) $X = ABC + D$

(e) $X = A + B + C$

(f) $X = ABCD$

(g) $X = A(CD + B)$

(h) $X = AB(C + DEF) + CE(A + B + F)$

285

11. Use AND gates, OR gates, and inverters as needed to implement the following logic expressions as stated:

(a) $X = AB + \overline{B}C$

(b) $X = A(B + \overline{C})$

(c) $X = A\overline{B} + AB$

(d) $X = \overline{ABC} + B(EF + \overline{G})$

(e) $X = A[BC(A + B + C + D)]$

(f) $X = B(C\overline{D}E + \overline{E}FG)(\overline{AB} + C)$

12. Use NAND gates, NOR gates, or combinations of both to implement the following logic expressions as stated:

(a) $X = \overline{A}B + CD + (\overline{A + B})(ACD + \overline{BE})$

(b) $X = AB\overline{CD} + D\overline{E}F + \overline{AF}$

(c) $X = \overline{A}[B + \overline{C}(D + E)]$

13. Implement a logic circuit for the truth table in Table 8.

▶ TABLE 8

INPUTS			OUTPUT
A	B	C	X
0	0	0	1
0	0	1	0
0	1	0	1
0	1	1	0
1	0	0	1
1	0	1	0
1	1	0	1
1	1	1	1

14. Implement a logic circuit for the truth table in Table 9.

▶ TABLE 9

INPUTS				OUTPUT
A	B	C	D	X
0	0	0	0	0
0	0	0	1	0
0	0	1	0	1
0	0	1	1	1
0	1	0	0	1
0	1	0	1	0
0	1	1	0	0
0	1	1	1	0
1	0	0	0	1
1	0	0	1	1
1	0	1	0	1
1	0	1	1	1
1	1	0	0	0
1	1	0	1	0
1	1	1	0	0
1	1	1	1	1

15. Simplify the circuit in Figure 57 as much as possible, and verify that the simplified circuit is equivalent to the original by showing that the truth tables are identical.

16. Repeat Problem 15 for the circuit in Figure 58.

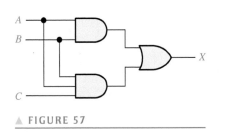

▲ FIGURE 57

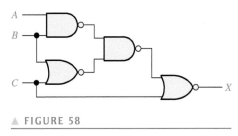

▲ FIGURE 58

17. Minimize the gates required to implement the functions in each part of Problem 11 in SOP form.

18. Minimize the gates required to implement the functions in each part of Problem 12 in SOP form.

19. Minimize the gates required to implement the function of the circuit in each part of Figure 56 in SOP form.

Section 3 **The Universal Property of NAND and NOR Gates**

20. Implement the logic circuits in Figure 54 using only NAND gates.

21. Implement the logic circuit in Figure 58 using only NAND gates.

22. Repeat Problem 20 using only NOR gates.

23. Repeat Problem 21 using only NOR gates.

Section 4 **Combinational Logic Using NAND and NOR Gates**

24. Show how the following expressions can be implemented as stated using only NOR gates:

(a) $X = ABC$ (b) $X = \overline{ABC}$ (c) $X = A + B$

(d) $X = A + B + \overline{C}$ (e) $X = \overline{AB} + \overline{CD}$ (f) $X = (A + B)(C + D)$

(g) $X = AB[C(\overline{DE} + \overline{AB}) + \overline{BCE}]$

25. Repeat Problem 24 using only NAND gates.

26. Implement each function in Problem 10 by using only NAND gates.

27. Implement each function in Problem 11 by using only NAND gates.

Section 5 **Logic Circuit Operation with Pulse Waveform Inputs**

28. Given the logic circuit and the input waveforms in Figure 59, draw the output waveform.

▶ FIGURE 59

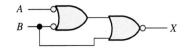

29. For the logic circuit in Figure 60, draw the output waveform in proper relationship to the inputs.

▶ FIGURE 60

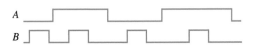
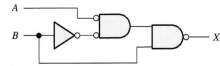

287

30. For the input waveforms in Figure 61, what logic circuit will generate the output waveform shown?

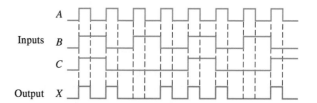

▲ FIGURE 61

31. Repeat Problem 30 for the waveforms in Figure 62.

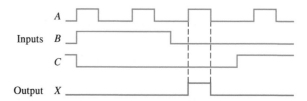

▲ FIGURE 62

32. For the circuit in Figure 63, draw the waveforms at the numbered points in the proper relationship to each other.

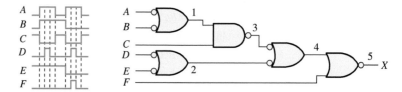

▲ FIGURE 63

33. Assuming a propagation delay through each gate of 10 nanoseconds (ns), determine if the *desired* output waveform *X* in Figure 64 (a pulse with a minimum $t_W = 25$ ns positioned as shown) will be generated properly with the given inputs.

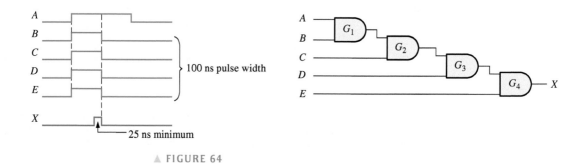

▲ FIGURE 64

Section 6   **Troubleshooting**

34. For the logic circuit and the input waveforms in Figure 65, the indicated output waveform is observed. Determine if this is the correct output waveform.

▶ FIGURE 65

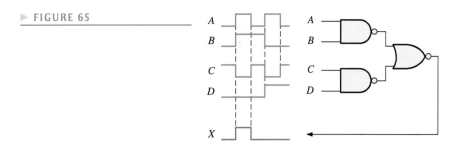

35. The output waveform in Figure 66 is incorrect for the inputs that are applied to the circuit. Assuming that one gate in the circuit has failed, with its output either an apparent constant HIGH or a constant LOW, determine the faulty gate and the type of failure (output open or shorted).

▶ FIGURE 66

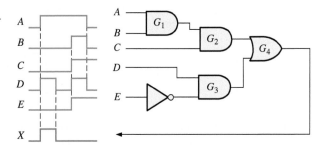

36. Repeat Problem 35 for the circuit in Figure 67, with input and output waveforms as shown.

▶ FIGURE 67

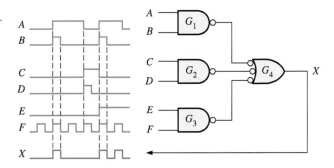

37. By examining the connections in Figure 68, determine the driving gate and load gate(s). Specify by device and pin numbers.

▶ FIGURE 68

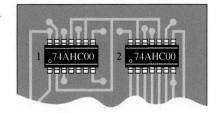

38. Figure 69(a) is a logic circuit under test. Figure 69(b) shows the waveforms as observed on a logic analyzer. The output waveform is incorrect for the inputs that are applied to the circuit. Assuming that one gate in the circuit has failed, with its output either an apparent constant HIGH or a constant LOW, determine the faulty gate and the type of failure.

▶ FIGURE 69

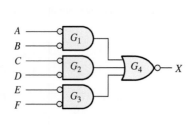

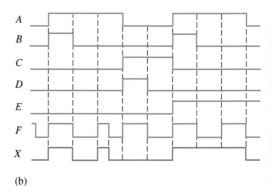

(a)   (b)

39. The logic circuit in Figure 70 has the input waveforms shown.

(a) Determine the correct output waveform in relation to the inputs.

(b) Determine the output waveform if the output of gate G_3 is open.

(c) Determine the output waveform if the upper input to gate G_5 is shorted to ground.

▶ FIGURE 70

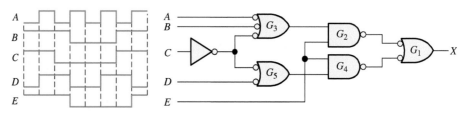

40. The logic circuit in Figure 71 has only one intermediate test point available besides the output, as indicated. For the inputs shown, you observe the indicated waveform at the test point. Is this waveform correct? If not, what are the possible faults that would cause it to appear as it does?

▶ FIGURE 71

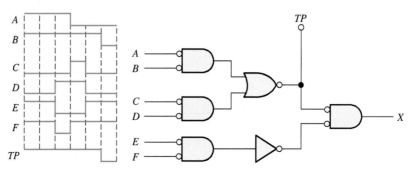

Section 7 **Combinational Logic with VHDL**

41. Describe a 3-input AND gate with VHDL.

42. Write a VHDL program using the data flow approach (Boolean expressions) to describe the logic circuit in Figure 54(b).

43. Write VHDL programs using the data flow approach (Boolean expressions) for the logic circuits in Figure 55(e) and (f).

44. Write a VHDL program using the structural approach for the logic circuit in Figure 56(d). Assume component declarations for each type of gate are already available.

45. Repeat Problem 44 for the logic circuit in Figure 56(f).

46. Describe the logic represented by the truth table in Table 8 using VHDL by first converting it to SOP form.

47. Develop a VHDL program for the logic in Figure 66, using both the data flow and the structural approach. Compare the resulting programs.

48. Develop a VHDL program for the logic in Figure 70, using both the data flow and the structural approach. Compare the resulting programs.

49. Given the following VHDL program, create the truth table that describes the logic circuit.

> entity CombLogic is
>> port (A, B, C, D: in bit; X: out bit);
>
> end entity CombLogic;
>
> architecture Example of CombLogic is
>> begin
>>> X <= not((not A and not B) or (not A and not C) or (not A and not D) or
>>>> (not B and not C) or (not B and not D) or (not D and not C));
>
> end architecture Example;

50. Describe the logic circuit shown in Figure 72 with a VHDL program, using the data flow approach.

▶ FIGURE 72

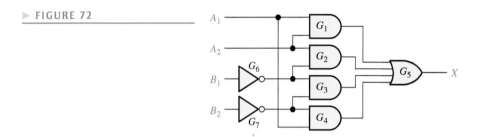

51. Repeat Problem 50 using the structural approach.

System Application Activity

52. Implement the inlet valve logic using NOR gates and inverters.

53. Repeat Problem 52 for the outlet valve logic.

54. Implement the temperature control logic using XNOR gates.

55. Design a circuit to enable an additive to be introduced into the syrup through another inlet only when the temperature is at the specified value and the syrup is at the low-level sensor.

Special Design Problems

56. Design a logic circuit to produce a HIGH output only if the input, represented by a 4-bit binary number, is greater than twelve or less than three. First develop the truth table and then draw the logic diagram.

57. Develop the logic circuit necessary to meet the following requirements:

A battery-powered lamp in a room is to be operated from two switches, one at the back door and one at the front door. The lamp is to be on if the front switch is on and the back switch is off, or if the front switch is off and the back switch is on. The lamp is to be off if both switches are off or if both switches are on. Let a HIGH output represent the on condition and a LOW output represent the off condition.

58. Develop the NAND logic for a hexadecimal keypad encoder that will convert each key closure to binary.

Multisim Troubleshooting Practice

59. Open file P05-59 on www.pearsoned.com/electronics and test the logic circuit to determine if there is a fault. If there is a fault, identify it if possible.

60. Open file P05-60 and test the logic circuit to determine if there is a fault. If there is a fault, identify it if possible.

61. Open file P05-61 and test the logic circuit to determine if there is a fault. If there is a fault, identify it if possible.

62. Open file P05-62 and test the logic circuit to determine if there is a fault. If there is a fault, identify it if possible.

ANSWERS

SECTION CHECKUPS

Section 1

Basic Combinational Logic Circuits

1. (a) $\overline{AB + CD} = \overline{1 \cdot 0 + 1 \cdot 0} = 1$ (b) $\overline{AB + CD} = \overline{1 \cdot 1 + 0 \cdot 1} = 0$
   (c) $\overline{AB + CD} = \overline{0 \cdot 1 + 1 \cdot 1} = 0$

2. (a) $A\overline{B} + \overline{A}B = 1 \cdot \overline{0} + \overline{1} \cdot 0 = 1$ (b) $A\overline{B} + \overline{A}B = 1 \cdot \overline{1} + \overline{1} \cdot 1 = 0$
   (c) $A\overline{B} + \overline{A}B = 0 \cdot \overline{1} + \overline{0} \cdot 1 = 1$ (d) $A\overline{B} + \overline{A}B = 0 \cdot \overline{0} + \overline{0} \cdot 0 = 0$

3. $X = 1$ when $ABC = 000, 011, 101, 110$, and 111; $X = 0$ when $ABC = 001, 010$, and 100

4. $X = AB + \overline{A}\,\overline{B}$; the circuit consists of two AND gates, one OR gate, and two inverters. See Figure 6(b) for diagram.

Section 2

Implementing Combinational Logic

1. (a) $X = ABC + AB + AC$: three AND gates, one OR gate

   (b) $X = AB(C + DE)$: three AND gates, one OR gate

2. $X = ABC + \overline{A}\,\overline{B}\,\overline{C}$; two AND gates, one OR gate, and three inverters

3. (a) $X = AB(C + 1) + AC = AB + AC$ (b) $X = AB(C + DE) = ABC + ABDE$

Section 3

The Universal Property of NAND and NOR Gates

1. (a) $X = \overline{A} + B$: a 2-input NAND gate with A and $\overline{B}$ on its inputs.

   (b) $X = A\overline{B}$: a 2-input NAND with A and $\overline{B}$ on its inputs, followed by one NAND used as an inverter.

2. (a) $X = \overline{A} + B$: a 2-input NOR with inputs $\overline{A}$ and B, followed by one NOR used as an inverter.

   (b) $X = A\overline{B}$: a 2-input NOR with $\overline{A}$ and B on its inputs.

Section 4

Combinational Logic Using NAND and NOR Gates

1. $X = (\overline{A} + \overline{B} + \overline{C})DE$: a 3-input NAND with inputs, A, B, and C, with its output connected to a second 3-input NAND with two other inputs, D and E

2. $X = \overline{A}\,\overline{B}\,\overline{C} + \overline{(D + E)}$: a 3-input NOR with inputs A, B, and C, with its output connected to a second 3-input NOR with two other inputs, D and E

Section 5

Logic Circuit Operation with Pulse Waveform Inputs

1. The exclusive-OR output is a 15 μs pulse followed by a 25 μs pulse, with a separation of 10 μs between the pulses.

2. The output of the exclusive-NOR is HIGH when both inputs are HIGH or when both inputs are LOW.

Section 6

Troubleshooting

1. Common gate failures are input or output open; input or output shorted to ground.

2. Input shorted to V_{CC} causes output to be stuck LOW.

3. (a) G_4 output is HIGH until rising edge of seventh pulse, then it goes LOW.

   (b) G_4 output is the same as input D.

   (c) G_4 output is the inverse of the G_2 output shown in Figure 42(b).

Section 7

Combinational Logic with VHDL

1. A VHDL component is a predefined program describing a specified logic function.

2. A component instantiation is used to call for a specified component in a program architecture.

3. Interconnections between components are made using VHDL signals.

4. Components are used in the structural approach.

RELATED PROBLEMS FOR EXAMPLES

1 $X = AB + AC + BC$

2 $X = \overline{AB + AC + BC}$

If $A = 0$ and $B = 0$, $X = \overline{0 \cdot 0 + 0 \cdot 1 + 0 \cdot 1} = \overline{0} = 1$

If $A = 0$ and $C = 0$, $X = \overline{0 \cdot 1 + 0 \cdot 0 + 1 \cdot 0} = \overline{0} = 1$

If $B = 0$ and $C = 0$, $X = \overline{1 \cdot 0 + 1 \cdot 0 + 0 \cdot 0} = \overline{0} = 1$

3 Determine the even-parity output for all 16 input combinations. Each combination should have an even number of 1s including the parity bit.

4 Apply codes with odd number of 1s and verify output is 1.

5 Cannot be simplified

6 Cannot be simplified

7 $X = A + B + C + D$ is valid.

8 See Figure 73.

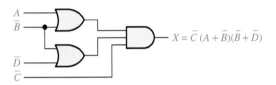

▲ FIGURE 73

9 $X = \overline{(\overline{\overline{ABC}})(\overline{\overline{DEF}})} = (\overline{AB})C + (\overline{DE})F = (\overline{A} + \overline{B})C + (\overline{D} + \overline{E})F$

10 See Figure 74.

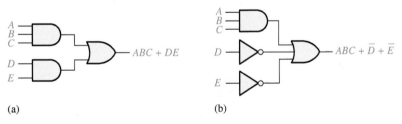

(a)　　　　　　　　　　(b)

▲ FIGURE 74

11 $X = \overline{\overline{(\overline{A + B} + C)} + \overline{(\overline{D + E} + F)}} = (\overline{A + B} + C)(\overline{D + E} + F) = (\overline{A}\overline{B} + C)(\overline{D}\overline{E} + F)$

12 See Figure 75.　　**13** See Figure 76.

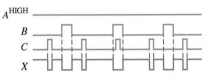

▲ FIGURE 75

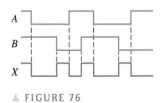

▲ FIGURE 76

14 See Figure 77.   **15** See Figure 78.
16 See Figure 79.

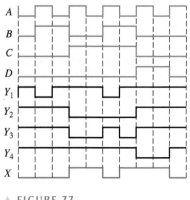

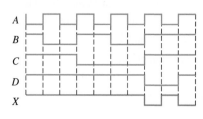

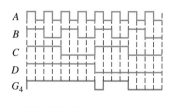

▲ FIGURE 77   ▲ FIGURE 78   ▲ FIGURE 79

17 G5: NAND_gate2 **port map** (A => IN9, B => IN10, X => OUT5);

ANSWERS TO ODD-NUMBERED PROBLEMS

1.   See Figure 80.

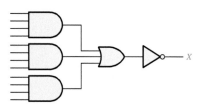   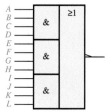

▲ FIGURE 80

3. (a) $X = ABB$ (b) $X = AB + B$
   (c) $\overline{}$ (d) $X = (A + B) + AB$
   (e) $X = \overline{A}BC$ (f) $X = (A + B)(\overline{B} + C)$
5. (a)   **5.** (b)

A	B	X
0	0	0
0	1	0
1	0	0
1	1	1

A	B	X
0	0	0
0	1	1
1	0	0
1	1	1

5. (c)

A	B	X
0	0	1
0	1	1
1	0	0
1	1	1

5. (d)

A	B	X
0	0	0
0	1	1
1	0	1
1	1	1

5. (e)

A	B	C	X
0	0	0	1
0	0	1	1
0	1	0	1
0	1	1	0
1	0	0	1
1	0	1	1
1	1	0	1
1	1	1	1

5. (f)

A	B	C	X
0	0	0	0
0	0	1	0
0	1	0	0
0	1	1	1
1	0	0	1
1	0	1	1
1	1	0	0
1	1	1	1

7. $X = \overline{A\overline{B} + \overline{A}B} = (\overline{A} + B)(A + \overline{B})$

9. $\overline{A\,B\,C\,D + E\,F\,G\,H}$

11. See Figure 81.

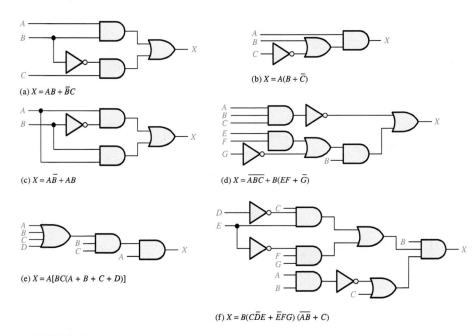

(a) $X = AB + \overline{B}C$

(b) $X = A(B + \overline{C})$

(c) $X = A\overline{B} + AB$

(d) $X = \overline{ABC} + B(EF + \overline{G})$

(e) $X = A[BC(A + B + C + D)]$

(f) $X = B(C\overline{D}E + \overline{E}FG)(\overline{AB} + C)$

▲ FIGURE 81

13. See Figure 82.

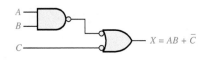

$X = AB + \overline{C}$

▲ FIGURE 82

15. $X = AB$

17. **(a)** No simplification

   (b) No simplification

   (c) $X = A$

   (d) $X = \overline{A} + \overline{B} + \overline{C} + EF + \overline{G}$

   (e) $X = ABC$

   (f) $X = BC\overline{D}E + \overline{A}B\overline{E}FG + BC\overline{E}FG$

19. **(a)** $X = AC + AD + BC + BD$

   (b) $X = \overline{A}CD + \overline{B}CD$

   (c) $X = ABD + CD + E$

   (d) $X = \overline{A} + B + D$

   (e) $X = ABD + \overline{C}D + \overline{E}$

   (f) $X = \overline{A}\,\overline{C} + \overline{A}\,\overline{D} + \overline{B}\,\overline{C} + \overline{B}\,\overline{D} + \overline{E}\,\overline{G} + \overline{E}\,\overline{H} + \overline{F}\,\overline{G} + \overline{F}\,\overline{H}$

21. See Figure 83.

23. See Figure 84.

25. See Figure 85.

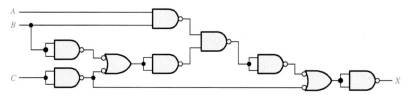

▲ FIGURE 83

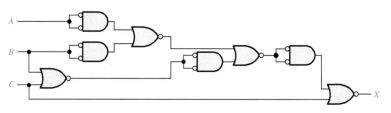

▲ FIGURE 84

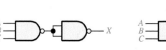 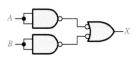 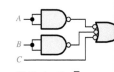

(a) $X = ABC$ (b) $X = \overline{ABC}$ (c) $X = A + B$ (d) $X = A + B + \overline{C}$

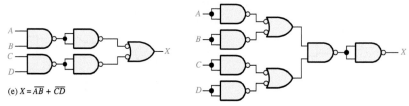

(e) $X = \overline{AB} + \overline{CD}$

(f) $X = (A + B)(C + D)$

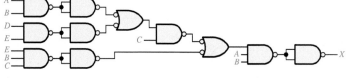

(g) $X = AB[C(\overline{DE} + \overline{AB}) + \overline{BCE}]$

▲ FIGURE 85

27. See Figure 86.

29. $X = A + \overline{B}$; see Figure 87.

31. $X = A\overline{B}\,\overline{C}$ see Figure 88.

33. The output pulse width is greater than the specified minimum.

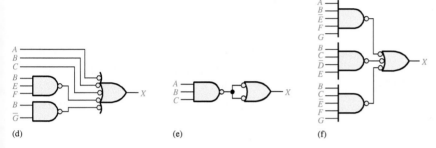

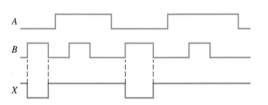

▲ FIGURE 86

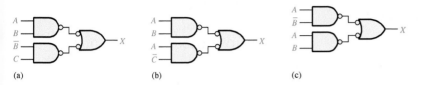

▲ FIGURE 87   ▲ FIGURE 88

35. $X = ABC + D\overline{E}$. Since X is the same as the G_3 output, either G_1 or G_2 has failed, with its output stuck LOW.

37. See Figure 89.

39. **(a)** See Figure 90.   **(b)** $X = E$

  (c) $X = E$

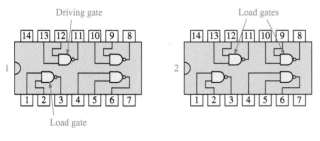

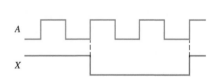

▲ FIGURE 89   ▲ FIGURE 90

41. X <= A and B and C

43. **(e)** **entity** Circuit 5_55e **is**

     port (A, B, C: **in** bit; X: **out** bit);

     end entity Circuit5_55e;

     architecture LogicFunction **of** Circuit5_55e **is**

     begin

X <= (**not** A **and** B) **or** B **or** (B **and not** C) **or**

     (**not** A **and not** C) **or** (B **and not** C) **or not** C;

     end architecture LogicFunction;

  (f) **entity** Circuit5_55f **is**

     port (A, B, C: **in** bit; X: **out** bit);

     end entity Circuit5_55f;

architecture LogicFunction **of** Circuit5_55f **is**

begin

    X <= (A **or** B) **and** (**not** B **or** C);

end architecture LogicFunction;

45. Number gates from top to bottom and left to right G1, G2, G3, etc. Relabel inputs IN1, IN2, IN3, etc. and output OUT.

entity Circuit5_56f **is**

    port (IN1, IN2, IN3, IN4, IN5, IN6, IN7, IN8: **in** bit; OUT: **out** bit);

end entity Circuit5_56f;

architecture LogicFunction **of** Circuit5_56f **is**

component NAND_gate **is**

    port (A, B: **in** bit; X: **out** bit);

end component NAND_gate;

    signal G1OUT, G2OUT, G3OUT, G4OUT, G5OUT, G6OUT: bit;

begin

    G1: NAND_gate **port map** (A => IN1, B => IN2, X => G1OUT);

    G2: NAND_gate **port map** (A => IN3, B => IN4, X => G2OUT);

    G3: NAND_gate **port map** (A => IN5, B => IN6, X => G3OUT);

    G4: NAND_gate **port map** (A => IN7, B => IN8, X => G4OUT);

    G5: NAND_gate **port map** (A => G1OUT, B => G2OUT, X => G5OUT);

    G6: NAND_gate **port map** (A => G3OUT, B => G4OUT, X => G6OUT);

    G7: NAND_gate **port map** (A => G5OUT, B => G6OUT, X => OUT);

end architecture LogicFunction;

47. –Data flow approach

entity Fig5_66 **is**

    port (A, B, C, D, E: **in** bit; X: **out** bit);

end entity Fig5_66;

architecture DataFlow **of** Fig5_66 **is**

begin

    X <= (A **and** B **and** C) **or** (D **and not** E);

end architecture DataFlow;

–Structural approach

entity Fig5_66 **is**

    port (IN1, IN2, IN3, IN4, IN5: **in** bit; OUT: **out** bit);

end entity Fig5_66;

architecture Structure **of** Fig5_66 **is**

component AND_gate **is**

    port (A, B: **in** bit; X: **out** bit);

end component AND_gate;

component OR_gate **is**

    port (A, B: **in** bit; X: **out** bit);

end component OR_gate;

component Inverter **is**

    port (A: **in** bit; X: **out** bit);

end component Inverter;

    signal G1OUT, G2OUT, G3OUT, INVOUT: bit;

begin

    G1: AND_gate **port map** (A => IN1, B => IN2, X => G1OUT);

    G2: AND_gate **port map** (A => G1OUT, B => IN3, X => G2OUT);

    INV: Inverter **port map** (A => IN5, X => INVOUT);

    G3: AND_gate **port map** (A => IN4, B => INVOUT, X => G3OUT);

    G4: OR_gate **port map** (A => G2OUT, B => G3OUT, X => OUT);

end architecture Structure;

49. See Table 9.

51. The AND gates are numbered top to bottom G1, G2, G3, G4. The OR gate is G5 and the inverters are, top to bottom. G6 and G7. Change A_1, A_2, B_1, B_2 to IN1, IN2, IN3, IN4 respectively. Change X to OUT.

entity Circuit5_72 **is**

    port (IN1, IN2, IN3, IN4: **in** bit; OUT: **out** bit);

end entity Circuit5_72;

architecture Logic **of** Circuit5_72 **is**

▼ TABLE 9

INPUTS				OUTPUT
A	B	C	D	X
0	0	0	0	0
1	0	0	0	0
0	1	0	0	0
1	1	0	0	0
0	0	1	0	0
1	0	1	0	0
0	1	1	0	0
1	1	1	0	0
0	0	0	1	0
1	0	0	1	0
0	1	0	1	0
1	1	0	1	1
0	0	1	1	0
1	0	1	1	1
0	1	1	1	1
1	1	1	1	1

component AND_gate **is**

    port (A, B: **in** bit; X: **out** bit);

end component AND_gate;

component OR_gate **is**

    port (A, B, C, D: **in** bit; X: **out** bit);

end component OR_gate;

component Inverter **is**

    port (A: **in** bit; X: **out** bit);

end component Inverter;

    signal G1OUT, G2OUT, G3OUT, G4OUT, G5OUT, G6OUT, G7OUT: bit;

begin

    G1: AND_gate **port map** (A => IN1, B => IN2, X => G1OUT);

    G2: AND_gate **port map** (A => IN2, B => G6OUT, X => G2OUT);

    G3: AND_gate **port map** (A => G6OUT, B => G7OUT, X => G3OUT);

    G4: AND_gate **port map** (A => G7OUT, B => IN1, X => G4OUT);

    G5: OR_gate **port map** (A => G1OUT, B => G2OUT, C => G3OUT, D => G4OUT, X => OUT);

    G6: Inverter **port map** (A => IN3, X => G6OUT);

    G7: Inverter **port map** (A => IN4, X => G7OUT);

end architecture Logic;

▶ FIGURE 91

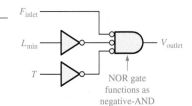

▶ FIGURE 92

▶ FIGURE 93

53. See Figure 91.

55. See Figure 92.

57. X = lamp on, A = front door switch on, B = back door switch on. See Figure 93.

59. Pin B of G1 open

61. Inverter input open.

FUNCTIONS OF COMBINATIONAL LOGIC

CHAPTER OBJECTIVES

- Distinguish between half-adders and full-adders
- Use full-adders to implement multibit parallel binary adders
- Explain the differences between ripple carry and look-ahead carry parallel adders
- Use the magnitude comparator to determine the relationship between two binary numbers and use cascaded comparators to handle the comparison of larger numbers
- Implement a basic binary decoder
- Use BCD-to-7-segment decoders in display systems
- Apply a decimal-to-BCD priority encoder in a simple keyboard application
- Convert from binary to Gray code, and Gray code to binary by using logic devices
- Apply data selectors/multiplexers in multiplexed displays and as a function generator
- Use decoders as demultiplexers
- Explain the meaning of parity
- Use parity generators and checkers to detect bit errors in digital systems
- Implement a simple data communications system
- Identify glitches, common bugs in digital systems

KEY TERMS

- Half-adder
- Full-adder
- Cascading
- Ripple carry
- Look-ahead carry
- Decoder

- Encoder
- Priority encoder
- Multiplexer (MUX)
- Demultiplexer (DEMUX)
- Parity bit
- Glitch

INTRODUCTION

In this chapter, several types of combinational logic circuits are introduced including adders, comparators, decoders, encoders, code converters, multiplexers (data selectors), demultiplexers, and parity generators/checkers. Examples of fixed-function IC devices are included. Each device introduced may also be available in other logic families.

FIXED-FUNCTION LOGIC DEVICES

74XX42	74XX47	74XX85
74XX138	74XX139	74XX147
74XX148	74XX151	74XX154
74XX157	74XX280	74XX283

SYSTEM APPLICATION ACTIVITY PREVIEW

The System Application Activity illustrates concepts from this chapter and deals with one portion of a traffic signal control system. The system applications in this chapter focus on various parts of the traffic signal control system. This system controls the traffic signal at the intersection of a busy street and a lightly traveled side street. The system includes a combinational logic section to which the topics in this chapter apply, plus a timing circuit and a sequential logic section. The Multisim activities are optional.

1 BASIC ADDERS

Adders are important in computers and also in other types of digital systems in which numerical data are processed. An understanding of the basic adder operation is fundamental to the study of digital systems. In this section, the half-adder and the full-adder are introduced.

After completing this section, you should be able to

- ◆ Describe the function of a half-adder
- ◆ Draw a half-adder logic diagram
- ◆ Describe the function of the full-adder
- ◆ Draw a full-adder logic diagram using half-adders
- ◆ Implement a full-adder using AND-OR logic

The Half-Adder

A half-adder adds two bits and produces a sum and an output carry.

Recall the basic rules for binary addition.

$$0 + 0 = 0$$
$$0 + 1 = 1$$
$$1 + 0 = 1$$
$$1 + 1 = 10$$

The operations are performed by a logic circuit called a **half-adder**.

The half-adder accepts two binary digits on its inputs and produces two binary digits on its outputs—a sum bit and a carry bit.

A half-adder is represented by the logic symbol in Figure 1.

▶ FIGURE 1

Logic symbol for a half-adder. Open file F06-01 on www.pearsoned.com/electronics to verify operation.

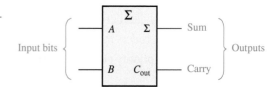

Half-Adder Logic   From the operation of the half-adder as stated in Table 1, expressions can be derived for the sum and the output carry as functions of the inputs. Notice that the output carry (C_{out}) is a 1 only when both A and B are 1s; therefore, C_{out} can be expressed as the AND of the input variables.

Equation 1

$$C_{out} = AB$$

▶ TABLE 1

Half-adder truth table.

A	B	C_{out}	Σ
0	0	0	0
0	1	0	1
1	0	0	1
1	1	1	0

Σ = sum

C_{out} = output carry

A and B = input variables (operands)

Now observe that the sum output (Σ) is a 1 only if the input variables, A and B, are not equal. The sum can therefore be expressed as the exclusive-OR of the input variables.

$$\Sigma = A \oplus B$$

Equation 2

From Equations 1 and 2, the logic implementation required for the half-adder function can be developed. The output carry is produced with an AND gate with A and B on the inputs, and the sum output is generated with an exclusive-OR gate, as shown in Figure 2. Remember that the exclusive-OR can be implemented with AND gates, an OR gate, and inverters.

$\Sigma = A \oplus B = A\bar{B} + \bar{A}B$

$C_{out} = AB$

A

B

◀ FIGURE 2

Half-adder logic diagram.

The Full-Adder

The second category of adder is the **full-adder.**

> **The full-adder accepts two input bits and an input carry and generates a sum output and an output carry.**

A full-adder has an input carry while the half-adder does not.

The basic difference between a full-adder and a half-adder is that the full-adder accepts an input carry. A logic symbol for a full-adder is shown in Figure 3, and the truth table in Table 2 shows the operation of a full-adder.

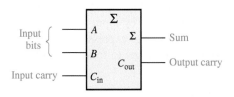

Input bits { A B

Input carry C_{in}

Σ

Σ — Sum

C_{out} — Output carry

◀ FIGURE 3

Logic symbol for a full-adder. Open file F06-03 to verify operation.

A	B	C_{in}	C_{out}	Σ
0	0	0	0	0
0	0	1	0	1
0	1	0	0	1
0	1	1	1	0
1	0	0	0	1
1	0	1	1	0
1	1	0	1	0
1	1	1	1	1

C_{in} = input carry, sometimes designated as CI
C_{out} = output carry, sometimes designated as CO
Σ = sum
A and B = input variables (operands)

◀ TABLE 2

Full-adder truth table.

Full-Adder Logic The full-adder must add the two input bits and the input carry. From the half-adder you know that the sum of the input bits A and B is the exclusive-OR of those two variables, $A \oplus B$. For the input carry (C_{in}) to be added to the input bits, it must be exclusive-ORed with $A \oplus B$, yielding the equation for the sum output of the full-adder.

Equation 3

$$\Sigma = (A \oplus B) \oplus C_{in}$$

This means that to implement the full-adder sum function, two 2-input exclusive-OR gates can be used. The first must generate the term $A \oplus B$, and the second has as its inputs the output of the first XOR gate and the input carry, as illustrated in Figure 4(a).

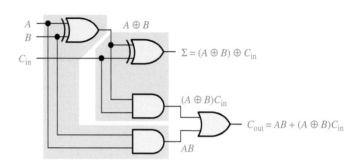

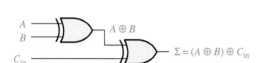

(a) Logic required to form the sum of three bits

(b) Complete logic circuit for a full-adder (each half-adder is enclosed by a shaded area)

▲ FIGURE 4

Full-adder logic. Open file F06-04 to verify operation.

The output carry is a 1 when both inputs to the first XOR gate are 1s or when both inputs to the second XOR gate are 1s. You can verify this fact by studying Table 2. The output carry of the full-adder is therefore produced by input A ANDed with input B and $A \oplus B$ ANDed with C_{in}. These two terms are ORed, as expressed in Equation 4. This function is implemented and combined with the sum logic to form a complete full-adder circuit, as shown in Figure 4(b).

Equation 4

$$C_{out} = AB + (A \oplus B)C_{in}$$

Notice in Figure 4(b) there are two half-adders, connected as shown in the block diagram of Figure 5(a), with their output carries ORed. The logic symbol shown in Figure 5(b) will normally be used to represent the full-adder.

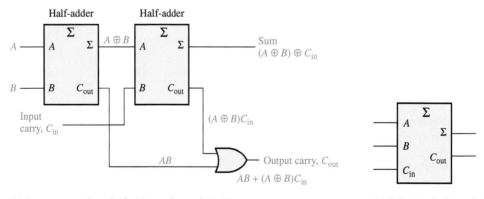

(a) Arrangement of two half-adders to form a full-adder

(b) Full-adder logic symbol

▲ FIGURE 5

Full-adder implemented with half-adders.

EXAMPLE 1

For each of the three full-adders in Figure 6, determine the outputs for the inputs shown.

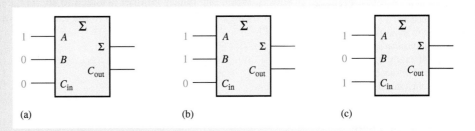

(a)   (b)   (c)

Solution

(a) The input bits are $A = 1$, $B = 0$, and $C_{in} = 0$.

$$1 + 0 + 0 = 1 \text{ with no carry}$$

Therefore, $\Sigma = \mathbf{1}$ and $C_{out} = \mathbf{0}.$

(b) The input bits are $A = 1$, $B = 1$, and $C_{in} = 0$.

$$1 + 1 + 0 = 0 \text{ with a carry of } 1$$

Therefore, $\Sigma = \mathbf{0}$ and $C_{out} = \mathbf{1}.$

(c) The input bits are $A = 1$, $B = 0$, and $C_{in} = 1$.

$$1 + 0 + 1 = 0 \text{ with a carry of } 1$$

Therefore, $\Sigma = \mathbf{0}$ and $C_{out} = \mathbf{1}.$

*Related Problem** What are the full-adder outputs for $A = 1$, $B = 1$, and $C_{in} = 1$?

*Answers are at the end of the chapter.

**SECTION 1
CHECKUP**
Answers are at the end of the chapter.

1. Determine the sum (Σ) and the output carry (C_{out}) of a half-adder for each set of input bits:
   (a) 01   (b) 00   (c) 10   (d) 11
2. A full-adder has $C_{in} = 1$. What are the sum (Σ) and the output carry (C_{out}) when $A = 1$ and $B = 1$?

---

2 PARALLEL BINARY ADDERS

Two or more full-adders are connected to form parallel binary adders. In this section, you will learn the basic operation of this type of adder and its associated input and output functions.

After completing this section, you should be able to

- ◆ Use full-adders to implement a parallel binary adder
- ◆ Explain the addition process in a parallel binary adder
- ◆ Use the truth table for a 4-bit parallel adder
- ◆ Apply two 74LS283s for the addition of two 4-bit numbers
- ◆ Expand the 4-bit adder to accommodate 8-bit or 16-bit addition

As you saw in Section 1, a single full-adder is capable of adding two 1-bit numbers and an input carry. To add binary numbers with more than one bit, you must use additional full-adders. When one binary number is added to another, each column generates a sum bit and a 1 or 0 carry bit to the next column to the left, as illustrated here with 2-bit numbers.

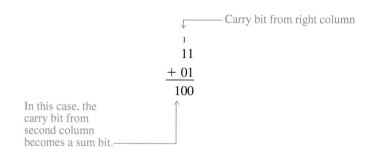

To add two binary numbers, a full-adder is required for each bit in the numbers. So for 2-bit numbers, two adders are needed; for 4-bit numbers, four adders are used; and so on. The carry output of each adder is connected to the carry input of the next higher-order adder, as shown in Figure 7 for a 2-bit adder. Notice that either a half-adder can be used for the least significant position or the carry input of a full-adder can be made 0 (grounded) because there is no carry input to the least significant bit position.

▶ FIGURE 7

Block diagram of a basic 2-bit parallel adder using two full-adders. Open file F06-07 to verify operation.

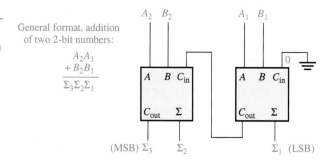

In Figure 7 the least significant bits (LSB) of the two numbers are represented by A_1 and B_1. The next higher-order bits are represented by A_2 and B_2. The three sum bits are Σ_1, Σ_2, and Σ_3. Notice that the output carry from the left-most full-adder becomes the most significant bit (MSB) in the sum, Σ_3.

EXAMPLE 2

Determine the sum generated by the 3-bit parallel adder in Figure 8 and show the intermediate carries when the binary numbers 101 and 011 are being added.

▶ FIGURE 8

Four-Bit Parallel Adders

A group of four bits is called a **nibble.** A basic 4-bit parallel adder is implemented with
four full-adder stages as shown in Figure 9. Again, the LSBs (A_1 and B_1) in each number
being added go into the right-most full-adder; the higher-order bits are applied as shown to
the successively higher-order adders, with the MSBs (A_4 and B_4) in each number being
applied to the left-most full-adder. The carry output of each adder is connected to the carry
input of the next higher-order adder as indicated. These are called *internal carries*.

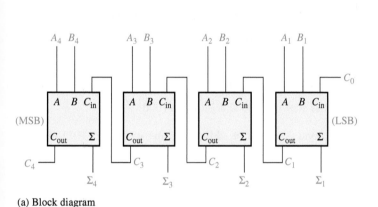
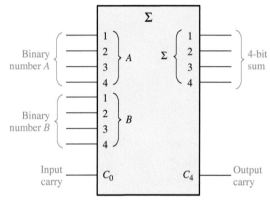

(a) Block diagram   (b) Logic symbol

▲ FIGURE 9

A 4-bit parallel adder.

In keeping with most manufacturers' data sheets, the input labeled C_0 is the input carry
to the least significant bit adder; C_4, in the case of four bits, is the output carry of the most
significant bit adder; and Σ_1 (LSB) through Σ_4 (MSB) are the sum outputs. The logic symbol is shown in Figure 9(b).

In terms of the method used to handle carries in a parallel adder, there are two types: the
ripple carry adder and the *carry look-ahead* adder. These are discussed in Section 3.

Truth Table for a 4-Bit Parallel Adder

Table 3 is the truth table for a 4-bit adder. On some data sheets, truth tables may be called
function tables or *functional truth tables*. The subscript n represents the adder bits and can

◄ TABLE 3

Truth table for each stage of a 4-bit
parallel adder.

C_{n-1}	A_n	B_n	Σ_n	C_n
0	0	0	0	0
0	0	1	1	0
0	1	0	1	0
0	1	1	0	1
1	0	0	1	0
1	0	1	0	1
1	1	0	0	1
1	1	1	1	1

be 1, 2, 3, or 4 for the 4-bit adder. C_{n-1} is the carry from the previous adder. Carries C_1, C_2, and C_3 are generated internally. C_0 is an external carry input and C_4 is an output. Example 3 illustrates how to use Table 3.

EXAMPLE 3

Use the 4-bit parallel adder truth table (Table 3) to find the sum and output carry for the addition of the following two 4-bit numbers if the input carry (C_{n-1}) is 0:

$$A_4A_3A_2A_1 = 1100 \quad \text{and} \quad B_4B_3B_2B_1 = 1100$$

Solution   For $n = 1$: $A_1 = 0$, $B_1 = 0$, and $C_{n-1} = 0$. From the 1st row of the table,

$$\Sigma_1 = \mathbf{0} \quad \text{and} \quad C_1 = 0$$

For $n = 2$: $A_2 = 0$, $B_2 = 0$, and $C_{n-1} = 0$. From the 1st row of the table,

$$\Sigma_2 = \mathbf{0} \quad \text{and} \quad C_2 = 0$$

For $n = 3$: $A_3 = 1$, $B_3 = 1$, and $C_{n-1} = 0$. From the 4th row of the table,

$$\Sigma_3 = \mathbf{0} \quad \text{and} \quad C_3 = 1$$

For $n = 4$: $A_4 = 1$, $B_4 = 1$, and $C_{n-1} = 1$. From the last row of the table,

$$\Sigma_4 = \mathbf{1} \quad \text{and} \quad C_4 = \mathbf{1}$$

C_4 becomes the output carry; the sum of 1100 and 1100 is 11000.

Related Problem   Use the truth table (Table 3) to find the result of adding the binary numbers 1011 and 1010.

THE 74LS283 4-BIT PARALLEL ADDER

An example of a 4-bit parallel adder that is available in IC form is the 74LS283. For the 74LS283, V_{CC} is pin 16 and ground is pin 8, which is a standard configuration. The pin diagram and logic symbol for this device are shown, with pin numbers in parentheses on the logic symbol, in Figure 10.

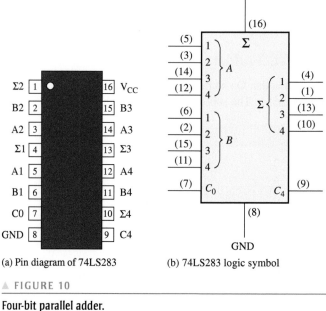

(a) Pin diagram of 74LS283   (b) 74LS283 logic symbol

▲ **FIGURE 10**

Four-bit parallel adder.

IC Data Sheet Characteristics Recall that logic gates have one specified propagation delay time, t_P, from an input to the output. For IC logic, there may be several different specifications for t_P. The 4-bit parallel adder has the four t_P specifications shown in Figure 11, which is part of a 74LS283 data sheet.

FIGURE 11

Propagation delay characteristics for the 74LS283.

Symbol	Parameter	Limits			Unit
		Min	Typ	Max	
t_{PLH} t_{PHL}	Propagation delay, C_0 input to any Σ output		16 15	24 24	ns
t_{PLH} t_{PHL}	Propagation delay, any A or B input to Σ outputs		15 15	24 24	ns
t_{PLH} t_{PHL}	Propagation delay, C_0 input to C_4 output		11 11	17 22	ns
t_{PLH} t_{PHL}	Propagation delay, any A or B input to C_4 output		11 12	17 17	ns

Adder Expansion

The 4-bit parallel adder can be expanded to handle the addition of two 8-bit numbers by using two 4-bit adders. The carry input of the low-order adder (C_0) is connected to ground because there is no carry into the least significant bit position, and the carry output of the low-order adder is connected to the carry input of the high-order adder, as shown in Figure 12(a). This process is known as **cascading**. Notice that, in this case, the output carry is designated

Adders can be expanded to handle more bits by cascading.

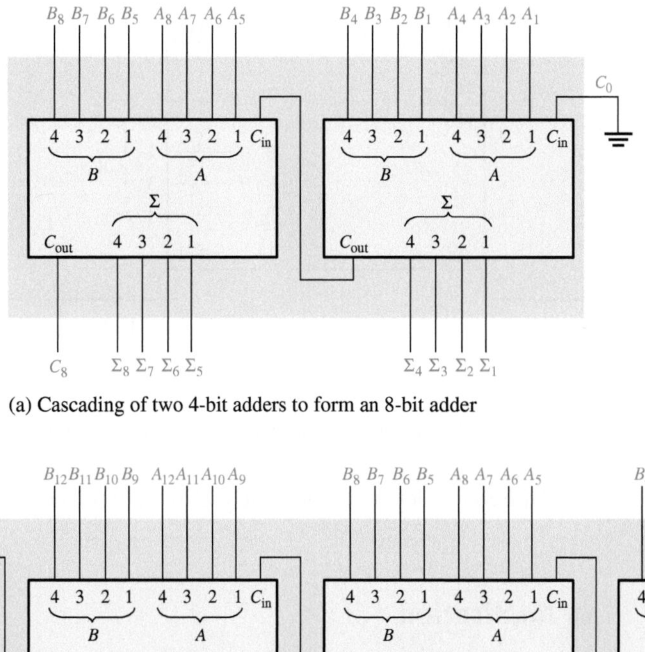

(a) Cascading of two 4-bit adders to form an 8-bit adder

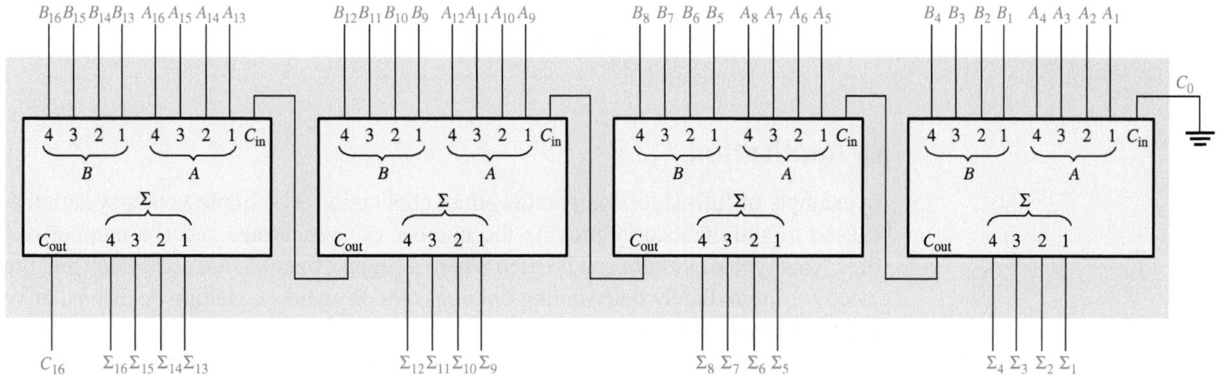

(b) Cascading of four 4-bit adders to form a 16-bit adder

FIGURE 12

Examples of adder expansion.

designated C_8 because it is generated from the eighth bit position. The low-order adder is the one that adds the lower or less significant four bits in the numbers, and the high-order adder is the one that adds the higher or more significant four bits in the 8-bit numbers.

Similarly, four 4-bit adders can be cascaded to handle two 16-bit numbers as shown in Figure 12(b). Notice that the output carry is designated C_{16} because it is generated from the sixteenth bit position.

EXAMPLE 4

Show how two 74LS283 adders can be connected to form an 8-bit parallel adder. Show output bits for the following 8-bit input numbers:

$$A_8A_7A_6A_5A_4A_3A_2A_1 = 10111001 \quad \text{and} \quad B_8B_7B_6B_5B_4B_3B_2B_1 = 10011110$$

Solution   Two 74LS283 4-bit parallel adders are used to implement the 8-bit adder. The only connection between the two 74LS283s is the carry output (pin 9) of the low-order adder to the carry input (pin 7) of the high-order adder, as shown in Figure 13. Pin 7 of the low-order adder is grounded (no carry input).

The sum of the two 8-bit numbers is

$$\Sigma_9\Sigma_8\Sigma_7\Sigma_6\Sigma_5\Sigma_4\Sigma_3\Sigma_2\Sigma_1 = 101010111$$

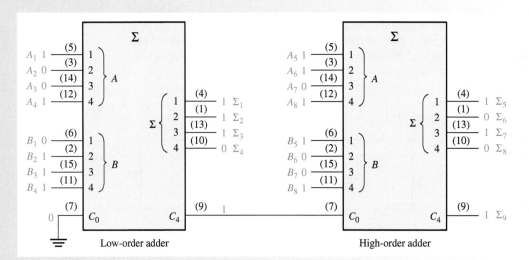

▲ FIGURE 13

Two 74LS283 adders connected as an 8-bit parallel adder (pin numbers are in parentheses).

Related Problem   Use 74LS283 adders to implement a 12-bit parallel adder.

An Application

An example of full-adder and parallel adder application is a simple voting system that can be used to simultaneously provide the number of "yes" votes and the number of "no" votes. This type of system can be used where a group of people are assembled and there is a need for immediately determining opinions (for or against), making decisions, or voting on certain issues or other matters.

In its simplest form, the system includes a switch for "yes" or "no" selection at each position in the assembly and a digital display for the number of yes votes and one for the number of no votes. The basic system is shown in Figure 14 for a 6-position setup, but it can be expanded to any number of positions with additional 6-position modules and additional parallel adder and display circuits.

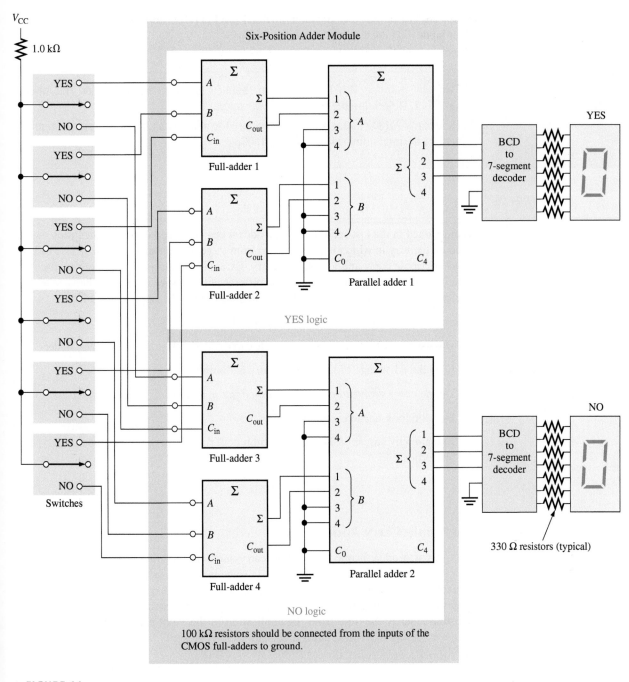

A voting system using full-adders and parallel binary adders.

In Figure 14 each full-adder can produce the sum of up to three votes. The sum and output carry of each full-adder then goes to the two lower-order inputs of a parallel binary adder. The two higher-order inputs of the parallel adder are connected to ground (0) because there is never a case where the binary input exceeds 0011 (decimal 3). For this basic 6-position system, the outputs of the parallel adder go to a BCD-to-7-segment decoder that drives the 7-segment display. As mentioned, additional circuits must be included when the system is expanded.

The resistors from the inputs of each full-adder to ground assure that each input is LOW when the switch is in the neutral position (CMOS logic is used). When a switch is moved to the "yes" or to the "no" position, a HIGH level (V_{CC}) is applied to the associated full-adder input.

3 RIPPLE CARRY VERSUS LOOK-AHEAD CARRY ADDERS

As mentioned in the last section, parallel adders can be placed into two categories based on the way in which internal carries from stage to stage are handled. Those categories are ripple carry and look-ahead carry. Externally, both types of adders are the same in terms of inputs and outputs. The difference is the speed at which they can add numbers. The look-ahead carry adder is much faster than the ripple carry adder.

After completing this section, you should be able to

◆ Discuss the difference between a ripple carry adder and a look-ahead carry adder

◆ State the advantage of look-ahead carry addition

◆ Define *carry generation* and *carry propagation* and explain the difference

◆ Develop look-ahead carry logic

◆ Explain why cascaded 74LS283s exhibit both ripple carry and look-ahead carry properties

The Ripple Carry Adder

A **ripple carry** adder is one in which the carry output of each full-adder is connected to the carry input of the next higher-order stage (a stage is one full-adder). The sum and the output carry of any stage cannot be produced until the input carry occurs; this causes a time delay in the addition process, as illustrated in Figure 15. The carry propagation delay for each full-adder is the time from the application of the input carry until the output carry occurs, assuming that the *A* and *B* inputs are already present.

▶ FIGURE 15

A 4-bit parallel ripple carry adder showing "worst-case" carry propagation delays.

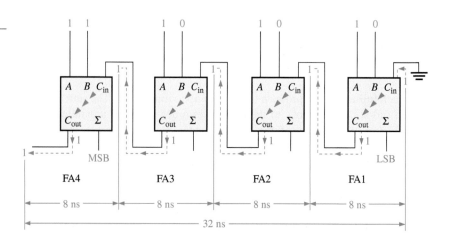

Full-adder 1 (FA1) cannot produce a potential output carry until an input carry is applied. Full-adder 2 (FA2) cannot produce a potential output carry until FA1 produces an output carry. Full-adder 3 (FA3) cannot produce a potential output carry until an output carry is produced by FA1 followed by an output carry from FA2, and so on. As you can see in Figure 15, the input carry to the least significant stage has to ripple through all the adders before a final sum is produced. The cumulative delay through all the adder stages is a "worst-case" addition time. The total delay can vary, depending on the carry bit produced by each full-adder. If two numbers are added such that no carries (0) occur between stages, the addition time is simply the propagation time through a single full-adder from the application of the data bits on the inputs to the occurrence of a sum output; however, worst-case addition time must always be assumed.

The Look-Ahead Carry Adder

The speed with which an addition can be performed is limited by the time required for the carries to propagate, or ripple, through all the stages of a parallel adder. One method of speeding up the addition process by eliminating this ripple carry delay is called **look-ahead carry** addition. The look-ahead carry adder anticipates the output carry of each stage, and based on the inputs, produces the output carry by either carry generation or carry propagation.

Carry generation occurs when an output carry is produced (generated) internally by the full-adder. A carry is generated only when both input bits are 1s. The generated carry, C_g, is expressed as the AND function of the two input bits, A and B.

$$C_g = AB$$

Equation 5

Carry propagation occurs when the input carry is rippled to become the output carry. An input carry may be propagated by the full-adder when either or both of the input bits are 1s. The propagated carry, C_p, is expressed as the OR function of the input bits.

$$C_p = A + B$$

Equation 6

The conditions for carry generation and carry propagation are illustrated in Figure 16. The three arrowheads symbolize ripple (propagation).

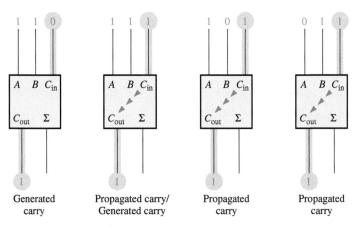

Illustration of conditions for carry generation and carry propagation.

Generated carry

Propagated carry/ Generated carry

Propagated carry

Propagated carry

The output carry of a full-adder can be expressed in terms of both the generated carry (C_g) and the propagated carry (C_p). The output carry (C_{out}) is a 1 if the generated carry is a 1 OR if the propagated carry is a 1 AND the input carry (C_{in}) is a 1. In other words, we get an output carry of 1 if it is generated by the full-adder ($A = 1$ AND $B = 1$) or if the adder propagates the input carry ($A = 1$ OR $B = 1$) AND $C_{in} = 1$. This relationship is expressed as

$$C_{out} = C_g + C_p C_{in}$$

Equation 7

Now let's see how this concept can be applied to a parallel adder, whose individual stages are shown in Figure 17 for a 4-bit example. For each full-adder, the output carry is dependent on the generated carry (C_g), the propagated carry (C_p), and its input carry (C_{in}). The C_g and C_p functions for each stage are *immediately* available as soon as the input bits A and B and the input carry to the LSB adder are applied because they are dependent only on these bits. The input carry to each stage is the output carry of the previous stage.

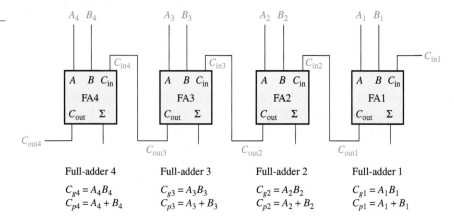

▶ FIGURE 17

Carry generation and carry propagation in terms of the input bits to a 4-bit adder.

Full-adder 4

$C_{g4} = A_4 B_4$
$C_{p4} = A_4 + B_4$

Full-adder 3

$C_{g3} = A_3 B_3$
$C_{p3} = A_3 + B_3$

Full-adder 2

$C_{g2} = A_2 B_2$
$C_{p2} = A_2 + B_2$

Full-adder 1

$C_{g1} = A_1 B_1$
$C_{p1} = A_1 + B_1$

Based on this analysis, we can now develop expressions for the output carry, C_{out}, of each full-adder stage for the 4-bit example.

Full-adder 1:

$$C_{out1} = C_{g1} + C_{p1}C_{in1}$$

Full-adder 2:

$$C_{in2} = C_{out1}$$
$$C_{out2} = C_{g2} + C_{p2}C_{in2} = C_{g2} + C_{p2}C_{out1} = C_{g2} + C_{p2}(C_{g1} + C_{p1}C_{in1})$$
$$= C_{g2} + C_{p2}C_{g1} + C_{p2}C_{p1}C_{in1}$$

Full-adder 3:

$$C_{in3} = C_{out2}$$
$$C_{out3} = C_{g3} + C_{p3}C_{in3} = C_{g3} + C_{p3}C_{out2} = C_{g3} + C_{p3}(C_{g2} + C_{p2}C_{g1} + C_{p2}C_{p1}C_{in1})$$
$$= C_{g3} + C_{p3}C_{g2} + C_{p3}C_{p2}C_{g1} + C_{p3}C_{p2}C_{p1}C_{in1}$$

Full-adder 4:

$$C_{in4} = C_{out3}$$
$$C_{out4} = C_{g4} + C_{p4}C_{in4} = C_{g4} + C_{p4}C_{out3}$$
$$= C_{g4} + C_{p4}(C_{g3} + C_{p3}C_{g2} + C_{p3}C_{p2}C_{g1} + C_{p3}C_{p2}C_{p1}C_{in1})$$
$$= C_{g4} + C_{p4}C_{g3} + C_{p4}C_{p3}C_{g2} + C_{p4}C_{p3}C_{p2}C_{g1} + C_{p4}C_{p3}C_{p2}C_{p1}C_{in1}$$

Notice that in each of these expressions, the output carry for each full-adder stage is dependent only on the initial input carry (C_{in1}), the C_g and C_p functions of that stage, and the C_g and C_p functions of the preceding stages. Since each of the C_g and C_p functions can be expressed in terms of the A and B inputs to the full-adders, all the output carries are immediately available (except for gate delays), and you do not have to wait for a carry to ripple through all the stages before a final result is achieved. Thus, the look-ahead carry technique speeds up the addition process.

The C_{out} equations are implemented with logic gates and connected to the full-adders to create a 4-bit look-ahead carry adder, as shown in Figure 18.

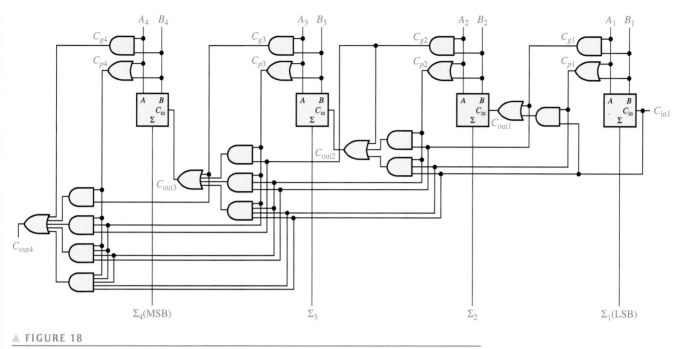

▲ FIGURE 18

Logic diagram for a 4-stage look-ahead carry adder.

Combination Look-Ahead and Ripple Carry Adders

As with most IC adders, the 74LS283 4-bit adder that was introduced in Section 2 is a look-ahead carry adder. When these adders are cascaded to expand their capability to handle binary numbers with more than four bits, the output carry of one adder is connected to the input carry of the next. This creates a ripple carry condition between the 4-bit adders so that when two or more 74LS283s are cascaded, the resulting adder is actually a combination look-ahead and ripple carry adder. The look-ahead carry operation is internal to each MSI adder and the ripple carry feature comes into play when there is a carry out of one of the adders to the next one.

SECTION 3 CHECKUP	1. The input bits to a full-adder are $A = 1$ and $B = 0$. Determine C_g and C_p.
	2. Determine the output carry of a full-adder when $C_{in} = 1$, $C_g = 0$, and $C_p = 1$.

4 COMPARATORS

The basic function of a comparator is to compare the magnitudes of two binary quantities to determine the relationship of those quantities. In its simplest form, a comparator circuit determines whether two numbers are equal.

After completing this section, you should be able to

◆ Use the exclusive-NOR gate as a basic comparator

◆ Analyze the internal logic of a magnitude comparator that has both equality and inequality outputs

◆ Apply the 74LS85 comparator to compare the magnitudes of two 4-bit numbers

◆ Cascade 74LS85s to expand a comparator to eight or more bits

Equality

The exclusive-NOR gate can be used as a basic comparator because its output is a 0 if the two input bits are not equal and a 1 if the input bits are equal. Figure 19 shows the exclusive-NOR gate as a 2-bit comparator.

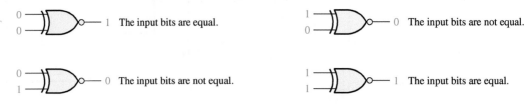

Basic comparator operation.

In order to compare binary numbers containing two bits each, an additional exclusive-NOR gate is necessary. The two least significant bits (LSBs) of the two numbers are compared by gate G_1, and the two most significant bits (MSBs) are compared by gate G_2, as shown in Figure 20. If the two numbers are equal, their corresponding bits are the same, and the output of each exclusive-NOR gate is a 1. If the corresponding sets of bits are not equal, a 0 occurs on that exclusive-NOR gate output.

▶ FIGURE 20

Logic diagram for equality comparison of two 2-bit numbers. Open file F06-20 to verify operation.

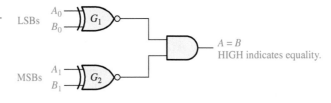

General format: Binary number $A \rightarrow A_1A_0$
Binary number $B \rightarrow B_1B_0$

A comparator determines if two binary numbers are equal or unequal.

In order to produce a single output indicating an equality or inequality of two numbers, an AND gate can be combined with XNOR gates, as shown in Figure 20. The output of each exclusive-NOR gate is applied to the AND gate input. When the two input bits for each exclusive-NOR are equal, the corresponding bits of the numbers are equal, producing a 1 on both inputs to the AND gate and thus a 1 on the output. When the two numbers are not equal, one or both sets of corresponding bits are unequal, and a 0 appears on at least one input to the AND gate to produce a 0 on its output. Thus, the output of the AND gate indicates equality (1) or inequality (0) of the two numbers. Example 5 illustrates this operation for two specific cases.

EXAMPLE 5

Apply each of the following sets of binary numbers to the comparator inputs in Figure 21, and determine the output by following the logic levels through the circuit.

(a) 10 and 10 **(b)** 11 and 10

$A_0 = 0$	$A_0 = 1$
$B_0 = 0$ ... 1	$B_0 = 0$ ... 0
	$1 \rightarrow$ equal	$0 \rightarrow$ not equal
$A_1 = 1$	$A_1 = 1$
$B_1 = 1$ ... 1	$B_1 = 1$ ... 1
(a)	(b)

▲ FIGURE 21

Solution **(a)** The output is **1** for inputs 10 and 10, as shown in Figure 21(a).

(b) The output is **0** for inputs 11 and 10, as shown in Figure 21(b).

Related Problem Repeat the process for binary inputs of 01 and 10.

The basic comparator can be expanded to any number of bits. The AND gate sets the condition that all corresponding bits of the two numbers must be equal if the two numbers themselves are equal.

Inequality

In addition to the equality output, many IC comparators provide additional outputs that indicate which of the two binary numbers being compared is the larger. That is, there is an output that indicates when number A is greater than number B ($A > B$) and an output that indicates when number A is less than number B ($A < B$), as shown in the logic symbol for a 4-bit comparator in Figure 22.

To determine an inequality of binary numbers A and B, you first examine the highest-order bit in each number. The following conditions are possible:

1. If $A_3 = 1$ and $B_3 = 0$, number A is greater than number B.

2. If $A_3 = 0$ and $B_3 = 1$, number A is less than number B.

3. If $A_3 = B_3$, then you must examine the next lower bit position for an inequality.

These three operations are valid for each bit position in the numbers. The general procedure used in a comparator is to check for an inequality in a bit position, starting with the highest-order bits (MSBs). When such an inequality is found, the relationship of the two numbers is established, and any other inequalities in lower-order bit positions must be ignored because it is possible for an opposite indication to occur; *the highest-order indication must take precedence.*

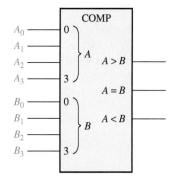

▲ FIGURE 22

Logic symbol for a 4-bit comparator with inequality indication.

EXAMPLE 6

Determine the $A = B$, $A > B$, and $A < B$ outputs for the input numbers shown on the comparator in Figure 23.

▶ FIGURE 23

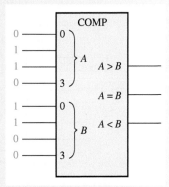

Solution   The number on the A inputs is 0110 and the number on the B inputs is 0011. The **$A > B$ output is HIGH and the other outputs are LOW.**

Related Problem   What are the comparator outputs when $A_3A_2A_1A_0 = 1001$ and $B_3B_2B_1B_0 = 1010$?

THE 74LS85 4-BIT MAGNITUDE COMPARATOR

The 74LS85 is a comparator that is also available in other IC families. The pin diagram and logic symbol are shown in Figure 24. Notice that this device has all the inputs and outputs of the generalized comparator previously discussed and, in addition, has three cascading inputs: $A < B$, $A = B$, $A > B$. These inputs allow several comparators to be cascaded for comparison of any number of bits greater than four. To expand the comparator, the $A < B$, $A = B$, and $A > B$ outputs of the lower-order comparator are connected to the corresponding cascading inputs of the next higher-order comparator. The lowest-order comparator must have a HIGH on the $A = B$ input and LOWs on the $A < B$ and $A > B$ inputs.

▶ FIGURE 24

Pin diagram and logic symbol for the 74LS85 4-bit magnitude comparator (pin numbers are in parentheses).

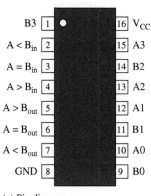

(a) Pin diagram

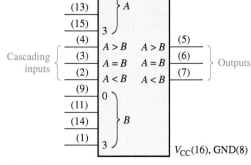

(b) Logic symbol

EXAMPLE 7

Use 74LS85 comparators to compare the magnitudes of two 8-bit numbers. Show the comparators with proper interconnections.

Solution   Two 74LS85s are required to compare two 8-bit numbers. They are connected as shown in Figure 25 in a cascaded arrangement.

▶ FIGURE 25

An 8-bit magnitude comparator using two 74LS85s.

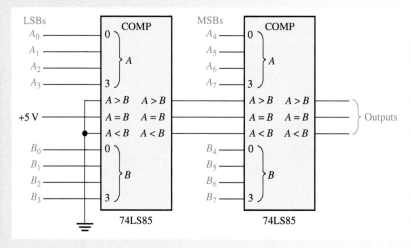

Related Problem   Expand the circuit in Figure 25 to a 16-bit comparator.

Hands-On Tip

Most CMOS devices contain protection circuitry to guard against damage from high static voltages or electric fields. However, precautions must be taken to avoid applications of any voltages higher than maximum rated voltages. For proper operation, input and output voltages should be between ground and V_{CC}. Also, remember that unused inputs must always be connected to an appropriate logic level (ground or V_{CC}). Unused outputs may be left open.

**SECTION 4
CHECKUP**

1. The binary numbers $A = 1011$ and $B = 1010$ are applied to the inputs of a 74LS85. Determine the outputs.

2. The binary numbers $A = 11001011$ and $B = 11010100$ are applied to the 8-bit comparator in Figure 25. Determine the states of the outputs on each comparator.

5 DECODERS

A **decoder** is a digital circuit that detects the presence of a specified combination of bits (code) on its inputs and indicates the presence of that code by a specified output level. In its general form, a decoder has n input lines to handle n bits and from one to 2^n output lines to indicate the presence of one or more n-bit combinations. In this section, several decoders are introduced. The basic principles can be extended to other types of decoders.

After completing this section, you should be able to

- Define *decoder*
- Design a logic circuit to decode any combination of bits
- Describe the 74HC154 binary-to-decimal decoder
- Expand decoders to accommodate larger numbers of bits in a code
- Describe the 74LS47 BCD-to-7-segment decoder
- Discuss zero suppression in 7-segment displays
- Apply decoders to specific applications

The Basic Binary Decoder

Suppose you need to determine when a binary 1001 occurs on the inputs of a digital circuit. An AND gate can be used as the basic decoding element because it produces a HIGH output only when all of its inputs are HIGH. Therefore, you must make sure that all of the inputs to the AND gate are HIGH when the binary number 1001 occurs; this can be done by inverting the two middle bits (the 0s), as shown in Figure 26.

The logic equation for the decoder of Figure 26(a) is developed as illustrated in Figure 26(b). You should verify that the output is 0 except when $A_0 = 1$, $A_1 = 0$, $A_2 = 0$, and $A_3 = 1$ are applied to the inputs. A_0 is the LSB and A_3 is the MSB. *In the representation of a binary number or other weighted code in this book, the LSB is the right-most bit in a*

319

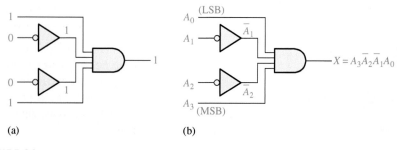

(a)   (b)

▲ FIGURE 26

Decoding logic for the binary code 1001 with an active-HIGH output.

horizontal arrangement and the topmost bit in a vertical arrangement, unless specified otherwise.

If a NAND gate is used in place of the AND gate in Figure 26, a LOW output will indicate the presence of the proper binary code, which is 1001 in this case.

EXAMPLE 8

Determine the logic required to decode the binary number 1011 by producing a HIGH level on the output.

Solution   The decoding function can be formed by complementing only the variables that appear as 0 in the desired binary number, as follows:

$$X = A_3\overline{A}_2A_1A_0 \quad (1011)$$

This function can be implemented by connecting the true (uncomplemented) variables A_0, A_1, and A_3 directly to the inputs of an AND gate, and inverting the variable A_2 before applying it to the AND gate input. The decoding logic is shown in Figure 27.

▶ FIGURE 27

Decoding logic for producing a HIGH output when 1011 is on the inputs.

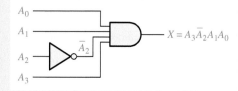

Related Problem   Develop the logic required to detect the binary code 10010 and produce an active-LOW output.

The 4-Bit Decoder

In order to decode all possible combinations of four bits, sixteen decoding gates are required ($2^4 = 16$). This type of decoder is commonly called either a *4-line-to-16-line decoder* because there are four inputs and sixteen outputs or a *1-of-16 decoder* because for any given code on the inputs, one of the sixteen outputs is activated. A list of the sixteen binary codes and their corresponding decoding functions is given in Table 4.

If an active-LOW output is required for each decoded number, the entire decoder can be implemented with NAND gates and inverters. In order to decode each of the sixteen binary codes, sixteen NAND gates are required (AND gates can be used to produce active-HIGH outputs).

▼ TABLE 4

Decoding functions and truth table for a 4-line-to-16-line (1-of-16) decoder with active-LOW outputs.

DECIMAL DIGIT	BINARY INPUTS				DECODING FUNCTION	OUTPUTS															
	A_3	A_2	A_1	A_0		0	1	2	3	4	5	6	7	8	9	10	11	12	13	14	15
0	0	0	0	0	$\bar{A_3}\bar{A_2}\bar{A_1}\bar{A_0}$	0	1	1	1	1	1	1	1	1	1	1	1	1	1	1	1
1	0	0	0	1	$\bar{A_3}\bar{A_2}\bar{A_1}A_0$	1	0	1	1	1	1	1	1	1	1	1	1	1	1	1	1
2	0	0	1	0	$\bar{A_3}\bar{A_2}A_1\bar{A_0}$	1	1	0	1	1	1	1	1	1	1	1	1	1	1	1	1
3	0	0	1	1	$\bar{A_3}\bar{A_2}A_1A_0$	1	1	1	0	1	1	1	1	1	1	1	1	1	1	1	1
4	0	1	0	0	$\bar{A_3}A_2\bar{A_1}\bar{A_0}$	1	1	1	1	0	1	1	1	1	1	1	1	1	1	1	1
5	0	1	0	1	$\bar{A_3}A_2\bar{A_1}A_0$	1	1	1	1	1	0	1	1	1	1	1	1	1	1	1	1
6	0	1	1	0	$\bar{A_3}A_2A_1\bar{A_0}$	1	1	1	1	1	1	0	1	1	1	1	1	1	1	1	1
7	0	1	1	1	$\bar{A_3}A_2A_1A_0$	1	1	1	1	1	1	1	0	1	1	1	1	1	1	1	1
8	1	0	0	0	$A_3\bar{A_2}\bar{A_1}\bar{A_0}$	1	1	1	1	1	1	1	1	0	1	1	1	1	1	1	1
9	1	0	0	1	$A_3\bar{A_2}\bar{A_1}A_0$	1	1	1	1	1	1	1	1	1	0	1	1	1	1	1	1
10	1	0	1	0	$A_3\bar{A_2}A_1\bar{A_0}$	1	1	1	1	1	1	1	1	1	1	0	1	1	1	1	1
11	1	0	1	1	$A_3\bar{A_2}A_1A_0$	1	1	1	1	1	1	1	1	1	1	1	0	1	1	1	1
12	1	1	0	0	$A_3A_2\bar{A_1}\bar{A_0}$	1	1	1	1	1	1	1	1	1	1	1	1	0	1	1	1
13	1	1	0	1	$A_3A_2\bar{A_1}A_0$	1	1	1	1	1	1	1	1	1	1	1	1	1	0	1	1
14	1	1	1	0	$A_3A_2A_1\bar{A_0}$	1	1	1	1	1	1	1	1	1	1	1	1	1	1	0	1
15	1	1	1	1	$A_3A_2A_1A_0$	1	1	1	1	1	1	1	1	1	1	1	1	1	1	1	0

A logic symbol for a 4-line-to-16-line (1-of-16) decoder with active-LOW outputs is shown in Figure 28. The BIN/DEC label indicates that a binary input makes the corresponding decimal output active. The input labels 8, 4, 2, and 1 represent the binary weights of the input bits ($2^3 2^2 2^1 2^0$).

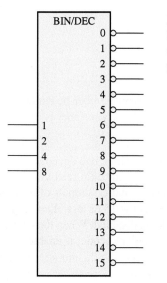

▶ FIGURE 28

Logic symbol for a 4-line-to-16-line (1-of-16) decoder. Open file F06-28 to verify operation.

THE 74HC154 1-OF-16 DECODER

The 74HC154 is a good example of an IC decoder. The logic symbol is shown in Figure 29. There is an enable function (*EN*) provided on this device, which is implemented with a NOR gate used as a negative-AND. A LOW level on each chip select input, $\overline{CS_1}$ and $\overline{CS_2}$, is required in order to make the enable gate output (*EN*) HIGH. The enable gate output is connected to an input of *each* NAND gate in the decoder, so it must be HIGH for the NAND gates to be enabled. If the enable gate is not activated by a LOW on both inputs, then all sixteen decoder outputs (*Y*) will be HIGH regardless of the states of the four input variables, A_0, A_1, A_2, and A_3.

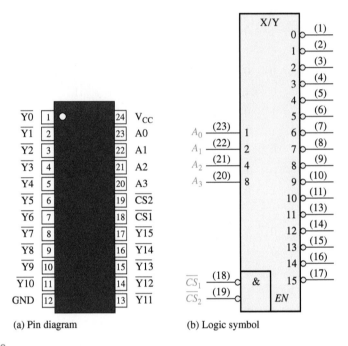

(a) Pin diagram

(b) Logic symbol

▲ FIGURE 29

Pin diagram and logic symbol for the 74HC154 1-of-16 decoder.

EXAMPLE 9

A certain application requires that a 5-bit number be decoded. Use 74HC154 decoders to implement the logic. The binary number is represented by the format $A_4A_3A_2A_1A_0$.

Solution   Since the 74HC154 can handle only four bits, two decoders must be used to decode five bits. The fifth bit, A_4, is connected to the chip select inputs, $\overline{CS_1}$ and $\overline{CS_2}$, of one decoder, and $\overline{A_4}$ is connected to the $\overline{CS_1}$ and $\overline{CS_2}$ inputs of the other decoder, as shown in Figure 30. When the decimal number is 15 or less, $A_4 = 0$, the low-order decoder is enabled, and the high-order decoder is disabled. When the decimal number is greater than 15, $A_4 = 1$ so $\overline{A_4} = 0$, the high-order decoder is enabled, and the low-order decoder is disabled.

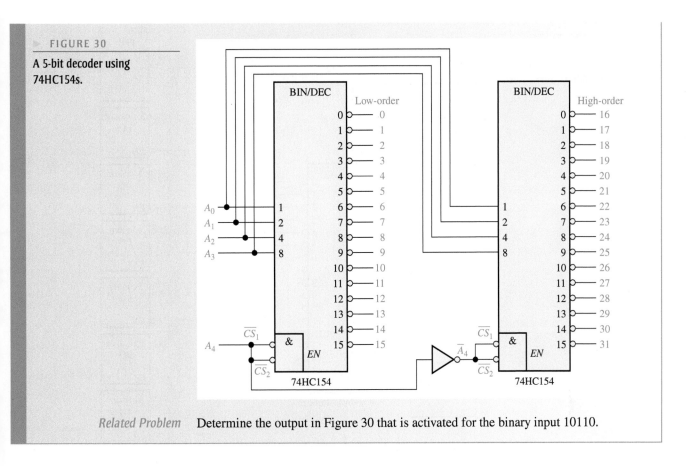

▶ FIGURE 30

A 5-bit decoder using 74HC154s.

Related Problem   Determine the output in Figure 30 that is activated for the binary input 10110.

An Application

Decoders are used in many types of applications. One example is in computers for input/output selection as depicted in the general diagram of Figure 31.

Computers must communicate with a variety of external devices called *peripherals* by sending and/or receiving data through what is known as input/output (I/O) ports. These external devices include printers, modems, scanners, external disk drives, keyboard, video monitors, and other computers. As illustrated in Figure 31, a decoder can be used to select the I/O port as determined by the computer so that data can be sent or received from a specific external device.

Each I/O port has a number, called an address, which uniquely identifies it. When the computer wants to communicate with a particular device, it issues the appropriate address code for the I/O port to which that particular device is connected. This binary port address is decoded and the appropriate decoder output is activated to enable the I/O port.

As shown in Figure 31, binary data are transferred within the computer on a data bus, which is a set of parallel lines. For example, an 8-bit bus consists of eight parallel lines that can carry one byte of data at a time. The data bus goes to all of the I/O ports, but any data coming in or going out will only pass through the port that is enabled by the port address decoder.

The BCD-to-Decimal Decoder

The BCD-to-decimal decoder converts each BCD code (8421 code) into one of ten possible decimal digit indications. It is frequently referred as a *4-line-to-10-line decoder* or a *1-of-10 decoder.*

A simplified computer I/O port system with a port address decoder with only four address lines shown.

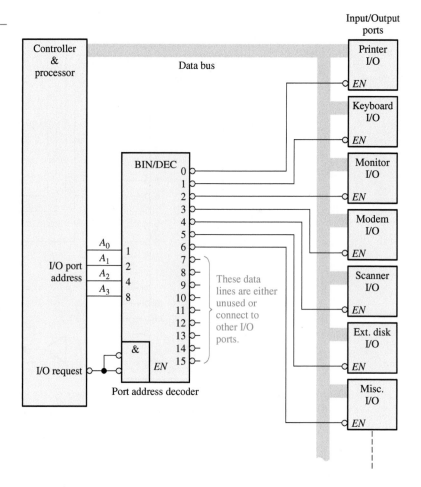

The method of implementation is the same as for the 1-of-16 decoder previously discussed, except that only ten decoding gates are required because the BCD code represents only the ten decimal digits 0 through 9. A list of the ten BCD codes and their corresponding decoding functions is given in Table 5. Each of these decoding functions is implemented with NAND gates to provide active-LOW outputs. If an active-HIGH output is required, AND gates are used for decoding. The logic is identical to that of the first ten decoding gates in the 1-of-16 decoder (see Table 4).

▶ TABLE 5

BCD decoding functions.

DECIMAL DIGIT	BCD CODE				DECODING FUNCTION
	A_3	A_2	A_1	A_0	
0	0	0	0	0	$\overline{A_3}\,\overline{A_2}\,\overline{A_1}\,\overline{A_0}$
1	0	0	0	1	$\overline{A_3}\,\overline{A_2}\,\overline{A_1}A_0$
2	0	0	1	0	$\overline{A_3}\,\overline{A_2}A_1\overline{A_0}$
3	0	0	1	1	$\overline{A_3}\,\overline{A_2}A_1A_0$
4	0	1	0	0	$\overline{A_3}A_2\overline{A_1}\,\overline{A_0}$
5	0	1	0	1	$\overline{A_3}A_2\overline{A_1}A_0$
6	0	1	1	0	$\overline{A_3}A_2A_1\overline{A_0}$
7	0	1	1	1	$\overline{A_3}A_2A_1A_0$
8	1	0	0	0	$A_3\overline{A_2}\,\overline{A_1}\,\overline{A_0}$
9	1	0	0	1	$A_3\overline{A_2}\,\overline{A_1}A_0$

THE 74HC42 BCD-TO-DECIMAL DECODER

The 74HC42 is an IC decoder with four BCD inputs and ten active-LOW decimal outputs. The logic symbol is shown in Figure 32.

▶ FIGURE 32

The 74HC42 BCD-to-decimal decoder.

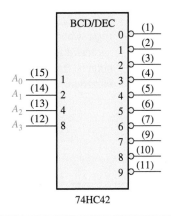

EXAMPLE 10

If the input waveforms in Figure 33(a) are applied to the inputs of the 74HC42, show the output waveforms.

▶ FIGURE 33

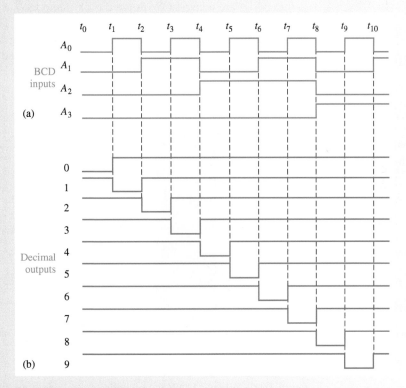

Solution The output waveforms are shown in Figure 33(b). As you can see, the inputs are sequenced through the BCD for digits 0 through 9. The output waveforms in the timing diagram indicate that sequence on the decimal-value outputs.

Related Problem Construct a timing diagram showing input and output waveforms for the case where the BCD inputs sequence through the decimal numbers as follows: 0, 2, 4, 6, 8, 1, 3, 5, and 9.

The BCD-to-7-Segment Decoder

The BCD-to-7-segment decoder accepts the BCD code on its inputs and provides outputs to drive 7-segment display devices to produce a decimal readout. The logic diagram for a basic 7-segment decoder is shown in Figure 34.

▶ FIGURE 34

Logic symbol for a BCD-to-7-segment decoder/driver with active-LOW outputs. Open file F06-34 to verify operation.

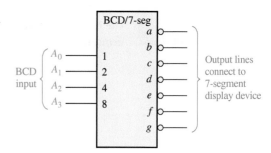

THE 74LS47 BCD-TO-7-SEGMENT DECODER/DRIVER

The 74LS47 is an example of an IC device that decodes a BCD input and drives a 7-segment display. In addition to its decoding and segment drive capability, the 74LS47 has several additional features as indicated by the $\overline{LT}$, $\overline{RBI}$, $\overline{BI}/\overline{RBO}$ functions in the logic symbol of Figure 35. As indicated by the bubbles on the logic symbol, all of the outputs (a through g) are active-LOW as are the $\overline{LT}$ (lamp test), $\overline{RBI}$ (ripple blanking input), and $\overline{BI}/\overline{RBO}$ (blanking input/ripple blanking output) functions. The outputs can drive a common-anode 7-segment display directly. In addition to decoding a BCD input and producing the appropriate 7-segment outputs, the 74LS47 has lamp test and zero suppression capability.

▶ FIGURE 35

Pin diagram and logic symbol for the 74LS47 BCD-to-7-segment decoder/driver.

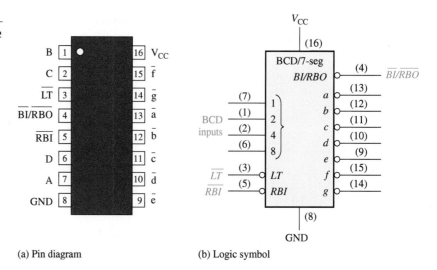

(a) Pin diagram   (b) Logic symbol

Lamp Test   When a LOW is applied to the $\overline{LT}$ input and the $\overline{BI}/\overline{RBO}$ is HIGH, all of the seven segments in the display are turned on. Lamp test is used to verify that no segments are burned out.

Zero Suppression   **Zero suppression** is a feature used for multidigit displays to blank out unnecessary zeros. For example, in a 6-digit display the number 6.4 may be displayed as 006.400 if the zeros are not blanked out. Blanking the zeros at the front of a number is called *leading zero suppression* and blanking the zeros at the back of the number is called

Zero suppression results in leading or trailing zeros in a number not showing on a display.

326

trailing zero suppression. Keep in mind that only nonessential zeros are blanked. With zero suppression, the number 030.080 will be displayed as 30.08 (the essential zeros remain).

Zero suppression in the 74LS47 is accomplished using the $\overline{RBI}$ and $\overline{BI}/\overline{RBO}$ functions. $\overline{RBI}$ is the ripple blanking input and $\overline{RBO}$ is the ripple blanking output on the 74LS47; these are used for zero suppression. $\overline{BI}$ is the blanking input that shares the same pin with $\overline{RBO}$; in other words, the $\overline{BI}/\overline{RBO}$ pin can be used as an input or an output. When used as a $\overline{BI}$ (blanking input), all segment outputs are HIGH (nonactive) when $\overline{BI}$ is LOW, which overrides all other inputs. The $\overline{BI}$ function is not part of the zero suppression capability of the device.

All of the segment outputs of the decoder are nonactive (HIGH) if a zero code (0000) is on its BCD inputs and if its $\overline{RBI}$ is LOW. This causes the display to be blank and produces a LOW $\overline{RBO}$.

The logic diagram in Figure 36(a) illustrates leading zero suppression for a whole number. The highest-order digit position (left-most) is always blanked if a zero code is on its BCD inputs because the $\overline{RBI}$ of the most-significant decoder is made LOW by connecting it to ground. The $\overline{RBO}$ of each decoder is connected to the $\overline{RBI}$ of the next lowest-order decoder so that all zeros to the left of the first nonzero digit are blanked. For example, in

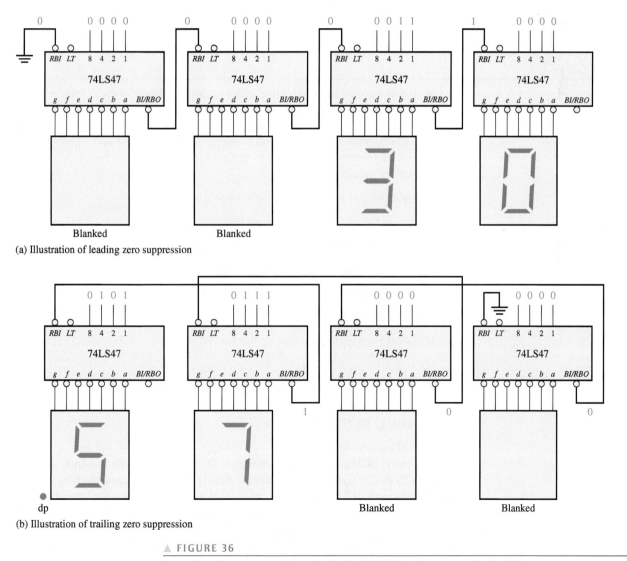

(a) Illustration of leading zero suppression

(b) Illustration of trailing zero suppression

▲ FIGURE 36

Examples of zero suppression using the 74LS47 BCD to 7-segment decoder/driver.

part (a) of the figure the two highest-order digits are zeros and therefore are blanked. The remaining two digits, 3 and 0 are displayed.

The logic diagram in Figure 36(b) illustrates trailing zero suppression for a fractional number. The lowest-order digit (right-most) is always blanked if a zero code is on its BCD inputs because the $\overline{RBI}$ is connected to ground. The $\overline{RBO}$ of each decoder is connected to the $\overline{RBI}$ of the next highest-order decoder so that all zeros to the right of the first nonzero digit are blanked. In part (b) of the figure, the two lowest-order digits are zeros and therefore are blanked. The remaining two digits, 5 and 7 are displayed. To combine both leading and trailing zero suppression in one display and to have decimal point capability, additional logic is required.

**SECTION 5
CHECKUP**

1. A 3-line-to-8-line decoder can be used for octal-to-decimal decoding. When a binary 101 is on the inputs, which output line is activated?
2. How many 74HC154 1-of-16 decoders are necessary to decode a 6-bit binary number?
3. Would you select a decoder/driver with active-HIGH or active-LOW outputs to drive a common-cathode 7-segment LED display?

---

6 ENCODERS

An **encoder** is a combinational logic circuit that essentially performs a "reverse" decoder function. An encoder accepts an active level on one of its inputs representing a digit, such as a decimal or octal digit, and converts it to a coded output, such as BCD or binary. Encoders can also be devised to encode various symbols and alphabetic characters. The process of converting from familiar symbols or numbers to a coded format is called *encoding*.

After completing this section, you should be able to

- Determine the logic for a decimal-to-BCD encoder
- Explain the purpose of the priority feature in encoders
- Describe the 74HC147 decimal-to-BCD priority encoder
- Describe the 74LS148 octal-to-binary priority encoder
- Expand an encoder
- Apply the encoder to a specific application

The Decimal-to-BCD Encoder

This type of encoder has ten inputs—one for each decimal digit—and four outputs corresponding to the BCD code, as shown in Figure 37. This is a basic 10-line-to-4-line encoder.

The BCD (8421) code is listed in Table 6. From this table you can determine the relationship between each BCD bit and the decimal digits in order to analyze the logic. For instance, the most significant bit of the BCD code, A_3, is always a 1 for decimal digit 8 or 9. An OR expression for bit A_3 in terms of the decimal digits can therefore be written as

$$A_3 = 8 + 9$$

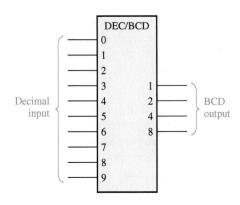

◀ FIGURE 37

Logic symbol for a decimal-to-BCD encoder.

◀ TABLE 6

DECIMAL DIGIT	BCD CODE			
	A_3	A_2	A_1	A_0
0	0	0	0	0
1	0	0	0	1
2	0	0	1	0
3	0	0	1	1
4	0	1	0	0
5	0	1	0	1
6	0	1	1	0
7	0	1	1	1
8	1	0	0	0
9	1	0	0	1

Bit A_2 is always a 1 for decimal digit 4, 5, 6 or 7 and can be expressed as an OR function as follows:

$$A_2 = 4 + 5 + 6 + 7$$

Bit A_1 is always a 1 for decimal digit 2, 3, 6, or 7 and can be expressed as

$$A_1 = 2 + 3 + 6 + 7$$

Finally, A_0 is always a 1 for decimal digit 1, 3, 5, 7, or 9. The expression for A_0 is

$$A_0 = 1 + 3 + 5 + 7 + 9$$

Now let's implement the logic circuitry required for encoding each decimal digit to a BCD code by using the logic expressions just developed. It is simply a matter of ORing the appropriate decimal digit input lines to form each BCD output. The basic encoder logic resulting from these expressions is shown in Figure 38.

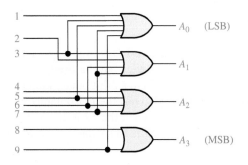

◀ FIGURE 38

Basic logic diagram of a decimal-to-BCD encoder. A 0-digit input is not needed because the BCD outputs are all LOW when there are no HIGH inputs.

The basic operation of the circuit in Figure 38 is as follows: When a HIGH appears on *one* of the decimal digit input lines, the appropriate levels occur on the four BCD output lines. For instance, if input line 9 is HIGH (assuming all other input lines are LOW), this condition will produce a HIGH on outputs A_0 and A_3 and LOWs on outputs A_1 and A_2, which is the BCD code (1001) for decimal 9.

The Decimal-to-BCD Priority Encoder This type of encoder performs the same basic encoding function as previously discussed. A **priority encoder** also offers additional flexibility in that it can be used in applications that require priority detection. The priority function means that the encoder will produce a BCD output corresponding to the *highest-order decimal digit* input that is active and will ignore any other lower-order active inputs. For instance, if the 6 and the 3 inputs are both active, the BCD output is 0110 (which represents decimal 6).

THE 74HC147 DECIMAL-TO-BCD ENCODER

The 74HC147 is a priority encoder with active-LOW inputs (0) for decimal digits 1 through 9 and active-LOW BCD outputs as indicated in the logic symbol in Figure 39. A BCD zero output is represented when none of the inputs is active. The device pin numbers are in parentheses.

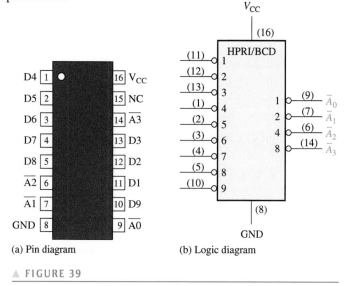

(a) Pin diagram

(b) Logic diagram

▲ FIGURE 39

Pin diagram and logic symbol for the 74HC147 decimal-to-BCD priority encoder (HPRI means highest value input has priority).

THE 74LS148 8-LINE-TO-3-LINE ENCODER

The 74LS148 is a priority encoder that has eight active-LOW inputs and three active-LOW binary outputs, as shown in Figure 40. This device can be used for converting octal inputs (recall that the octal digits are 0 through 7) to a 3-bit binary code. To enable the device, the *EI* (enable input) must be LOW. It also has the *EO* (enable output) and *GS* output for expansion purposes. The *EO* is LOW when the *EI* is LOW and none of the inputs (0 through 7) is active. *GS* is LOW when *EI* is LOW and any of the inputs is active.

▶ FIGURE 40

Logic symbol for the 74LS148 8-line-to-3-line encoder.

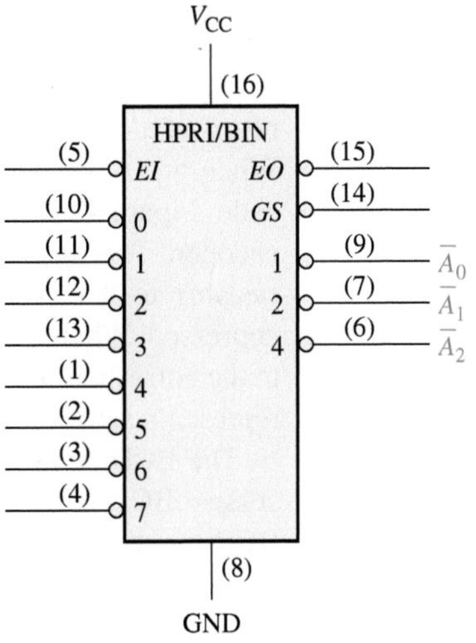

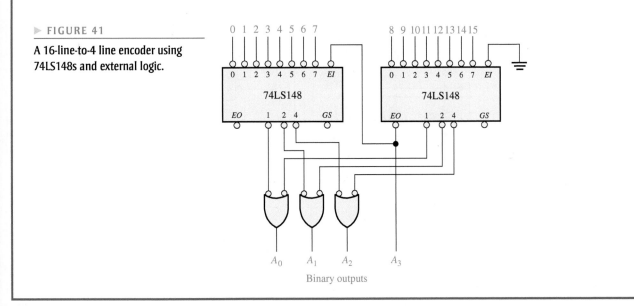

The 74LS148 can be expanded to a 16-line-to-4-line encoder by connecting the EO of the higher-order encoder to the EI of the lower-order encoder and negative-ORing the corresponding binary outputs as shown in Figure 41. The EO is used as the fourth and most-significant bit. This particular configuration produces active-HIGH outputs for the 4-bit binary number.

▶ FIGURE 41

A 16-line-to-4 line encoder using 74LS148s and external logic.

EXAMPLE 11

If LOW levels appear on pins, 1, 4, and 13 of the 74HC147 shown in Figure 39, indicate the state of the four outputs. All other inputs are HIGH.

Solution   Pin 4 is the highest-order decimal digit input having a LOW level and represents decimal 7. Therefore, the output levels indicate the BCD code for decimal 7 where $\overline{A}_0$ is the LSB and $\overline{A}_3$ is the MSB. Output $\overline{A}_0$ is LOW, $\overline{A}_1$ is LOW, $\overline{A}_2$ is LOW, and $\overline{A}_3$ is HIGH.

Related Problem   What are the outputs of the 74HC147 if all its inputs are LOW? If all its inputs are HIGH?

An Application

A classic application example is a keyboard encoder. The ten decimal digits on the keyboard of a computer, for example, must be encoded for processing by the logic circuitry. When one of the keys is pressed, the decimal digit is encoded to the corresponding BCD code. Figure 42 shows a simple keyboard encoder arrangement using a 74HC147 priority encoder. The keys are represented by ten push-button switches, each with a **pull-up resistor** to $+V$. The pull-up resistor ensures that the line is HIGH when a key is not depressed. When a key is depressed, the line is connected to ground, and a LOW is applied to the corresponding encoder input. The zero key is not connected because the BCD output represents zero when none of the other keys is depressed.

The BCD complement output of the encoder goes into a storage device, and each successive BCD code is stored until the entire number has been entered. Methods of storing BCD numbers and binary data are covered in later chapters.

▶ FIGURE 42

A simplified keyboard encoder.

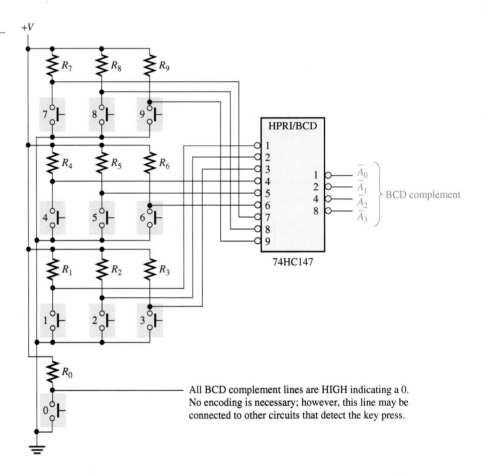

All BCD complement lines are HIGH indicating a 0.
No encoding is necessary; however, this line may be connected to other circuits that detect the key press.

SECTION 6 CHECKUP

1. Suppose the HIGH levels are applied to the 2 input and the 9 input of the circuit in Figure 38.
   (a) What are the states of the output lines?
   (b) Does this represent a valid BCD code?
   (c) What is the restriction on the encoder logic in Figure 38?

2. (a) What is the $\overline{A}_3 \overline{A}_2 \overline{A}_1 \overline{A}_0$ output when LOWs are applied to pins 1 and 5 of the 74HC147 in Figure 39?
   (b) What does this output represent?

7   CODE CONVERTERS

In this section, we will examine some methods of using combinational logic circuits to convert from one code to another.

After completing this section, you should be able to

+ Explain the process for converting BCD to binary
+ Use exclusive-OR gates for conversions between binary and Gray codes

BCD-to-Binary Conversion

One method of BCD-to-binary code conversion uses adder circuits. The basic conversion process is as follows:

1. The value, or weight, of each bit in the BCD number is represented by a binary number.

2. All of the binary representations of the weights of bits that are 1s in the BCD number are added.

3. The result of this addition is the binary equivalent of the BCD number.

A more concise statement of this operation is

The binary numbers representing the weights of the BCD bits are summed to produce the total binary number.

Let's examine an 8-bit BCD code (one that represents a 2-digit decimal number) to understand the relationship between BCD and binary. For instance, you already know that the decimal number 87 can be expressed in BCD as

$$\underbrace{1000}_{8} \quad \underbrace{0111}_{7}$$

The left-most 4-bit group represents 80, and the right-most 4-bit group represents 7. That is, the left-most group has a weight of 10, and the right-most group has a weight of 1. Within each group, the binary weight of each bit is as follows:

	Tens Digit				Units Digit			
Weight:	80	40	20	10	8	4	2	1
Bit designation:	B_3	B_2	B_1	B_0	A_3	A_2	A_1	A_0

The binary equivalent of each BCD bit is a binary number representing the weight of that bit within the total BCD number. This representation is given in Table 7.

BCD BIT	BCD WEIGHT	(MSB) 64	32	BINARY REPRESENTATION 16	8	4	2	(LSB) 1
A_0	1	0	0	0	0	0	0	1
A_1	2	0	0	0	0	0	1	0
A_2	4	0	0	0	0	1	0	0
A_3	8	0	0	0	1	0	0	0
B_0	10	0	0	0	1	0	1	0
B_1	20	0	0	1	0	1	0	0
B_2	40	0	1	0	1	0	0	0
B_3	80	1	0	1	0	0	0	0

◄ TABLE 7

Binary representations of BCD bit weights.

If the binary representations for the weights of all the 1s in the BCD number are added, the result is the binary number that corresponds to the BCD number. Example 12 illustrates this.

EXAMPLE 12

Convert the BCD numbers 00100111 (decimal 27) and 10011000 (decimal 98) to binary.

Solution

Write the binary representations of the weights of all 1s appearing in the numbers, and then add them together.

```
80  40  20  10   8   4   2   1
 0   0   1   0   0   1   1   1
                              ──────→   0000001    1
                          ──────────→   0000010    2
                      ──────────────→   0000100    4
          ──────────────────────────→ + 0010100   20
                                        0011011    Binary number for decimal 27
```

```
80  40  20  10   8   4   2   1
 1   0   0   1   1   0   0   0
                      ──────────→   0001000    8
                  ──────────────→   0001010   10
 ──────────────────────────────→ + 1010000   80
                                    1100010    Binary number for decimal 98
```

Related Problem   Show the process of converting 01000001 in BCD to binary.

Open file EX06-12 and run the simulation to observe the operation of a BCD-to-binary logic circuit.

Binary-to-Gray and Gray-to-Binary Conversion

Exclusive-OR gates can be used for Gray-binary conversions. Programmable logic devices (PLDs) can also be programmed for these code conversions. Figure 43 shows a 4-bit binary-to-Gray code converter, and Figure 44 illustrates a 4-bit Gray-to-binary converter.

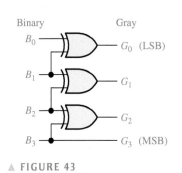

▲ FIGURE 43

Four-bit binary-to-Gray conversion logic. Open file F06-43 to verify operation.

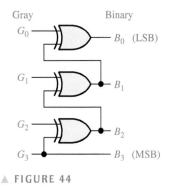

▲ FIGURE 44

Four-bit Gray-to-binary conversion logic. Open file F06-44 to verify operation.

EXAMPLE 13

(a) Convert the binary number 0101 to Gray code with exclusive-OR gates.

(b) Convert the Gray code 1011 to binary with exclusive-OR gates.

Solution

(a) 0101_2 is 0111 Gray. See Figure 45(a).

(b) 1011 Gray is 1101_2. See Figure 45(b).

▶ FIGURE 45

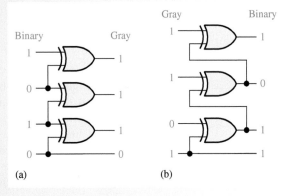

(a)   (b)

Related Problem How many exclusive-OR gates are required to convert 8-bit binary to Gray?

**SECTION 7
CHECKUP**

1. Convert the BCD number 10000101 to binary.

2. Draw the logic diagram for converting an 8-bit binary number to Gray code.

---

8   MULTIPLEXERS (DATA SELECTORS)

A **multiplexer (MUX)** is a device that allows digital information from several sources to be routed onto a single line for transmission over that line to a common destination. The basic multiplexer has several data-input lines and a single output line. It also has data-select inputs, which permit digital data on any one of the inputs to be switched to the output line. Multiplexers are also known as data selectors.

After completing this section, you should be able to

* Explain the basic operation of a multiplexer
* Describe the 74HC157 and the 74LS151 multiplexers
* Expand a multiplexer to handle more data inputs
* Use the multiplexer as a logic function generator

A logic symbol for a 4-input multiplexer (MUX) is shown in Figure 46. Notice that there are two data-select lines because with two select bits, any one of the four data-input lines can be selected.

In a multiplexer, data goes from several lines to one line.

▶ FIGURE 46

Logic symbol for a 1-of-4 data selector/multiplexer.

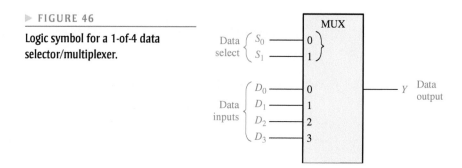

In Figure 46, a 2-bit code on the data-select (S) inputs will allow the data on the selected data input to pass through to the data output. If a binary 0 ($S_1 = 0$ and $S_0 = 0$) is applied to the data-select lines, the data on input D_0 appear on the data-output line. If a binary 1 ($S_1 = 0$ and $S_0 = 1$) is applied to the data-select lines, the data on input D_1 appear on the data output. If a binary 2 ($S_1 = 1$ and $S_0 = 0$) is applied, the data on D_2 appear on the output. If a binary 3 ($S_1 = 1$ and $S_0 = 1$) is applied, the data on D_3 are switched to the output line. A summary of this operation is given in Table 8.

▼ TABLE 8

Data selection for a 1-of-4-multiplexer.

DATA-SELECT INPUTS		INPUT SELECTED
S_1	S_0	
0	0	D_0
0	1	D_1
1	0	D_2
1	1	D_3

Now let's look at the logic circuitry required to perform this multiplexing operation. The data output is equal to the state of the *selected* data input. You can therefore, derive a logic expression for the output in terms of the data input and the select inputs.

The data output is equal to D_0 only if $S_1 = 0$ and $S_0 = 0$: $Y = D_0\overline{S_1}\overline{S_0}$.

The data output is equal to D_1 only if $S_1 = 0$ and $S_0 = 1$: $Y = D_1\overline{S_1}S_0$.

The data output is equal to D_2 only if $S_1 = 1$ and $S_0 = 0$: $Y = D_2 S_1\overline{S_0}$.

The data output is equal to D_3 only if $S_1 = 1$ and $S_0 = 1$: $Y = D_3 S_1 S_0$.

When these terms are ORed, the total expression for the data output is

$$Y = D_0\overline{S_1}\overline{S_0} + D_1\overline{S_1}S_0 + D_2 S_1\overline{S_0} + D_3 S_1 S_0$$

The implementation of this equation requires four 3-input AND gates, a 4-input OR gate, and two inverters to generate the complements of S_1 and S_0, as shown in Figure 47. Because data can be selected from any one of the input lines, this circuit is also referred to as a **data selector.**

COMPUTER NOTE

A *bus* is a multiple conductor pathway along which electrical signals are sent from one part of a computer to another. In computer networks, a *shared bus* is one that is connected to all the microprocessors in the system in order to exchange data. A shared bus may contain memory and input/output devices that can be accessed by all the microprocessors in the system. Access to the shared bus is controlled by a *bus arbiter* (a multiplexer of sorts) that allows only one microprocessor at a time to use the system's shared bus.

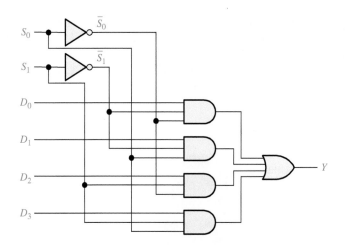

◄ FIGURE 47

Logic diagram for a 4-input multiplexer. Open file F06-47 to verify operation.

EXAMPLE 14

The data-input and data-select waveforms in Figure 48(a) are applied to the multiplexer in Figure 47. Determine the output waveform in relation to the inputs.

FIGURE 48

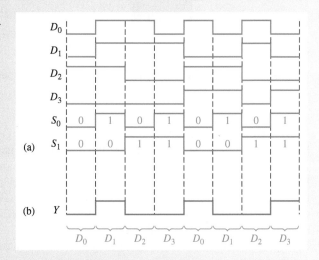

Solution   The binary state of the data-select inputs during each interval determines which data input is selected. Notice that the data-select inputs go through a repetitive binary sequence 00, 01, 10, 11, 00, 01, 10, 11, and so on. The resulting output waveform is shown in Figure 48(b).

Related Problem   Construct a timing diagram showing all inputs and the output if the S_0 and S_1 waveforms in Figure 48 are interchanged.

THE 74HC157 QUAD 2-INPUT DATA SELECTOR/MULTIPLEXER

The 74HC157, as well as its LS version, consists of four separate 2-input multiplexers. Each of the four multiplexers shares a common data-select line and a common *Enable*. Because there are only two inputs to be selected in each multiplexer, a single data-select input is sufficient.

A LOW on the $\overline{Enable}$ input allows the selected input data to pass through to the output. A HIGH on the $\overline{Enable}$ input prevents data from going through to the output; that is, it disables the multiplexers.

The ANSI/IEEE Logic Symbol   The pin diagram for the 74HC157 is shown in Figure 49(a). The ANSI/IEEE logic symbol for the 74HC157 is shown in Figure 49(b). Notice that the four multiplexers are indicated by the partitioned outline and that the inputs common to all four multiplexers are indicated as inputs to the notched block at the top, which is called the *common control block*. All labels within the upper MUX block apply to the other blocks below it.

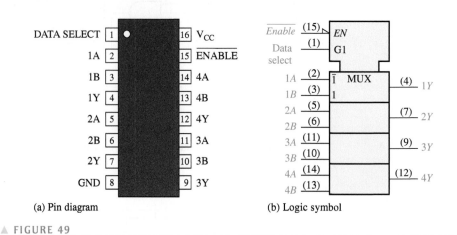

(a) Pin diagram   (b) Logic symbol

▲ FIGURE 49

Pin diagram and logic symbol for the 74HC157 quadruple 2-input data selector/multiplexer.

Notice the 1 and $\overline{1}$ labels in the MUX blocks and the G1 label in the common control block. These labels are an example of the **dependency notation** system specified in the ANSI/IEEE Standard 91-1984. In this case G1 indicates an AND relationship between the data-select input and the data inputs with 1 or $\overline{1}$ labels. (The $\overline{1}$ means that the AND relationship applies to the complement of the G1 input.) In other words, when the data-select input is HIGH, the *B* inputs of the multiplexers are selected; and when the data-select input is LOW, the *A* inputs are selected. A "G" is always used to denote AND dependency. Other aspects of dependency notation are introduced as appropriate throughout the book.

THE 74LS151 8-INPUT DATA SELECTOR/MULTIPLEXER

The 74LS151 has eight data inputs (D_0–D_7) and, therefore, three data-select or address input lines (S_0–S_2). Three bits are required to select any one of the eight data inputs ($2^3 = 8$). A LOW on the $\overline{Enable}$ input allows the selected input data to pass through to the output. Notice that the data output and its complement are both available. The pin diagram is shown in Figure 50(a), and the ANSI/IEEE logic symbol is shown in part (b). In this case there is no need for a common control block on the logic symbol because there is only one multiplexer to be controlled, not four as in the 74HC157. The $G\frac{0}{7}$ label within the logic symbol indicates the AND relationship between the data-select inputs and each of the data inputs 0 through 7.

▶ FIGURE 50

Pin diagram and logic symbol for the 74LS151 8-input data selector/multiplexer.

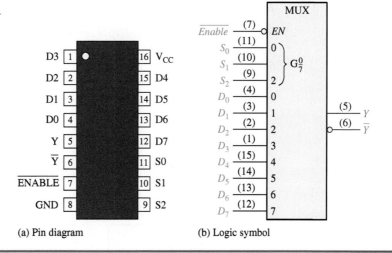

(a) Pin diagram   (b) Logic symbol

EXAMPLE 15

Use 74LS151s and any other logic necessary to multiplex 16 data lines onto a single data-output line.

Solution An implementation of this system is shown in Figure 51. Four bits are required to select one of 16 data inputs ($2^4 = 16$). In this application the *Enable* input is used as the most significant data-select bit. When the MSB in the data-select code is LOW, the left 74LS151 is enabled, and one of the data inputs (D_0 through D_7) is selected by the other three data-select bits. When the data-select MSB is HIGH, the right 74LS151 is enabled, and one of the data inputs (D_8 through D_{15}) is selected. The selected input data are then passed through to the negative-OR gate and onto the single output line.

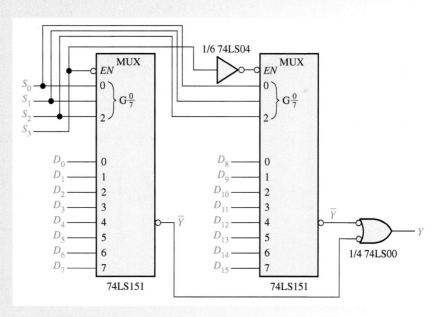

▲ FIGURE 51

A 16-input multiplexer.

Related Problem Determine the codes on the select inputs required to select each of the following data inputs: D_0, D_4, D_8, and D_{13}.

Applications

A 7-Segment Display Multiplexer Figure 52 shows a simplified method of multiplexing BCD numbers to a 7-segment display. In this example, 2-digit numbers are displayed on the 7-segment readout by the use of a single BCD-to-7-segment decoder. This basic method of display multiplexing can be extended to displays with any number of digits.

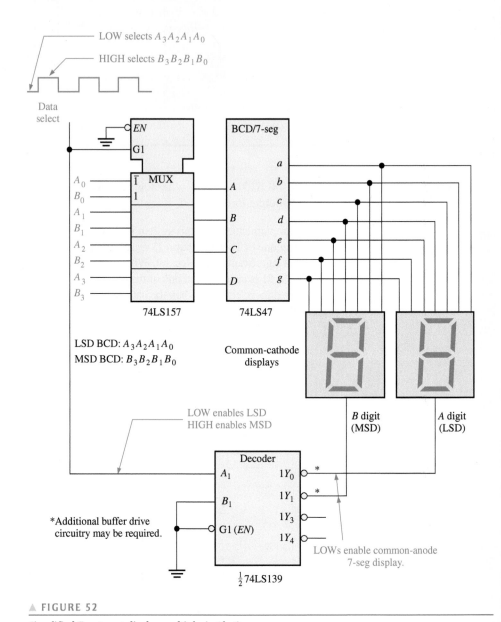

Simplified 7-segment display multiplexing logic.

The basic operation is as follows. Two BCD digits ($A_3A_2A_1A_0$ and $B_3B_2B_1B_0$) are applied to the multiplexer inputs. A square wave is applied to the data-select line, and when it is LOW, the A bits ($A_3A_2A_1A_0$) are passed through to the inputs of the 74LS47 BCD-to-7-segment decoder. The LOW on the data-select also puts a LOW on the A_1 input of the 74LS139 2-line-to-4-line decoder, thus activating its 0 output and enabling the A-digit display by effectively connecting its common terminal to ground. The A digit is now *on* and the B digit is *off*.

340

When the data-select line goes HIGH, the B bits $(B_3B_2B_1B_0)$ are passed through to the inputs of the BCD-to-7-segment decoder. Also, the 74LS139 decoder's 1 output is activated, thus enabling the B-digit display. The B digit is now *on* and the A digit is *off*. The cycle repeats at the frequency of the data-select square wave. This frequency must be high enough to prevent visual flicker as the digit displays are multiplexed.

A Logic Function Generator A useful application of the data selector/multiplexer is in the generation of combinational logic functions in sum-of-products form. When used in this way, the device can replace discrete gates, can often greatly reduce the number of ICs, and can make design changes much easier.

To illustrate, a 74LS151 8-input data selector/multiplexer can be used to implement any specified 3-variable logic function if the variables are connected to the data-select inputs and each data input is set to the logic level required in the truth table for that function. For example, if the function is a 1 when the variable combination is $\overline{A}_2A_1\overline{A}_0$, the 2 input (selected by 010) is connected to a HIGH. This HIGH is passed through to the output when this particular combination of variables occurs on the data-select lines. Example 16 will help clarify this application.

EXAMPLE 16

Implement the logic function specified in Table 9 by using a 74LS151 8-input data selector/multiplexer. Compare this method with a discrete logic gate implementation.

▽ TABLE 9

INPUTS			OUTPUT
A_2	A_1	A_0	Y
0	0	0	0
0	0	1	1
0	1	0	0
0	1	1	1
1	0	0	0
1	0	1	1
1	1	0	1
1	1	1	0

Solution Notice from the truth table that Y is a 1 for the following input variable combinations: 001, 011, 101, and 110. For all other combinations, Y is 0. For this function to be implemented with the data selector, the data input selected by each of the above-mentioned combinations must be connected to a HIGH (5 V). All the other data inputs must be connected to a LOW (ground), as shown in Figure 53.

The implementation of this function with logic gates would require four 3-input AND gates, one 4-input OR gate, and three inverters unless the expression can be simplified.

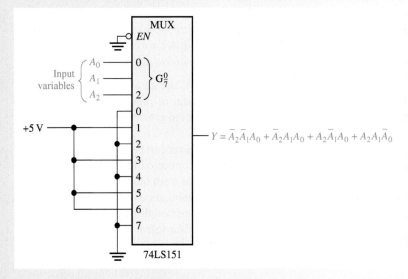

Data selector/multiplexer connected as a 3-variable logic function generator.

$$Y = \overline{A}_2\overline{A}_1 A_0 + \overline{A}_2 A_1 A_0 + A_2 \overline{A}_1 A_0 + A_2 A_1 \overline{A}_0$$

Related Problem   Use the 74LS151 to implement the following expression:

$$Y = \overline{A}_2\overline{A}_1\overline{A}_0 + A_2\overline{A}_1\overline{A}_0 + \overline{A}_2 A_1 \overline{A}_0$$

Example 16 illustrated how the 8-input data selector can be used as a logic function generator for three variables. Actually, this device can be also used as a 4-variable logic function generator by the utilization of one of the bits (A_0) in conjunction with the data inputs.

A 4-variable truth table has sixteen combinations of input variables. When an 8-bit data selector is used, each input is selected twice: the first time when A_0 is 0 and the second time when A_0 is 1. With this in mind, the following rules can be applied (Y is the output, and A_0 is the least significant bit):

1. If $Y = 0$ both times a given data input is selected by a certain combination of the input variables, $A_3 A_2 A_1$, connect that data input to ground (0).

2. If $Y = 1$ both times a given data input is selected by a certain combination of the input variables, $A_3 A_2 A_1$, connect the data input to $+V$ (1).

3. If Y is different the two times a given data input is selected by a certain combination of the input variables, $A_3 A_2 A_1$, and if $Y = A_0$, connect that data input to A_0.

4. If Y is different the two times a given data input is selected by a certain combination of the input variables, $A_3 A_2 A_1$, and if $Y = \overline{A}_0$, connect that data input to $\overline{A}_0$.

EXAMPLE 17

Implement the logic function in Table 10 by using a 74LS151 8-input data selector/multiplexer. Compare this method with a discrete logic gate implementation.

Solution   The data-select inputs are $A_3 A_2 A_1$. In the first row of the table, $A_3 A_2 A_1 = 000$ and $Y = A_0$. In the second row, where $A_3 A_2 A_1$ again is 000, $Y = A_0$. Thus, A_0 is connected to the 0 input. In the third row of the table, $A_3 A_2 A_1 = 001$ and $Y = \overline{A}_0$. Also, in the fourth row, when $A_3 A_2 A_1$ again is 001, $Y = \overline{A}_0$. Thus, A_0 is inverted

DECIMAL DIGIT	INPUTS				OUTPUT Y
	A_3	A_2	A_1	A_0	
0	0	0	0	0	0
1	0	0	0	1	1
2	0	0	1	0	1
3	0	0	1	1	0
4	0	1	0	0	0
5	0	1	0	1	1
6	0	1	1	0	1
7	0	1	1	1	1
8	1	0	0	0	1
9	1	0	0	1	0
10	1	0	1	0	1
11	1	0	1	1	0
12	1	1	0	0	1
13	1	1	0	1	1
14	1	1	1	0	0
15	1	1	1	1	1

and connected to the 1 input. This analysis is continued until each input is properly connected according to the specified rules. The implementation is shown in Figure 54.

▶ FIGURE 54

Data selector/multiplexer connected as a 4-variable logic function generator.

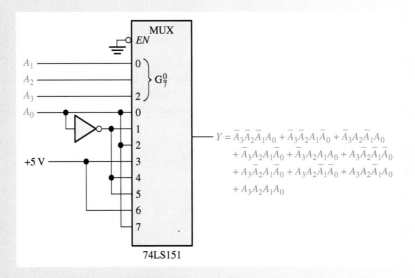

$$Y = \bar{A_3}\bar{A_2}\bar{A_1}A_0 + \bar{A_3}\bar{A_2}A_1\bar{A_0} + \bar{A_3}A_2\bar{A_1}A_0$$
$$+ \bar{A_3}A_2A_1\bar{A_0} + \bar{A_3}A_2A_1A_0 + A_3\bar{A_2}\bar{A_1}\bar{A_0}$$
$$+ A_3\bar{A_2}A_1\bar{A_0} + A_3A_2\bar{A_1}\bar{A_0} + A_3A_2\bar{A_1}A_0$$
$$+ A_3A_2A_1A_0$$

If implemented with logic gates, the function would require as many as ten 4-input AND gates, one 10-input OR gate, and four inverters, although possible simplification would reduce this requirement.

Related Problem   In Table 10, if $Y = 0$ when the inputs are all zeros and is alternately a 1 and a 0 for the remaining rows in the table, use a 74LS151 to implement the resulting logic function.

**SECTION 8
CHECKUP**

1. In Figure 47, $D_0 = 1$, $D_1 = 0$, $D_2 = 1$, $D_3 = 0$, $S_0 = 1$, and $S_1 = 0$. What is the output?

2. Identify each device.

   (a) 74LS157   (b) 74LS151

3. A 74LS151 has alternating LOW and HIGH levels on its data inputs beginning with $D_0 = 0$. The data-select lines are sequenced through a binary count (000, 001, 010, and so on) at a frequency of 1 kHz. The enable input is LOW. Describe the data output waveform.

4. Briefly describe the purpose of each of the following devices in Figure 52:

   (a) 74LS157   (b) 74LS47   (c) 74LS139

9 DEMULTIPLEXERS

A **demultiplexer (DEMUX)** basically reverses the multiplexing function. It takes digital information from one line and distributes it to a given number of output lines. For this reason, the demultiplexer is also known as a data distributor. As you will learn, decoders can also be used as demultiplexers.

After completing this section, you should be able to

♦ Explain the basic operation of a demultiplexer

♦ Describe how the 74HC154 4-line-to-16-line decoder can be used as a demultiplexer

♦ Develop the timing diagram for a demultiplexer with specified data and data selection inputs

In a demultiplexer, data goes from one line to several lines.

Figure 55 shows a 1-line-to-4-line demultiplexer (DEMUX) circuit. The data-input line goes to all of the AND gates. The two data-select lines enable only one gate at a time, and the data appearing on the data-input line will pass through the selected gate to the associated data-output line.

▶ FIGURE 55

A 1-line-to-4-line demultiplexer.

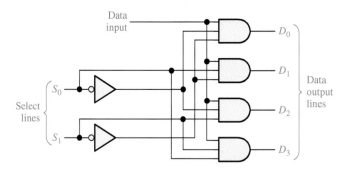

EXAMPLE 18

The serial data-input waveform (Data in) and data-select inputs (S_0 and S_1) are shown in Figure 56. Determine the data-output waveforms on D_0 through D_3 for the demultiplexer in Figure 55.

▶ FIGURE 56

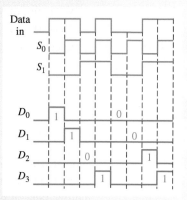

Solution   Notice that the select lines go through a binary sequence so that each successive input bit is routed to D_0, D_1, D_2, and D_3 in sequence, as shown by the output waveforms in Figure 56.

Related Problem   Develop the timing diagram for the demultiplexer if the S_0 and S_1 waveforms are both inverted.

THE 74HC154 DEMULTIPLEXER

We have already discussed the 74HC154 decoder in its application as a 4-line-to-16-line decoder (Section 5). This device and other decoders can also be used in demultiplexing applications. The logic symbol for this device when used as a demultiplexer is shown in Figure 57. In demultiplexer applications, the input lines are used as the data-select lines. One of the chip select inputs is used as the data-input line, with the other chip select input held LOW to enable the internal negative-AND gate at the bottom of the diagram.

▶ FIGURE 57

The 74HC154 decoder used as a demultiplexer.

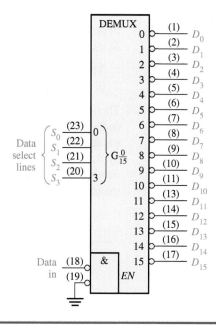

| SECTION 9 CHECKUP | 1. Generally, how can a decoder be used as a demultiplexer? |
| | 2. The 74HC154 demultiplexer in Figure 57 has a binary code of 1010 on the data-select lines, and the data-input line is LOW. What are the states of the output lines? |

10 PARITY GENERATORS/CHECKERS

Errors can occur as digital codes are being transferred from one point to another within a digital system or while codes are being transmitted from one system to another. The errors take the form of undesired changes in the bits that make up the coded information; that is, a 1 can change to a 0, or a 0 to a 1, because of component malfunctions or electrical noise. In most digital systems, the probability that even a single bit error will occur is very small, and the likelihood that more than one will occur is even smaller. Nevertheless, when an error occurs undetected, it can cause serious problems in a digital system.

After completing this section, you should be able to

- Explain the concept of parity
- Implement a basic parity circuit with exclusive-OR gates
- Describe the operation of basic parity generating and checking logic
- Discuss the 74LS280 9-bit parity generator/checker
- Discuss how error detection can be implemented in a data transmission

The parity method of error detection is where a **parity bit** is attached to a group of information bits in order to make the total number of 1s either even or odd (depending on the system). In addition to parity bits, several specific codes also provide inherent error detection.

Basic Parity Logic

A parity bit indicates if the number of 1s in a code is even or odd for the purpose of error detection.

In order to check for or to generate the proper parity in a given code, a basic principle can be used:

The sum (disregarding carries) of an even number of 1s is always 0, and the sum of an odd number of 1s is always 1.

Therefore, to determine if a given code has **even parity** or **odd parity,** all the bits in that code are summed. As you know, the modulo-2 sum of two bits can be generated by an exclusive-OR gate, as shown in Figure 58(a); the modulo-2 sum of four bits can be formed by three exclusive-OR gates connected as shown in Figure 58(b); and so on. When the number of 1s on the inputs is even, the output X is 0 (LOW). When the number of 1s is odd, the output X is 1 (HIGH).

▶ FIGURE 58

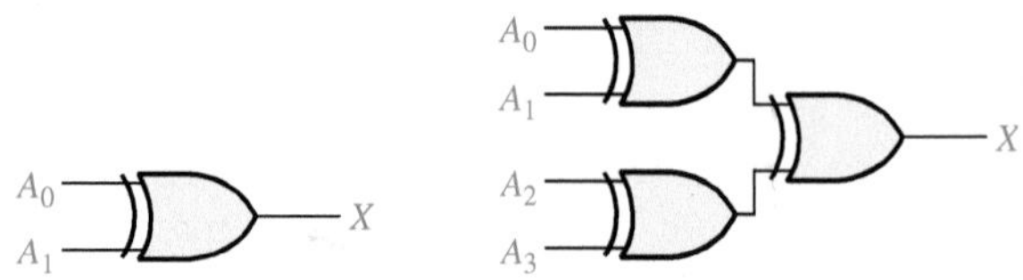

(a) Summing of two bits   (b) Summing of four bits

THE 74LS280 9-BIT PARITY GENERATOR/CHECKER

The logic symbol and function table for a 74LS280 are shown in Figure 59. This particular device can be used to check for odd or even parity on a 9-bit code (eight data bits and one parity bit), or it can be used to generate a parity bit for a binary code with up to nine bits. The inputs are A through I; when there is an even number of 1s on the inputs, the Σ Even output is HIGH and the Σ Odd output is LOW.

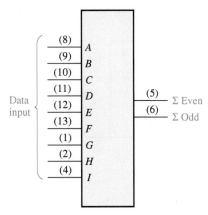

| NUMBER OF INPUTS | OUTPUTS | |
A–I THAT ARE HIGH	Σ EVEN	Σ ODD
0, 2, 4, 6, 8	H	L
1, 3, 5, 7, 9	L	H

(a) Traditional logic symbol

(b) Function table

▲ FIGURE 59

The 74LS280 9-bit parity generator/checker.

Parity Checker   When this device is used as an even parity checker, the number of input bits should always be even; and when a parity error occurs, the Σ Even output goes LOW and the Σ Odd output goes HIGH. When it is used as an odd parity checker, the number of input bits should always be odd; and when a parity error occurs, the Σ Odd output goes LOW and the Σ Even output goes HIGH.

Parity Generator   If this device is used as an even parity generator, the parity bit is taken at the Σ Odd output because this output is a 0 if there is an even number of input bits and it is a 1 if there is an odd number. When used as an odd parity generator, the parity bit is taken at the Σ Even output because it is a 0 when the number of inputs bits is odd.

A Data Transmission System with Error Detection

A simplified data transmission system is shown in Figure 60 to illustrate an application of parity generators/checkers, as well as multiplexers and demultiplexers, and to illustrate the need for data storage in some applications.

In this application, digital data from seven sources are multiplexed onto a single line for transmission to a distant point. The seven data bits (D_0 through D_6) are applied to the multiplexer data inputs and, at the same time, to the even parity generator inputs. The Σ Odd output of the parity generator is used as the even parity bit. This bit is 0 if the number of 1s on the inputs A through I is even and is a 1 if the number of 1s on A through I is odd. This bit is D_7 of the transmitted code.

The data-select inputs are repeatedly cycled through a binary sequence, and each data bit, beginning with D_0, is serially passed through and onto the transmission line ($\overline{Y}$). In this example, the transmission line consists of four conductors: one carries the serial data and three carry the timing signals (data selects). There are more sophisticated ways of

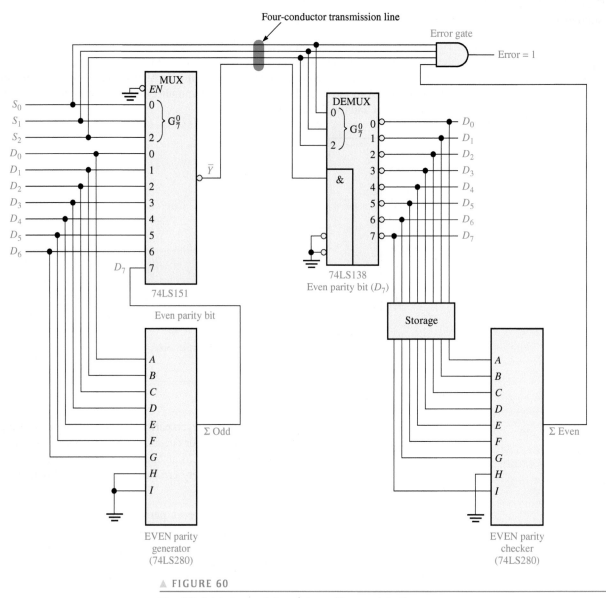

▲ FIGURE 60

Simplified data transmission system with error detection.

sending the timing information, but we are using this direct method to illustrate a basic principle.

At the demultiplexer end of the system, the data-select signals and the serial data stream are applied to the demultiplexer. The data bits are distributed by the demultiplexer onto the output lines in the order in which they occurred on the multiplexer inputs. That is, D_0 comes out on the D_0 output, D_1 comes out on the D_1 output, and so on. The parity bit comes out on the D_7 output. These eight bits are temporarily stored and applied to the even parity checker. Not all of the bits are present on the parity checker inputs until the parity bit D_7 comes out and is stored. At this time, the error gate is enabled by the data-select code 111. If the parity is correct, a 0 appears on the Σ Even output, keeping the Error output at 0. If the parity is incorrect, all 1s appear on the error gate inputs, and a 1 on the Error output results.

This particular application has demonstrated the need for data storage.

The timing diagram in Figure 61 illustrates a specific case in which two 8-bit words are transmitted, one with correct parity and one with an error.

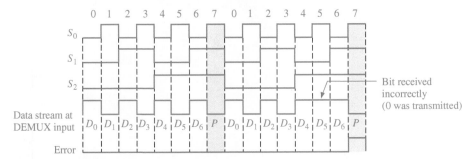

Data stream at DEMUX input D_0 D_1 D_2 D_3 D_4 D_5 D_6 P D_0 D_1 D_2 D_3 D_4 D_5 D_6 P

Error

Bit received incorrectly (0 was transmitted)

◀ FIGURE 61

Example of data transmission with and without error for the system in Figure 60.

SECTION 10 CHECKUP

1. Add an even parity bit to each of the following codes:
   (a) 110100   (b) 01100011
2. Add an odd parity bit to each of the following codes:
   (a) 1010101   (b) 1000001
3. Check each of the even parity codes for an error.
   (a) 100010101   (b) 1110111001

---

11 TROUBLESHOOTING

In this section, the problem of decoder glitches is introduced and examined from a troubleshooting standpoint. A **glitch** is any undesired voltage or current spike (pulse) of very short duration. A glitch can be interpreted as a valid signal by a logic circuit and may cause improper operation.

After completing this section, you should be able to

* Explain what a glitch is

* Determine the cause of glitches in a decoder application

* Use the method of output strobing to eliminate glitches

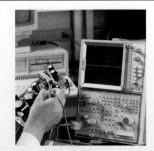

The 74LS138 was used as a DEMUX in the data transmission system in Figure 60. Now the 74HC138 is used as a 3-line-to-8-line decoder (binary-to-octal) in Figure 62 to illustrate how glitches occur and how to identify their cause. The $A_2A_1A_0$ inputs of the decoder are sequenced through a binary count, and the resulting waveforms of the inputs and outputs can be displayed on the screen of a logic analyzer, as shown in Figure 62. A_2 transitions are delayed from A_1 transitions and A_1 transitions are delayed from A_0 transitions. This commonly occurs when waveforms are generated by a binary counter.

The output waveforms are correct except for the glitches that occur on some of the output signals. A logic analyzer or an oscilloscope can be used to display glitches, which are normally very difficult to see. Generally, the logic analyzer is preferred, especially for low repetition rates (less than 10 kHz) and/or irregular occurrence because most logic analyzers have a *glitch capture* capability. Oscilloscopes can be used to observe glitches with reasonable success, particularly if the glitches occur at a regular high repetition rate (greater than 10 kHz).

Decoder waveforms with output glitches.

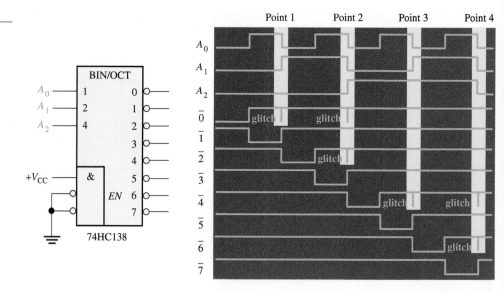

The points of interest indicated by the highlighted areas on the input waveforms in Figure 62 are displayed as shown in Figure 63. At point 1 there is a transitional state of 000 due to delay differences in the waveforms. This causes the first glitch on the $\overline{0}$ output of the decoder. At point 2 there are two transitional states, 010 and 000. These cause the glitch on the $\overline{2}$ output of the decoder and the second glitch on the $\overline{0}$ output, respectively. At point 3

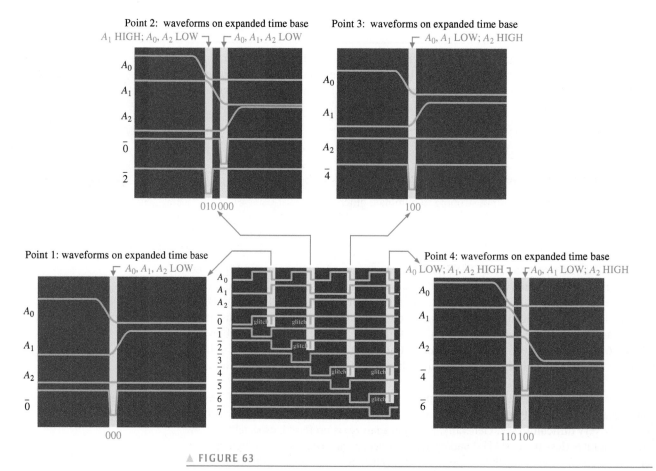

▲ FIGURE 63

Decoder waveform displays showing how transitional input states produce glitches in the output waveforms.

KEY TERMS

Cascading Connecting two or more similar devices in a manner that expands the capability of one device.

Decoder A digital circuit that converts coded information into a familiar or noncoded form.

Demultiplexer (DEMUX) A circuit that switches digital data from one input line to several output lines in a specified time sequence.

Encoder A digital circuit that converts information to a coded form.

Full-adder A digital circuit that adds two bits and an input carry to produce a sum and an output carry.

Glitch A voltage or current spike of short duration, usually unintentionally produced and unwanted.

Half-adder A digital circuit that adds two bits and produces a sum and an output carry. It cannot handle input carries.

Look-ahead carry A method of binary addition whereby carries from preceding adder stages are anticipated, thus eliminating carry propagation delays.

Multiplexer (MUX) A circuit that switches digital data from several input lines onto a single output line in a specified time sequence.

Parity bit A bit attached to each group of information bits to make the total number of 1s odd or even for every group of bits.

Priority encoder An encoder in which only the highest value input digit is encoded and any other active input is ignored.

Ripple carry A method of binary addition in which the output carry from each adder becomes the input carry of the next higher-order adder.

TRUE/FALSE QUIZ

Answers are at the end of the chapter.

1. A half-adder adds two binary bits.
2. A half-adder has a sum output only.
3. A full-adder adds three bits and produces two outputs.
4. Two 4-bit numbers can be added using two full-adders.
5. When the two input bits are both 1 and the carry input bit is a 1, the sum output of a full adder is 0.
6. A comparator determines when two binary numbers are equal.
7. A decoder detects the presence of a specified combination of input bits.
8. The 4-line-to-10-line decoder and the 1-of-10 decoder are two different types.
9. An encoder essentially performs a reverse decoder function.
10. A multiplexer is a logic circuit that allows digital information from a single source to be routed onto several lines.

SELF-TEST

Answers are at the end of the chapter.

1. A half-adder is characterized by
   (a) two inputs and two outputs
   (b) three inputs and two outputs
   (c) two inputs and three outputs
   (d) two inputs and one output

2. A full-adder is characterized by
   (a) two inputs and two outputs
   (b) three inputs and two outputs
   (c) two inputs and three outputs
   (d) two inputs and one output

3. The inputs to a full-adder are $A = 1$, $B = 1$, $C_{in} = 0$. The outputs are
   (a) $\Sigma = 1$, $C_{out} = 1$
   (b) $\Sigma = 1$, $C_{out} = 0$
   (c) $\Sigma = 0$, $C_{out} = 1$
   (d) $\Sigma = 0$, $C_{out} = 0$

4. A 4-bit parallel adder can add
   (a) two 4-bit binary numbers   (b) two 2-bit binary numbers
   (c) four bits at a time   (d) four bits in sequence

5. To expand a 4-bit parallel adder to an 8-bit parallel adder, you must
   (a) use four 4-bit adders with no interconnections
   (b) use two 4-bit adders and connect the sum outputs of one to the bit inputs of the other
   (c) use eight 4-bit adders with no interconnections
   (d) use two 4-bit adders with the carry output of one connected to the carry input of the other

6. If a 74LS85 magnitude comparator has $A = 1011$ and $B = 1001$ on its inputs, the outputs are
   (a) $A > B = 0, A < B = 1, A = B = 0$ (b) $A > B = 1, A < B = 0, A = B = 0$
   (c) $A > B = 1, A < B = 1, A = B = 0$ (d) $A > B = 0, A < B = 0, A = B = 1$

7. If a 1-of-16 decoder with active-LOW outputs exhibits a LOW on the decimal 12 output, what are the inputs?
   (a) $A_3A_2A_1A_0 = 1010$ (b) $A_3A_2A_1A_0 = 1110$
   (c) $A_3A_2A_1A_0 = 1100$ (d) $A_3A_2A_1A_0 = 0100$

8. A BCD-to-7 segment decoder has 0100 on its inputs. The active outputs are
   (a) a, c, f, g (b) b, c, f, g
   (c) b, c, e, f (d) b, d, e, g

9. If an octal-to-binary priority encoder has its 0, 2, 5, and 6 inputs at the active level, the active-HIGH binary output is
   (a) 110   (b) 010
   (c) 101   (d) 000

10. In general, a multiplexer has
    (a) one data input, several data outputs, and selection inputs
    (b) one data input, one data output, and one selection input
    (c) several data inputs, several data outputs, and selection inputs
    (d) several data inputs, one data output, and selection inputs

11. Data selectors are basically the same as
    (a) decoders   (b) demultiplexers
    (c) multiplexers   (d) encoders

12. Which of the following codes exhibit even parity?
    (a) 10011000   (b) 01111000
    (c) 11111111   (d) 11010101
    (e) all   (f) both answers (b) and (c)

PROBLEMS

Answers to odd-numbered problems are at the end of the chapter.

Section 1   **Basic Adders**

1. For the full-adder of Figure 4, determine the logic state (1 or 0) at each gate output for the following inputs:
   (a) $A = 1, B = 1, C_{in} = 1$
   (b) $A = 0, B = 1, C_{in} = 1$
   (c) $A = 0, B = 1, C_{in} = 0$

2. What are the full-adder inputs that will produce each of the following outputs:
   (a) $\Sigma = 0, C_{out} = 0$
   (b) $\Sigma = 1, C_{out} = 0$
   (c) $\Sigma = 1, C_{out} = 1$
   (d) $\Sigma = 0, C_{out} = 1$

3. Determine the outputs of a full-adder for each of the following inputs:
   (a) $A = 1, B = 0, C_{in} = 0$
   (b) $A = 0, B = 0, C_{in} = 1$
   (c) $A = 0, B = 1, C_{in} = 1$
   (d) $A = 1, B = 1, C_{in} = 1$

Section 2 **Parallel Binary Adders**

4. For the parallel adder in Figure 73, determine the complete sum by analysis of the logical operation of the circuit. Verify your result by longhand addition of the two input numbers.

▶ FIGURE 73

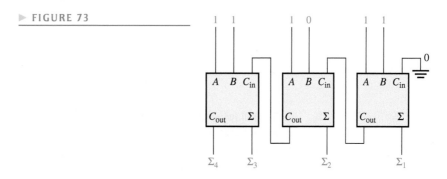

5. Repeat Problem 4 for the circuit and input conditions in Figure 74.

▶ FIGURE 74

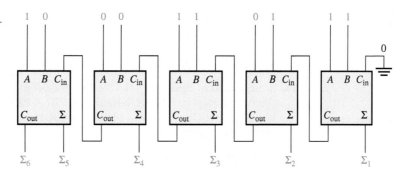

6. The circuit shown in Figure 75 is a 4-bit circuit that can add or subtract numbers in a form used in computers (positive numbers in true form; negative numbers in complement form). (a) Explain what happens when the $\overline{Add/Subt.}$ input is HIGH. (b) What happens when $\overline{Add/Subt.}$ is LOW?

7. For the circuit in Figure 75, assume the inputs are $\overline{Add/Subt.} = 1, A = 1001$ and $B = 1100$. What is the output?

▶ FIGURE 75

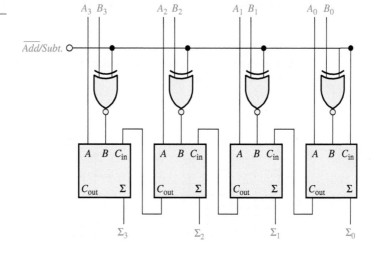

8. The input waveforms in Figure 76 are applied to a 2-bit adder. Determine the waveforms for the sum and the output carry in relation to the inputs by constructing a timing diagram.

▶ FIGURE 76

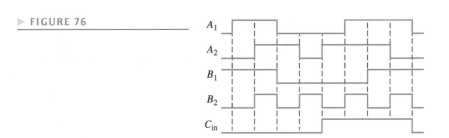

9. The following sequences of bits (right-most bit first) appear on the inputs to a 4-bit parallel adder. Determine the resulting sequence of bits on each sum output.

A_1	1001
A_2	1110
A_3	0000
A_4	1011
B_1	1111
B_2	1100
B_3	1010
B_4	0010

10. In the process of checking a 74LS283 4-bit parallel adder, the following logic levels are observed on its pins: 1-HIGH, 2-HIGH, 3-HIGH, 4-HIGH, 5-LOW, 6-LOW, 7-LOW, 9-HIGH, 10-LOW, 11-HIGH, 12-LOW, 13-HIGH, 14-HIGH, and 15-HIGH. Determine if the IC is functioning properly.

Section 3

Ripple Carry Versus Look-Ahead Carry Adders

11. Each of the eight full-adders in an 8-bit parallel ripple carry adder exhibits the following propagation delays:

A to Σ and C_{out}:	40 ns
B to Σ and C_{out}:	40 ns
C_{in} to Σ:	35 ns
C_{in} to C_{out}:	25 ns

Determine the maximum total time for the addition of two 8-bit numbers.

12. Show the additional logic circuitry necessary to make the 4-bit look-ahead carry adder in Figure 18 into a 5-bit adder.

Section 4

Comparators

13. The waveforms in Figure 77 are applied to the comparator as shown. Determine the output $(A = B)$ waveform.

▶ FIGURE 77

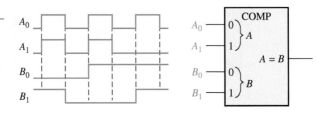

14. For the 4-bit comparator in Figure 78, plot each output waveform for the inputs shown. The outputs are active-HIGH.

▶ FIGURE 78

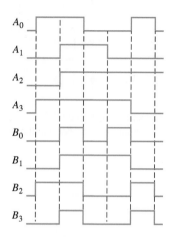

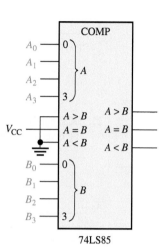

74LS85

15. For each set of binary numbers, determine the output states for the comparator of Figure 22.

(a) $A_3A_2A_1A_0 = 1100$ (b) $A_3A_2A_1A_0 = 1000$ (c) $A_3A_2A_1A_0 = 0100$
 $B_3B_2B_1B_0 = 1001$ $B_3B_2B_1B_0 = 1011$ $B_3B_2B_1B_0 = 0100$

Section 5 **Decoders**

16. When a HIGH is on the output of each of the decoding gates in Figure 79, what is the binary code appearing on the inputs? The MSB is A_3.

▶ FIGURE 79

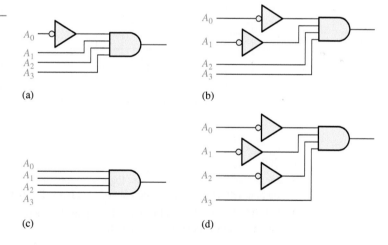

(a)   (b)

(c)   (d)

17. Show the decoding logic for each of the following codes if an active-HIGH (1) output is required:

(a) 1101 (b) 1000 (c) 11011 (d) 11100
(e) 101010 (f) 111110 (g) 000101 (h) 1110110

18. Solve Problem 17, given that an active-LOW (0) output is required.

19. You wish to detect only the presence of the codes 1010, 1100, 0001, and 1011. An active-HIGH output is required to indicate their presence. Develop the minimum decoding logic with a single output that will indicate when any one of these codes is on the inputs. For any other code, the output must be LOW.

20. If the input waveforms are applied to the decoding logic as indicated in Figure 80, sketch the output waveform in proper relation to the inputs.

▶ FIGURE 80

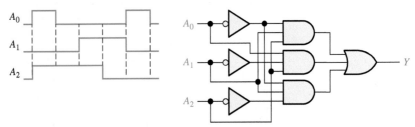

21. BCD numbers are applied sequentially to the BCD-to-decimal decoder in Figure 81. Draw a timing diagram, showing each output in the proper relationship with the others and with the inputs.

▶ FIGURE 81

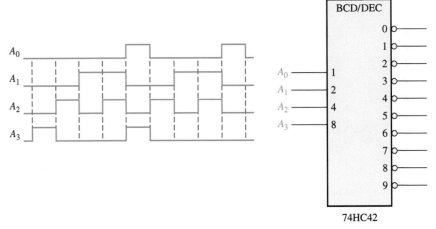

22. A 7-segment decoder/driver drives the display in Figure 82. If the waveforms are applied as indicated, determine the sequence of digits that appears on the display.

▶ FIGURE 82

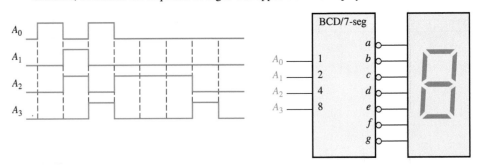

Section 6   Encoders

23. For the decimal-to-BCD encoder logic of Figure 38, assume that the 9 input and the 3 input are both HIGH. What is the output code? Is it a valid BCD (8421) code?

24. A 74HC147 encoder has LOW levels on pins 2, 5, and 12. What BCD code appears on the outputs if all the other inputs are HIGH?

Section 7   Code Converters

25. Convert the following decimal numbers to BCD and then to binary.

(a) 2   (b) 8   (c) 13   (d) 26   (e) 33

26. Show the logic required to convert a 10-bit binary number to Gray code, and use that logic to convert the following binary numbers to Gray code:

(a) 1010101010   (b) 1111100000   (c) 0000001110   (d) 1111111111

27. Show the logic required to convert a 10-bit Gray code to binary, and use that logic to convert the following Gray code words to binary:

(a) 1010000000   (b) 0011001100   (c) 1111000111   (d) 0000000001

Section 8   **Multiplexers (Data Selectors)**

28. For the multiplexer in Figure 83, determine the output for the following input states: $D_0 = 0$, $D_1 = 1$, $D_2 = 1$, $D_3 = 0$, $S_0 = 1$, $S_1 = 0$.

▷ FIGURE 83

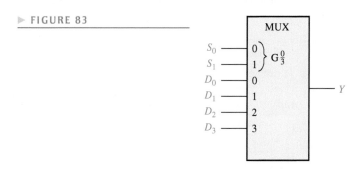

29. If the data-select inputs to the multiplexer in Figure 83 are sequenced as shown by the waveforms in Figure 84, determine the output waveform with the data inputs specified in Problem 28.

▷ FIGURE 84

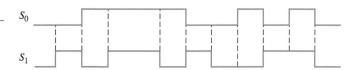

30. The waveforms in Figure 85 are observed on the inputs of a 74LS151 8-input multiplexer. Sketch the Y output waveform.

▷ FIGURE 85

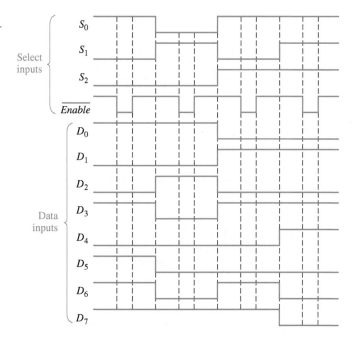

Section 9   **Demultiplexers**

31. Develop the total timing diagram (inputs and outputs) for a 74HC154 used in a demultiplexing application in which the inputs are as follows: The data-select inputs are repetitively sequenced through a straight binary count beginning with 0000, and the data input is a serial data stream carrying BCD data representing the decimal number 2468. The least significant digit (8) is first in the sequence, with its LSB first, and it should appear in the first 4-bit positions of the output.

Section 10 **Parity Generators/Checkers**

32. The waveforms in Figure 86 are applied to the 4-bit parity logic. Determine the output waveform in proper relation to the inputs. For how many bit times does even parity occur, and how is it indicated? The timing diagram includes eight bit times.

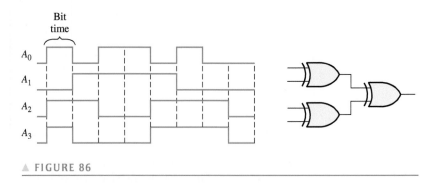

▲ FIGURE 86

33. Determine the Σ Even and the Σ Odd outputs of a 74LS280 9-bit parity generator/checker for the inputs in Figure 87. Refer to the function table in Figure 59.

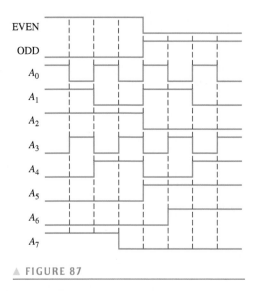

▲ FIGURE 87

Section 11 **Troubleshooting**

34. The full-adder in Figure 88 is tested under all input conditions with the input waveforms shown. From your observation of the Σ and C_{out} waveforms, is it operating properly, and if not, what is the most likely fault?

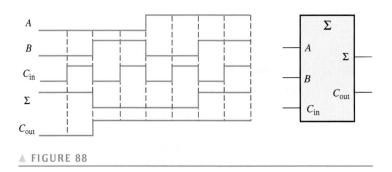

▲ FIGURE 88

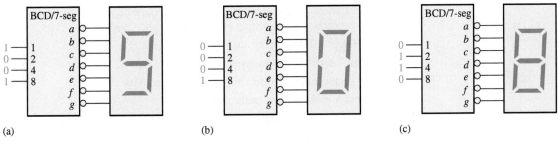

(a)

(b)

(c)

▲ FIGURE 89

35. List the possible faults for each decoder/display in Figure 89.

36. Develop a systematic test procedure to check out the complete operation of the keyboard encoder in Figure 42.

37. You are testing a BCD-to-binary converter consisting of 4-bit adders as shown in Figure 90. First verify that the circuit converts BCD to binary. The test procedure calls for applying BCD numbers in sequential order beginning with 0_{10} and checking for the correct binary output. What symptom or symptoms will appear on the binary outputs in the event of each of the following faults? For what BCD number is each fault *first* detected?

(a) The A_1 input is open (top adder).

(b) The C_{out} is open (top adder).

(c) The Σ_4 output is shorted to ground (top adder).

(d) The 32 output is shorted to ground (bottom adder).

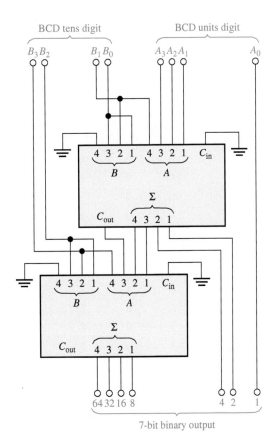

▲ FIGURE 90

367

38. For the 7-segment display multiplexing system in Figure 52, determine the most likely cause or causes for each of the following symptoms:

   (a) The B-digit (MSD) display does not turn on at all.

   (b) Neither 7-segment display turns on.

   (c) The f-segment of both displays appears to be on all the time.

   (d) There is a visible flicker on the displays.

39. Develop a systematic procedure to fully test the 74LS151 data selector IC.

40. During the testing of the data transmission system in Figure 60, a code is applied to the D_0 through D_6 inputs that contains an odd number of 1s. A single bit error is deliberately introduced on the serial data transmission line between the MUX and the DEMUX, but the system does not indicate an error (error output = 0). After some investigation, you check the inputs to the even parity checker and find that D_0 through D_6 contain an even number of 1s, as you would expect. Also, you find that the D_7 parity bit is a 1. What are the possible reasons for the system not indicating the error?

41. In general, describe how you would fully test the data transmission system in Figure 60, and specify a method for the introduction of parity errors.

System Application Activity

42. Use a 74LS00 (quad NAND gates) and any other devices that may be required to produce active-HIGH outputs for the given inputs.

43. Implement the light output logic with the 74LS00 if active-LOW outputs are required.

Special Design Problems

44. Modify the design of the 7-segment display multiplexing system in Figure 52 to accommodate two additional digits.

45. Using Table 2, write the SOP expressions for the Σ and C_{out} of a full-adder. Use a Karnaugh map to minimize the expressions and then implement them with inverters and AND-OR logic. Show how you can replace the AND-OR logic with 74LS151 data selectors.

46. Implement the logic function specified in Table 12 by using a 74LS151 data selector.

▷ TABLE 12

INPUTS				OUTPUT
A_3	A_2	A_1	A_0	Y
0	0	0	0	0
0	0	0	1	0
0	0	1	0	1
0	0	1	1	1
0	1	0	0	0
0	1	0	1	0
0	1	1	0	1
0	1	1	1	1
1	0	0	0	1
1	0	0	1	0
1	0	1	0	1
1	0	1	1	1
1	1	0	0	0
1	1	0	1	1
1	1	1	0	0
1	1	1	1	1

47. Using two of the 6-position adder modules from Figure 14, design a 12-position voting system.

48. The adder block in the tablet-bottling system in Figure 91 performs the addition of the 8-bit binary number from the counter and the 16-bit binary number from Register B. The result from the adder goes back into Register B. Use 74LS283s to implement this function and draw a complete logic diagram including pin numbers.

49. Use 74LS85s to implement the comparator block in the tablet-bottling system in Figure 91 and draw a complete logic diagram including pin numbers. The comparator compares the 8-bit binary number (actually only seven bits are required) from the BCD-to-binary converter with the 8-bit binary number from the counter.

50. Two BCD-to-7-segment decoders are used in the tablet-bottling system in Figure 91. One is required to drive the 2-digit *tablets/bottle* display and the other to drive the 5-digit *total tablets bottled* display. Use 74LS47s to implement each decoder and draw a complete logic diagram including pin numbers.

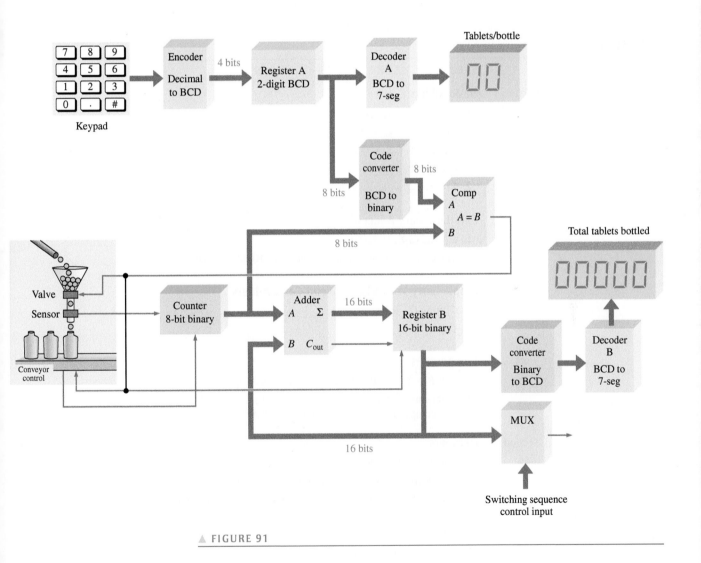

▲ FIGURE 91

51. The encoder shown in the system block diagram of Figure 91 encodes each decimal key closure and converts it to BCD. Use a 74LS147 to implement this function and draw a complete logic diagram including pin numbers.

52. The system in Figure 91 requires two code converters. The BCD-to-binary converter changes the 2-digit BCD number in Register A to an 8-bit binary code (actually only 7 bits are required because the MSB is always 0). Use appropriate IC code converters to implement the BCD-to-binary converter function and draw a complete logic diagram including pin numbers.

Multisim Troubleshooting Practice

53. Open file P06-53 on www.pearsoned.com/electronics and test the logic circuit to determine if there is a fault. If there is a fault, identify it if possible.

54. Open file P06-54 and test the logic circuit to determine if there is a fault. If there is a fault, identify it if possible.

55. Open file P06-55 and test the logic circuit to determine if there is a fault. If there is a fault, identify it if possible.

56. Open file P06-56 and test the logic circuit to determine if there is a fault. If there is a fault, identify it if possible.

ANSWERS

SECTION CHECKUPS

Section 1 **Basic Adders**

1. (a) $\Sigma = 1, C_{\text{out}} = 0$
   (b) $\Sigma = 0, C_{\text{out}} = 0$
   (c) $\Sigma = 1, C_{\text{out}} = 0$
   (d) $\Sigma = 0, C_{\text{out}} = 1$
2. $\Sigma = 1, C_{\text{out}} = 1$

Section 2 **Parallel Binary Adders**

1. $C_{\text{out}}\Sigma_4\Sigma_3\Sigma_2\Sigma_1 = 11001$
2. Three 74LS283s are required to add two 10-bit numbers.

Section 3 **Ripple Carry Versus Look-Ahead Carry Adders**

1. $C_g = 0, C_p = 1$
2. $C_{\text{out}} = 1$

Section 4 **Comparators**

1. $A > B = 1, A < B = 0, A = B = 0$ when $A = 1011$ and $B = 1010$
2. Right comparator: $A < B = 1; A = B = 0; A > B = 0$
   Left comparator: $A < B = 0; A = B = 0; A > B = 1$

Section 5 **Decoders**

1. Output 5 is active when 101 is on the inputs.
2. Four 74HC154s are used to decode a 6-bit binary number.
3. Active-HIGH output drives a common-cathode LED display.

Section 6 **Encoders**

1. (a) $A_0 = 1, A_1 = 1, A_2 = 0, A_3 = 1$
   (b) No, this is not a valid BCD code.
   (c) Only one input can be active for a valid output.
2. (a) $\overline{A}_3 = 0, \overline{A}_2 = 1, \overline{A}_1 = 1, \overline{A}_0 = 1$
   (b) The output is 0111, which is the complement of 1000 (8).

370

Section 7 **Code Converters**

1. 10000101 (BCD) = 1010101_2

2. An 8-bit binary-to-Gray converter consists of seven exclusive-OR gates in an arrangement like that in Figure 43 but with inputs B_0–B_7.

Section 8 **Multiplexers (Data Selectors)**

1. The output is 0.

2. (a) 74LS157: Quad 2-input data selector

   (b) 74LS151: 8-input data selector

3. The data output alternates between LOW and HIGH as the data-select inputs sequence through the binary states.

4. (a) The 74LS157 multiplexes the two BCD codes to the 7-segment decoder.

   (b) The 74LS47 decodes the BCD to energize the display.

   (c) The 74LS139 enables the 7-segment displays alternately.

Section 9 **Demultiplexers**

1. A decoder can be used as a multiplexer by using the input lines for data selection and an Enable line for data input.

2. The outputs are all HIGH except D_{10}, which is LOW.

Section 10 **Parity Generators/Checkers**

1. (a) Even parity: $\underline{1}$110100   (b) Even parity: $\underline{0}$01100011

2. (a) Odd parity: $\underline{1}$1010101   (b) Odd parity: $\underline{1}$1000001

3. (a) Code is correct, four 1s.   (b) Code is in error, seven 1s

Section 11 **Troubleshooting**

1. A glitch is a very short-duration voltage spike (usually unwanted).

2. Glitches are caused by transition states.

3. Strobe is the enabling of a device for a specified period of time when the device is not in transition.

RELATED PROBLEMS FOR EXAMPLES

1 $\Sigma = 1$, $C_{\text{out}} = 1$ **2** $\Sigma_1 = 0$, $\Sigma_2 = 0$, $\Sigma_3 = 1$, $\Sigma_4 = 1$

3 $1011 + 1010 = 10101$ **4** See Figure 92.

▶ FIGURE 92

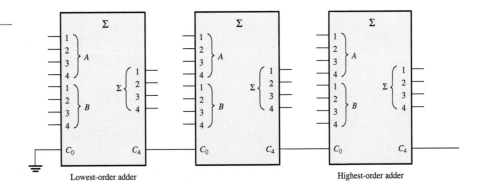

Lowest-order adder   Highest-order adder

5 See Figure 93.

▷ FIGURE 93

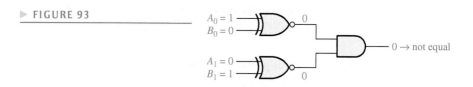

6 $A > B = 0, A = B = 0, A < B = 1$

7 See Figure 94.

▷ FIGURE 94

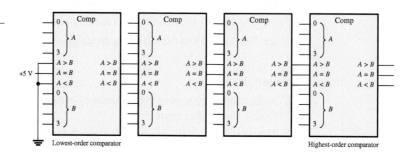

8 See Figure 95.

9 Output 22

▷ FIGURE 95

10 See Figure 96.

▷ FIGURE 96

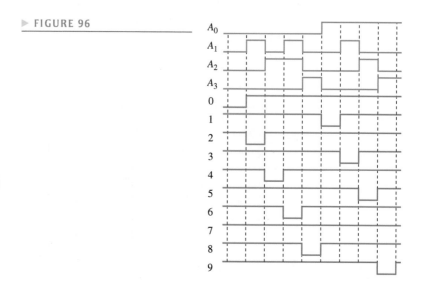

11 All inputs LOW: $\bar{A}_0 = 0, \bar{A}_1 = 1, \bar{A}_2 = 1, \bar{A}_3 = 0$

All inputs HIGH: All outputs HIGH.

12 BCD 01000001

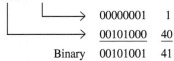

$$
\begin{array}{ll}
00000001 & 1 \\
\underline{00101000} & \underline{40} \\
\text{Binary} \quad 00101001 & 41
\end{array}
$$

13 Seven exclusive-OR gates

14 See Figure 97.

▷ FIGURE 97

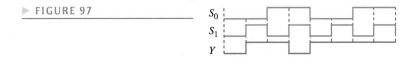

15 D_0: $S_3 = 0, S_2 = 0, S_1 = 0, S_0 = 0$

D_4: $S_3 = 0, S_2 = 1, S_1 = 0, S_0 = 0$

D_8: $S_3 = 1, S_2 = 0, S_1 = 0, S_0 = 0$

D_{13}: $S_3 = 1, S_2 = 1, S_1 = 0, S_0 = 1$

▷ FIGURE 98

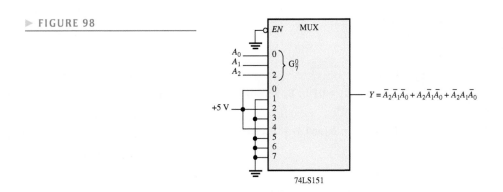

16 See Figure 98.

▷ FIGURE 99

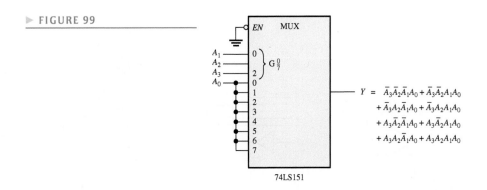

17 See Figure 99.

▷ FIGURE 100

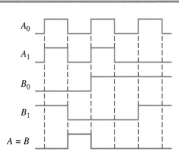

18 See Figure 100.

TRUE/FALSE QUIZ

1. T 2. F 3. T 4. F 5. F 6. T 7. T 8. F 9. T 10. F

SELF-TEST

1. (a) 2. (b) 3. (c) 4. (a) 5. (d) 6. (b)

ANSWERS TO ODD-NUMBERED PROBLEMS

1. (a) $A \oplus B = 0, \Sigma = 1, (A \oplus B)C_{in} = 0, AB = 1, C_{out} = 1$
    (b) $A \oplus B = 1, \Sigma = 0, (A \oplus B)C_{in} = 1, AB = 0, C_{out} = 1$
    (c) $A \oplus B = 1, \Sigma = 1, (A \oplus B)C_{in} = 0, AB = 0, C_{out} = 0$

3. (a) $\Sigma = 1, C_{out} = 0$;
    (b) $\Sigma = 1, C_{out} = 0$;
    (c) $\Sigma = 0, C_{out} = 1$;
    (d) $\Sigma = 1, C_{out} = 1$

5. 11100

7. $\Sigma_3\Sigma_2\Sigma_1\Sigma_0 = 1101$

9. $\Sigma_1 = 0110; \Sigma_2 = 1011; \Sigma_3 = 0110; \Sigma_4 = 0001; \Sigma_5 = 1000$

11. 225 ns

13. $A = B$ is HIGH when $A_0 = B_0$ and $A_1 = B_1$; see Figure 101.

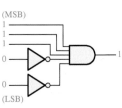

▲ FIGURE 101

15. (a) $A > B = 1; A = B = 0; A < B = 0$
    (b) $A < B = 1; A = B = 0; A > B = 0$
    (c) $A = B = 1; A < B = 0; A > B = 0$

17. See Figure 102.

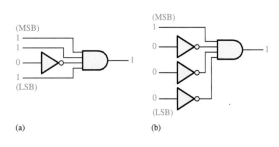

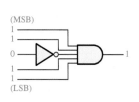

(a)   (b)   (c)   (d)

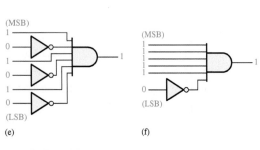

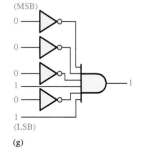

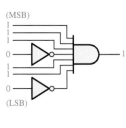

(e)   (f)   (g)   (h)

▲ FIGURE 102

19. $X = A_3 A_2 \overline{A_1} \overline{A_0} + \overline{A_3} \overline{A_2} \overline{A_1} A_0 + A_3 \overline{A_2} A_1$

21. See Figure 103.

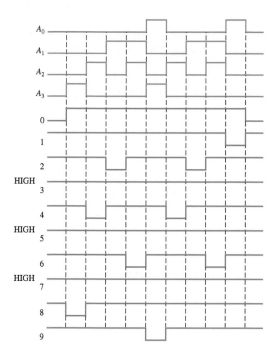

23. $A_3 A_2 A_1 A_0 = 1011$, invalid BCD

25. (a) $2 = 0010 = 0010_2$

(b) $8 = 1000 = 1000_2$

(c) $13 = 00010011 = 1101_2$

(d) $26 = 00100110 = 11010_2$

(e) $33 = 00110011 = 100001_2$

27. (a) 1010000000 Gray → 1100000000 binary

(b) 0011001100 Gray → 0010001000 binary

(c) 1111000111 Gray → 1010000101 binary

(d) 0000000001 Gray → 0000000001 binary

See Figure 104.

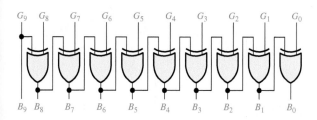

▲ FIGURE 104

29. See Figure 105.

31. See Figure 106.

33. See Figure 107.

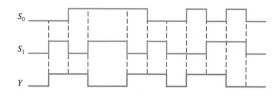

▲ FIGURE 105

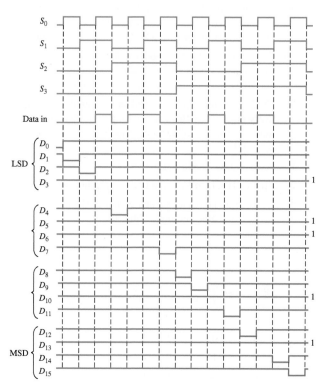

▲ FIGURE 106

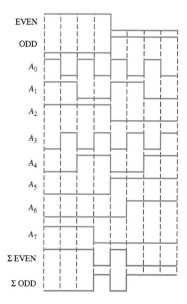

▲ FIGURE 107

35. (a) OK

   (b) segment g burned out; output G open

   (c) Segment b output stuck LOW

37. (a) The A_1 input of the top adder is open: All binary values corresponding to a BCD number having a value of 0, 1, 4, 5, 8, or 9 will be off by 2. This will first be seen for a BCD value of 0000 0000.

   (b) The carry out of the top adder is open: All values not normally involving an output carry will be off by 32. This will first be seen for a BCD value of 0000 0000.

   (c) The Σ_4 output of the top adder is shorted to ground: Same binary values above 15 will be short by 16. The first BCD value to indicate this will be 0001 1000.

   (d) The Σ_3 output of the bottom adder is shorted to ground: Every other set of 16 values starting with 16 will be short 16. The first BCD value to indicate this will be 0001 0110.

39. 1. Place a LOW on pin 7 (Enable).

   2. Apply a HIGH to D_0 and a LOW to D_1 through D_7.

   3. Go through the binary sequence on the select inputs and check Y and $\overline{Y}$ according to Table 13.

▼ TABLE 13

S_2	S_1	S_0	Y	$\overline{Y}$
0	0	0	1	0
0	0	1	0	1
0	1	0	0	1
0	1	1	0	1
1	0	0	0	1
1	0	1	0	1
1	1	0	0	1
1	1	1	0	1

4. Repeat the binary sequence of select inputs for each set of data inputs listed in Table 14. A HIGH on the Y output should occur only for the corresponding combinations of select inputs shown.

41. Apply a HIGH in turn to each Data input, D_0 through D_7 with LOWs on all the other inputs. For each HIGH applied to a data input, sequence through all eight binary combinations of select inputs ($S_2S_1S_0$) and check for HIGH on the corresponding data output and LOWs on all the other data outputs.

43. See Figure 108.

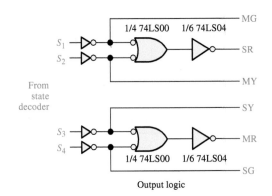

From state decoder

Output logic

▲ FIGURE 108

45. $\Sigma = \overline{A}\,\overline{B}C_{in} + \overline{A}B\overline{C}_{in} + A\overline{B}\,\overline{C}_{in} + ABC_{in}$
   $C_{out} = \overline{A}BC_{in} + A\overline{B}C_{in} + AB\overline{C}_{in} + ABC_{in}$
   See Figure 109.

47. See the block diagram in Figure 110.

▼ TABLE 14

D_0	D_1	D_2	D_3	D_4	D_5	D_6	D_7	Y	$\overline{Y}$	S_2	S_1	S_0
L	H	L	L	L	L	L	L	1	0	0	0	1
L	L	H	L	L	L	L	L	1	0	0	1	0
L	L	L	H	L	L	L	L	1	0	0	1	1
L	L	L	L	H	L	L	L	1	0	1	0	0
L	L	L	L	L	H	L	L	1	0	1	0	1
L	L	L	L	L	L	H	L	1	0	1	1	0
L	L	L	L	L	L	L	H	1	0	1	1	1

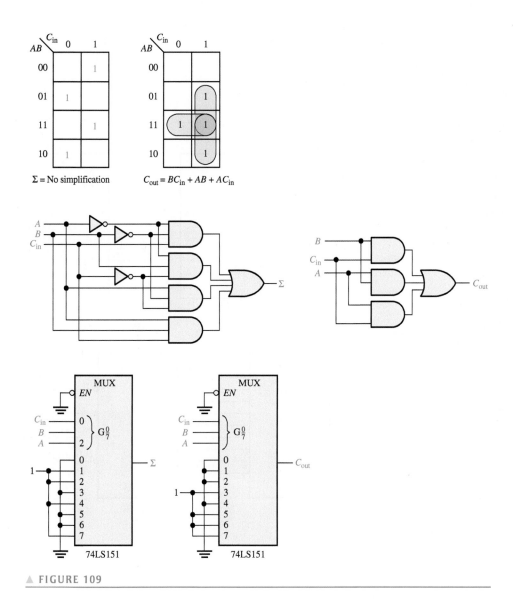

Σ = No simplification

$C_{\text{out}} = BC_{\text{in}} + AB + AC_{\text{in}}$

▲ FIGURE 109

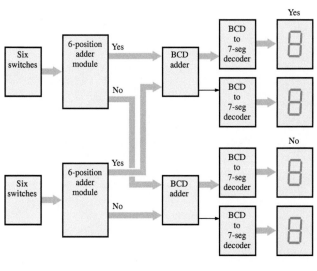

▲ FIGURE 110

49. See Figure 111.

51. See Figure 112.

53. LSB adder carry out open

55. Pin 12 of upper 74148 open

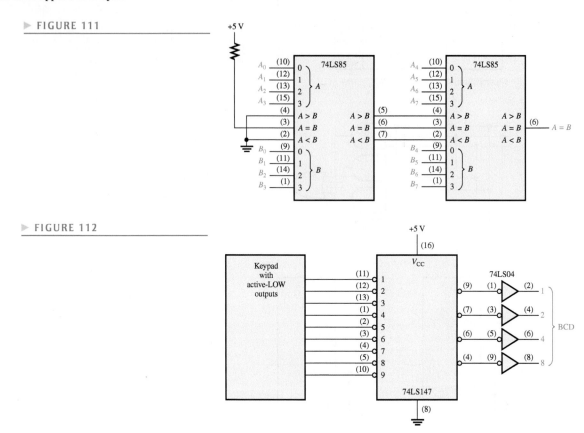

▶ FIGURE 111

▶ FIGURE 112